INTRODUCTION TO

Nuclear Engineering

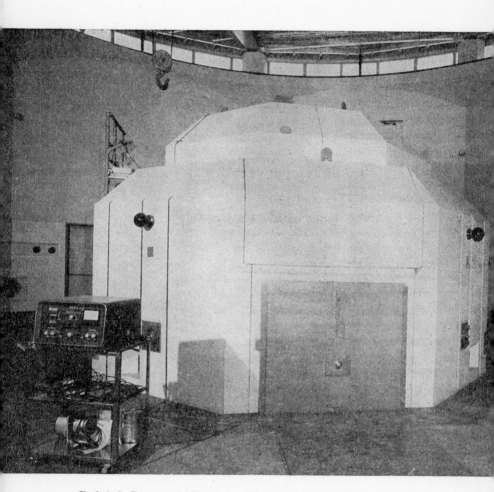

Raleigh Research Reactor, North Carolina State College

PHOTO BY JOHN MATTOX, VISUAL AIDS DEPARTMENT
NORTH CAROLINA STATE COLLEGE

INTRODUCTION TO
Nuclear Engineering

BY

Raymond L. Murray

Professor of Physics
North Carolina State College of
Agriculture and Engineering

PRENTICE-HALL, INC.
Englewood Cliffs, N. J.

A SELECTIVE LIST OF OTHER PRENTICE-HALL
TECHNICAL BOOKS:

APPLIED ATOMIC POWER, *by Fox, Smith, Sawyer, and Austin*
CHEMICAL THERMODYNAMICS: BASIC THEORY AND METHODS, *by I. Klotz*
COSMIC RAYS, *by L. Leprince-Ringuet*
EXPERIMENTAL SPECTROSCOPY, 2d Ed., *by R. Sawyer*
FUNDAMENTAL FORMULAS OF PHYSICS, *editor, D. Menzel*
FUNDAMENTALS OF QUANTUM MECHANICS, *by E. Persico*
HIGH-ENERGY PARTICLES, *by B. Rossi*
INDUSTRIAL ELECTRONIC ENGINEERING, *by W. Davis and H. Weed*
INTRODUCTION TO EXPERIMENTAL PHYSICS, *by W. Fretter*
MATHEMATICAL METHODS FOR SCIENTISTS AND ENGINEERS, *by L. Smith*
MODERN PHYSICS, *by F. Van Name*
NUCLEAR RADIATION PHYSICS, 2d Ed., *by R. Lapp and H. Andrews*
OXIDATION POTENTIALS, 2d Ed., *by W. Latimer*
PRACTICAL SPECTROSCOPY, *by Harrison, Lord, and Loofbourow*
PRINCIPLES OF AUTOMATIC CONTROLS, *by F. Nixon*
PROCEDURES IN EXPERIMENTAL PHYSICS, *by Strong, Cartwright, et al.*
QUANTUM CHEMISTRY, *by K. Pitzer*
STATISTICAL THERMODYNAMICS, *by M. Dole*
THERMODYNAMICS OF FLUID FLOW, *by N. Hall*

First printing............*March, 1954*
Second printing.........*November, 1954*
Third printing...............*June, 1955*
Fourth printing.........*September, 1955*
Fifth printing.................*April, 1956*
Sixth printing..............*March, 1957*

PRINTED IN THE UNITED STATES OF AMERICA
49096

To My Wife

PREFACE

Whether or not there exists a field of study that may be designated "nuclear engineering" or whether any individuals may be described as "nuclear engineers" is the subject of some controversy. One attitude is that each of the schools in conventional engineering should make available information on nuclear physics and atomic energy. Their students learn to modify their approaches to technical problems required by unusual processes and properties of materials. On this basis there is no distinct field of engineering that bears the prefix *nuclear*. The second point of view, to which the author subscribes, is that the term nuclear engineering may be validly applied to the design, construction, testing, and operation of equipment that makes use of or relates to nuclear processes and materials—particularly fissionable elements and their by-products. One immediately thinks of the nuclear reactor in this connection since it plays a central role in the atomic energy program. The staff at North Carolina State College take a broader view of the field, to include many related activities—the accumulation of nuclear fuel and other materials with unusual properties, the handling of radioactive chemicals or wastes, design of instruments for experimental particle detection, establishment of standards and practices in radiation protection, and the use of isotopes or neutrons for industrial or biological purposes. A very simple definition of the nuclear engineer is proposed: a person who has a strong background in the fundamentals of conventional engineering, plus a working understanding of the newer physics and chemistry and their relation to practical problems. Those who do not agree with the foregoing classifications are willing to grant that the results of research and development during World War II have had considerable impact on the engineering fields, and that some specialized training in atomic energy is of value, regardless of what descriptions and categories are used.

It is recognized that the on-the-job assignment of a new graduate with nuclear engineering training in an atomic energy project may be to a specialized field, such as shielding, heat transfer, reactor instruments, or reactor calculations. The overlapping and interrelation of the several aspects of the program require, however, that each worker be appreciative of the considerations and restrictions under which his colleagues work. The author feels strongly that the individual worker should have a concept of the over-all problems in addition to strength in his field of specialization. This book has been organized with this point of view. In the present nuclear energy field it is not possible for physicists to submit the design from the nuclear aspect to the mechanical or chemical engineers for construction, who later call in the electrical engineers to provide instrumentation. The distinction between "systems" and "components" as sometimes applied to the type of work done in the nuclear energy program is believed to be nonexistent at the level of the undergraduate engineering student and of little importance at the level of the graduate student.

This book is intended to serve as an introduction to the new developments in atomic energy, providing junior or senior engineering students with a perspective of the field and of the typical engineering problems that are encountered. Mathematical approaches to aspects that are not yet fully covered in standard engineering or physics courses are developed—isotope separation, reactor design and operation, special requirements on materials, heat transfer by liquid metals, regenerative production of fissionable materials (breeding), protection from nuclear radiations, and the application of reactors to transportation and power generation. The processes and functions of apparatus in the field of nuclear engineering can usually be understood with a background in college physics, chemistry and mathematics through calculus. The bulk of the contents of this book will be geared to the level of the engineering college junior or senior with the above prerequisites. Throughout the text, the teaching approach that has been adopted is to present first the qualitative concept, then an elementary mathematical analysis, and finally a review of the applications and significance of the material. Illustrative examples and problems for the student are provided. More elaborate subject matter is relegated to the Appendix, or reference is made to available papers or books on the subject. The reader or student may become concerned with the terseness with which many of the topics are treated. The author's conviction in this regard is that a direct, concise presentation of facts and principles is most urgently needed in this field, where the material is diffused through such a variety of isolated reports and articles.

Since most of the present activity in the field of nuclear energy, except for research in pure physics, is under the direction of the U.S. Atomic Energy Commission, much reference will be made to the publications of that organization, including the many declassified documents. With reference to the problem of information security, it will be understood that the discussion of some topics must remain on a general or strictly theoretical basis, since actual designs and operation characteristics remain classified. In keeping with AEC policy no discussion of details of atomic weapons, either of fissionable or thermonuclear type, has been undertaken.

The material included is based on a series of lectures given by the author in the undergraduate and graduate curricula in Nuclear Engineering at North Carolina State College. He is particularly indebted to former students for their interest and assistance. Appreciation is extended to Dr. Harry Soodak for his instructive lectures at the Oak Ridge National Laboratory in 1946 and to Dr. Clifford K. Beck, who initiated the course of study at North Carolina State College; the suggestions of Dean K. Pitzer, and Professors N. Hall, C. Bonilla, E. Creutz, and H. Gomberg, who read the book in manuscript form, are also received with thanks. The author is grateful, lastly, to his wife, Ilah Mae Rengler Murray, for suggestions and for preparation of the manuscript.

RAYMOND L. MURRAY

Raleigh, North Carolina

CONTENTS

CHAPTER 1

ATOMIC AND NUCLEAR PHYSICS

The new field that we call nuclear engineering arose as an application of the science of nuclear physics, much as the practical field of communications followed the theoretical predictions of electromagnetic waves, or as the present chemical industry has grown from the laboratory studies of a few early investigators. The principal achievement in the nuclear energy field to date has been the development of weapons of such destructiveness as to provide an important impact on world politics. Benefits to peacetime research and application to medicine, agriculture, and the physical sciences are the byproducts of the effort in World War II. The possibility is revealed of utilizing the newly discovered source of natural energy, uranium fission, for the practical generation of electricity or the propulsion of airplanes, submarines and other vehicles. Predictions on the length of time needed to demonstrate fully this possibility range from five to fifty years, depending on the degree of optimism of the authority on the subject. It seems clear, however, that the government, industry, and the scientific world are committed to continue the program until it is successful or conclusively proved impractical. Such a large scale endeavor requires workers with new training—in a field where facts, theories, standards and practices are different and unusual.

In the solution of most engineering problems it is sufficient to know the gross physical or chemical properties of substances, such as density, strength, melting and boiling points, electrical or heat conductivity and corrosion resistance. In the design of equipment, structures or machinery involving nuclear processes, however, the properties of the atoms of a material must be considered as well.*

* In this chapter we shall merely review the properties of atoms and nuclei with emphasis on basic working facts and formulas. A more extensive presentation of modern physics is deemed inadvisable in view of the many good texts available. The reader with a prior course in modern physics may read the following sections for review or may proceed immediately to Chapter 2; the student with a background of college introductory engineering physics may profit by more careful study.

1

1.1 The atomic nature of matter

The atom is usually defined as the smallest unit of matter that remains unchanged in a chemical reaction. Before the discovery of radioactivity, just before the beginning of the century, the atom was believed to be indivisible, since the only forces then known were chemical in nature. Experiments since have shown that the atom actually has a structure of its own, and is composed of more fundamental particles. The presence of one set of components, the electrons, was revealed by applying electric and magnetic fields in studies of electrical discharges in gases; the existence of the nucleus was demonstrated by bombarding atoms with particles from radioactive elements; the internal structure and constituents of nuclei were deduced from the effects produced by charged projectiles from particle accelerators such as the cyclotron. We shall first review the properties of atoms and molecules as such and progress toward the detailed examination of their internal structure.

Chemical reactions. The fact that the combining weights of elements and compounds always have the same proportions provides good evidence for the existence of elementary atomic particles. For example, 2 grams of hydrogen will react with 16 grams of oxygen to form water, or any fraction or multiple of these weights will do so. It was first concluded that one particle of each element, bearing an appropriate unique weight, engaged in the reaction. We now know, however, that for this case *2* hydrogen molecules and 1 oxygen molecule are involved. Equations of the type

$$2H_2 + O_2 \rightarrow 2H_2O$$

express our knowledge of either the single reactions or bulk reactions. The (relative) weights of the hydrogen molecule H_2 and the oxygen molecule O_2 are 2 and 32. The scale of relative weights (called atomic weights or molecular weights) was built up with the oxygen atom having the arbitrary value of 16. All such atoms were assumed to have the same weight. The terms "gram atomic weight" or "gram molecular weight" refer to a weight in grams equal to the relative weight. The term "valence" measures the number of atoms of hydrogen with which an atom of an element can combine (a negative valence), or that it can displace (a positive valence). Thus the existence of H_2O demonstrates that oxygen has a valence of -2; by comparing HCl and NaCl, it is shown that Na has a valence of $+1$.

It appears that the average student has a periodic table "vocabulary" of about 20 of the 98 elements. Much time and embarrassment can be saved by learning the names and symbols of the elements as given in Table 1.1, page 4.

Gases. A gas or vapor is pictured as composed of a large number of molecules or atoms in continuous random motion. The volume occupied at 0°C temperature and atmospheric pressure by a gram molecular weight (mole) is the same for all gases, 22.4 liters. Further, the number of molecules in a gram molecular weight is the same for all substances, 6.023×10^{23}, labeled Avogadro's number. Thus the number of molecules in a cubic centimeter of gas is $6.023 \times 10^{23}/22{,}400$ or 2.7×10^{19}. The weight of any atom or molecule may be computed from Avogadro's number and the weight of a mole. For example the hydrogen molecule with a molecular weight of approximately 2 g has a particle weight of $2/(6.023 \times 10^{23}) = 3.32 \times 10^{-24}$ gram. The particles are small, of the order of 10^{-8} cm in diameter, with a slow increase in size with molecular weight. The particle speeds cover a range from zero to infinity (in principle) with an average of about 10^5 cm/sec at ordinary temperatures. The average kinetic energy $\frac{1}{2}mv^2$ is recalled to be a measure of the temperature of the substance. The higher the temperature, the greater is the molecular agitation. A more exact connection is provided by the relation $\frac{1}{2}mv^2 = 3kT/2$ where T is expressed in absolute degrees and k is Boltzmann's constant, 1.38×10^{-16} erg/°K. It may be assumed for many purposes that when molecules collide with each other or with the walls of their container, they lose no energy. There is however, a reversal of the normal component of momentum upon collision with the wall that provides the mechanism of gas pressure. The rate of collision between particles is high, because of their speed and the large number of particles per unit volume. The average distance traveled in free flight between collisions at atmospheric pressure is around 10^{-6} cm.

Relation of atoms and electricity. The conduction of an electric current by a salt solution has long been explained on the assumption that molecules dissociate into *ions* bearing charges of opposite signs, for example

$$\mathrm{NaCl} \quad \rightarrow \quad \mathrm{Na^+ + Cl^-}$$

The positively-charged $\mathrm{Na^+}$ ions may be extracted by a negative electrode (cathode) immersed in the solution, while the $\mathrm{Cl^-}$ ions flow

TABLE 1.1

ATOMIC WEIGHTS OF THE ELEMENTS

Element	Symbol	Atomic Number	Atomic Weight	Element	Symbol	Atomic Number	Atomic Weight
Actinium	Ac	89	225.	Mercury	Hg	80	200.61
Aluminum	Al	13	26.97	Molybdenum	Mo	42	95.95
Americium	Am	95	241.	Neodymium	Nd	60	144.27
Antimony	Sb	51	121.76	Neon	Ne	10	20.183
Argon	A	18	39.944	Neptunium	Np	93	239.
Arsenic	As	33	74.91	Nickel	Ni	28	58.69
Astatine	At	85	211.	Nitrogen	N	7	14.008
Barium	Ba	56	137.36	Osmium	Os	76	190.2
Berkelium	Bk	97	243.	Oxygen	O	8	16.0000
Beryllium	Be	4	9.013	Palladium	Pd	46	106.7
Bismuth	Bi	83	209.00	Phosphorus	P	15	30.98
Boron	B	5	10.82	Platinum	Pt	78	195.23
Bromine	Br	35	79.916	Plutonium	Pu	94	239.
Cadmium	Cd	48	112.41	Polonium	Po	84	210.
Californium	Cf	98	244.	Potassium	K	19	39.096
Calcium	Ca	20	40.08	Praseodymium	Pr	59	140.92
Carbon	C	6	12.010	Promethium	Pm	61	147.
Cerium	Ce	58	140.13	Protactinium	Pa	91	231.
Cesium	Cs	55	132.91	Radium	Ra	88	226.05
Chlorine	Cl	17	35.457	Radon	Rn	86	222.
Chromium	Cr	24	52.01	Rhenium	Re	75	186.31
Cobalt	Co	27	58.94	Rhodium	Rh	45	102.91
Columbium	Cb	41	92.91	Rubidium	Rb	37	85.48
Copper	Cu	29	63.54	Ruthenium	Ru	44	101.7
Curium	Cm	96	242.	Samarium	Sm	62	150.43
Dysprosium	Dy	66	162.46	Scandium	Sc	21	45.10
Erbium	Er	68	167.2	Selenium	Se	34	78.96
Europium	Eu	63	152.0	Silicon	Si	14	28.06
Fluorine	F	9	19.00	Silver	Ag	47	107.880
Francium	Fr	87	221.	Sodium	Na	11	22.997
Gadolinium	Gd	64	156.9	Strontium	Sr	38	87.63
Gallium	Ga	31	69.72	Sulfur	S	16	32.066
Germanium	Ge	32	72.60	Tantalum	Ta	73	180.88
Gold	Au	79	197.2	Technetium	Tc	43	99.
Hafnium	Hf	72	178.6	Tellurium	Te	52	127.61
Helium	He	2	4.003	Terbium	Tb	65	159.2
Holmium	Ho	67	164.94	Thallium	Tl	81	204.39
Hydrogen	H	1	1.0080	Thorium	Th	90	232.12
Indium	In	49	114.76	Thulium	Tm	69	169.4
Iodine	I	53	126.92	Tin	Sn	50	118.70
Iridium	Ir	77	193.1	Titanium	Ti	22	47.90
Iron	Fe	26	55.85	Tungsten	W	74	183.92
Krypton	Kr	36	83.7	Uranium	U	92	238.07
Lanthanum	La	57	138.92	Vanadium	V	23	50.95
Lead	Pb	82	207.21	Xenon	Xe	54	131.3
Lithium	Li	3	6.940	Ytterbium	Yb	70	173.04
Lutetium	Lu	71	174.99	Yttrium	Y	39	88.92
Magnesium	Mg	12	24.32	Zinc	Zn	30	65.38
Manganese	Mn	25	54.93	Zirconium	Zr	40	91.22

toward the positive electrode (anode). Faraday's law of electrolysis expresses quantitatively the relation between current and the weights of chemicals that are liberated by or deposited on the electrodes. For example, if two electrodes of opposite polarity are inserted in a silver nitrate solution ($AgNO_3$), the Ag^+ ions deposit out on the negative electrode. A weight of 107.88 g, the atomic weight of silver, is liberated on the passage of 96,500 coulombs of electricity. The same amount of electricity will also deposit one atomic weight of any other (monovalent) element. If the element has a valence n, then 96,500 coulombs will deposit only a fraction $1/n$ of a gram atomic weight. Since the number of atoms in a mole is the same for all elements (6.023×10^{23}), it immediately follows that each monovalent atom carries the same unit of electricity. The value of this basic charge is 96,500 coulombs/$6.023 \times 10^{23} = 1.60 \times 10^{-19}$ coulomb. We attribute this quantity of electricity to an elementary particle, the *electron*. An ion of an atom of positive valence lacks one or more electrons, and an ion of an atom of negative valence has an excess. A gas may also be made to conduct electricity by applying a high electrical potential between two electrodes in a glass discharge tube. Ions are created from the neutral gas by dissociation analogous to the effects in a salt solution. The conduction and the characteristic luminosity is enhanced by reducing the pressure within the tube. At very low pressures, however, the discharge will disappear for lack of a medium to carry it. By virtue of the light emitted by the ionized gas, the path of the "rays" that emanate from the cathode may be detected. The rays may be deflected by an electric or a magnetic field, which indicates that they are composed of charged particles (electrons) rather than light. A simple experiment devised by Thomson in England may be performed to measure the ratio of charge to mass of the electron. The stream of electrons that flows toward the anode in a discharge tube is allowed to pass through a small opening in the anode into the space behind it. See Fig. 1.1. A luminous spot indicates the end of the electron path. The electron beam may be deflected either by the electric field between a pair of electrically charged plates or by a magnetic field between the poles of an electromagnet. The ratio of charge e to mass m of the electron can be computed from the measured deflections under these influences and the magnitudes of the electric potential difference and magnet current. From the experimental value of $e/m = 1.76 \times 10^{10}$ coulombs/g, and the electronic charge of 1.60×10^{-19} coulomb, the electronic mass is found to be 9.11×10^{-28} gram. The electron mass is smaller by a factor of 1/1837 than the lightest atom, that of hydrogen. Because

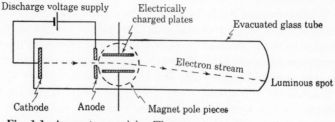

Fig. 1.1. Apparatus used by Thomson to measure ratio e/m for electrons.

of this small mass, the speeds attained by electrons under the influence of electric forces are very much higher than speeds of familiar moving objects. Let us compute the energy and velocity of an electron that traverses the space between two condenser plates differing in potential by 1 volt. By the definition of potential difference, the work done on the particle is $E = V$ (volts) $\times e$ (coulombs) $= (1.0)(1.6 \times 10^{-19}) = 1.6 \times 10^{-19}$ joule $= 1.6 \times 10^{-12}$ erg. The work done on the electron results in a gain in kinetic energy of an amount $\frac{1}{2}mv^2$. For consistency of units we must express the mass in grams and the speed in centimeters per second. Solving for v, we find

$$v = \sqrt{2Ve/m}$$
$$= \sqrt{2(1.60 \times 10^{-12})/(9.11 \times 10^{-28})} = 6 \times 10^7 \text{ cm/sec}$$

The amount of energy required to transfer an electron through a 1-v potential difference serves as a convenient energy unit, the *electron volt*, abbreviated "ev." The conversion factors are

$$1 \text{ ev} = 1.60 \times 10^{-19} \text{ (volt-coulomb)} = 1.60 \times 10^{-12} \text{ erg}$$

Although the ev unit is commonly defined by invoking the electron, it may be applied to any moving particle, or to stored energy. For example, let us find the energy in ev for a hydrogen atom moving at a speed of 2.2×10^5 cm/sec. This would correspond to the most likely speed of particles of atomic hydrogen gas (if it could be maintained at room temperature).

$$E = \tfrac{1}{2}mv^2 = \tfrac{1}{2}(1.66 \times 10^{-24} \text{ g})(2.2 \times 10^5 \text{ cm/sec})^2$$
$$= 4.0 \times 10^{-14} \text{ erg}$$

or $E = 4.0 \times 10^{-14} \text{ (erg)}/1.60 \times 10^{-12} \text{ (erg/ev)} = 0.025 \text{ ev}$

One of the convenient uses of the electron volt unit is in comparing particle energies with chemical binding energies. For instance, it is evident from the experimental fact that it requires about 2-v potential difference to dissociate water into its component gases that the energy of motion of the hydrogen atom above is considerably less than the potential energy of binding in the water molecule. The energies characteristic of nuclear reactions are much higher than those of chemical reactions. As we shall see later, the fission of a uranium atom results in the liberation of 200 *million* ev. The unit "mev," representing 1 million electron volts, is convenient in describing nuclear processes.

1.2 The Rutherford-Bohr picture of the atom

Many optical effects may be explained by assuming that light is an electromagnetic wave. One of the most striking examples is the striated interference patterns from light that has passed through a narrow slit. (Look at a light source through the space between two closed fingers, with the eye about two inches away.) The bright and dark may be associated with addition or subtraction of wave amplitudes. The phenomenon of refraction, or bending of light in passing from a less dense medium (optically) such as air to a more dense medium such as glass can also be explained in terms of waves with different velocities of propagation. The conventional attributes of a wave: velocity c (3×10^{10} cm/sec for light in a vacuum), wavelength λ, and frequency ν, related by $c = \lambda\nu$, were firmly established as describing light. For example, one yellow sodium D line has a wavelength of 5890 Ångstroms (1 Å = 10^{-8} cm). Its frequency is thus

$$(3 \times 10^{10} \text{ cm/sec})/(5890 \times 10^{-8}) = 5.1 \times 10^{14}/\text{sec}$$

The deductions made by Planck, however, at the start of the twentieth century, led to the sharply conflicting point of view that light consisted of individual particles of energy (in ergs) $E = h\nu$ where h was a constant 6.62×10^{-27} erg-sec. Prior to his analysis, the amount of light of different frequencies that is emitted from an internally-heated metal object had been measured by crystal prisms and sensitive heat radiation detectors as sketched in Fig. 1.2. Attempts to explain the shape of the typical graphs of intensity against wavelength by imagining the solid to be vibrating with different modes failed to give agreement with experiment. Planck proposed that the

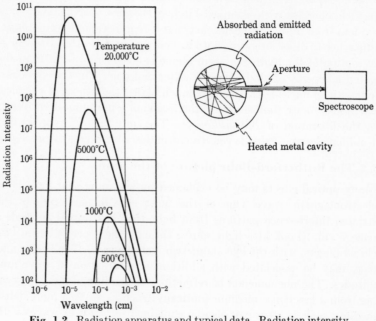

Fig. 1.2. Radiation apparatus and typical data. Radiation intensity is in ergs/sec-cm²-millimicron.

light was stored, absorbed and emitted within the cavity in units of energy of amount $h\nu$ by individual "oscillators" embedded in the walls of the substance. One of the phenomena that could be explained by these new particles, called quanta or photons, was the photoelectric effect. If the surface of one of two metal electrodes in an evacuated tube is illuminated with light, electrons are ejected from the metal, and can be measured by a closed circuit joining the plates. A photo-electric cell is shown in Fig. 1.3. The electrons are released with enough energy to move against an electric field designed to repel them. Estimates show that the time it would take for light *as a wave motion* to be absorbed and its energy concentrated on one electron in the metal far exceeds the measured response time of the photocell. Thus a duality of nature must be recognized—that under certain circumstances light has the properties of a wave, under others that of a particle. Rather than engaging in fruitless arguments as to which of these pictures is correct, the modern view is to state that

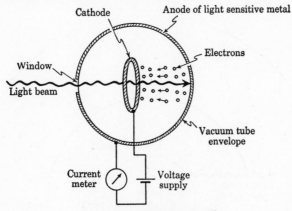

Fig. 1.3. Photoelectric cell.

both are aspects of reality that transcend models. As far as is known, the finer details of physical processes can only be described by the abstract mathematical terms of quantum mechanics.

The discovery of natural radioactivity, in which atomic particles

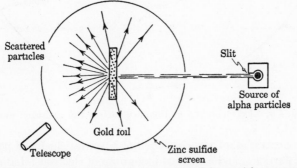

Fig. 1.4. Rutherford's method of measuring alpha particle scattering.

such as helium ions (alpha particles) are emitted by certain heavy elements such as radium, made available a new research tool. Rutherford in England found that the scattering of a high-velocity charged particle in a thin foil of gold, with apparatus shown in Fig. 1.4, could be explained in terms of a coulomb force interaction between the alpha particle and a very small positively charged "nucleus." The amount of charge carried by the central core was found to be numerically equal to about one-half of the atomic weight, which suggested

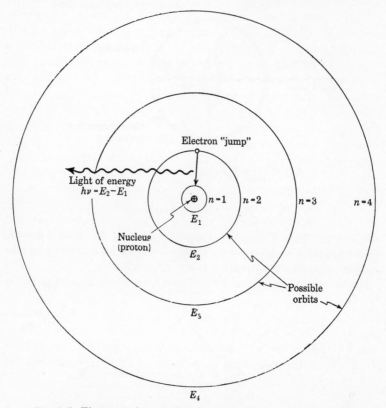

Fig. 1.5. Electron orbits in Bohr's model of the nydrogen atom.

that the neutral atom was composed of a central cluster of positively charged particles, and a surrounding group of electrons. Later it was proved that the nuclear charge and the total electron charge were each equal to the atomic number Z. The diameter of the nucleus studied by Rutherford was approximately 10^{-12} cm. It will be recalled that the atomic diameter was about 10^{-8} cm, which means that the nucleus is very small and dense in comparison with the complete atom. This qualitative picture was put on an accurate numerical basis by Niels Bohr of Denmark in 1913, with his now-famous hydrogen atom model. In one stroke the atomic structure and the nature of emission of light were explained by his theory. Bohr pictured the hydrogen atom as being composed of a single negative electron moving in a circular planetary orbit about the positive nucleus. He blended basic laws of mechanics and electricity with the quantum concept. In his analysis, for example, the electrostatic attraction of the two charges provided the necessary centripetal force mv^2/r to keep the electron in its circular path. The electron was assumed to have many possible orbits, each characterized by a definite radius r and by an energy E_r. One law of classical electricity, that accelerated charges radiate energy, was abandoned. Electrons would spiral into the nucleus if this law were applicable. The production of spectral lines of frequency ν was taken as the result of a "jump" of the electron to a smaller orbit, satisfying the Planck relation $\Delta E = h\nu$. These "stationary" orbits, Fig. 1.5, were determined by an entirely new relation in physics, that the angular momentum mvr of the electron about the nucleus had to be an integer times $h/2\pi$ where h is again Planck's constant. The integers, labeled n, were called quantum numbers. The formulas derived by Bohr for the hydrogen atom are listed below.

$$r = n^2 r_0 \qquad \text{(orbit radius)}$$

where $r_0 = \hbar^2/me^2$ is the radius of the smallest orbit. The symbol $\hbar$ is merely $h/2\pi = 1.05 \times 10^{-27}$ erg-sec. Inserting $m = 9.11 \times 10^{-28}$ g and $e = 4.80 \times 10^{-10}$ statcoulomb, we find $r_0 = 0.53 \times 10^{-8}$ cm. That atomic dimensions are of the order of 10^{-8} cm is thus checked.

$$E = -me^4/2n^2\hbar^2 \qquad \text{(orbit energy)}$$

The negative sign implies that work must be done in completely removing the electron from the atom. The maximum amount of energy E_1 must be supplied when the electron is originally in its smallest orbit, for which $n = 1$. Substituting known numbers, $E_1 = 2.2 \times 10^{-11}$ erg or 13.5 ev. This result agrees very well with the experimentally measured energy of ionization. The frequency of light due to electron jumps between any two orbits characterized by n_1 and n_2 is computed from

$$\nu = \Delta E/h = E_1/h(1/n_1^2 - 1/n_2^2)$$

The real test of the theory was the explanation of long-established empirical relations between the observed frequencies of the light from a hydrogen discharge. Since 1913, Bohr's theory has been found to be incomplete, in light of the more rigorous wave mechanics. It still stands as a brilliant analysis that greatly stimulated future scientific work, and as a useful means of visualizing atomic structure. As an example, the process of x-ray production is explained from a model of the more complicated atoms that is analogous to the hydrogen atom. An x-ray tube consists of an evacuated envelope with an electron emitting cathode and a metal target anode, as illustrated in Fig. 1.6. Electrons, accelerated across the space, bombard the target,

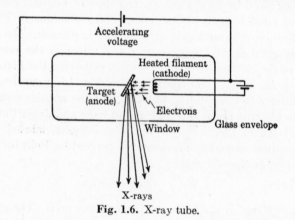

Fig. 1.6. X-ray tube.

resulting in the liberation of high-energy light rays that display certain dominant frequencies. An atom of a heavy element that serves as target is assumed to consist of a nucleus, about which two electrons circulate in what is labeled the K shell. Farther out is the L shell with eight electrons, the M shell with eighteen, and so on. If the atomic number is less than the sum of the number of electrons that it takes to fill all shells, the last shell is incomplete. The exclusion principle, first stated by Pauli, gives a more fundamental justification of the number of electrons allowed in each orbit. Electrons may be characterized by a set of four quantum numbers, related to their angular momentum in the orbit and their intrinsic angular momentum or "spin." Pauli's principle is that no two electrons can have the same set of quantum numbers. It may be shown that only two electrons may occupy the K shell, only eight may be in the L shell, etc. From this atom model, shown in Fig. 1.7, these radiations can be explained. An incoming electron dislodges a like particle from the K shell of the atom. The system is more stable the closer the elec-

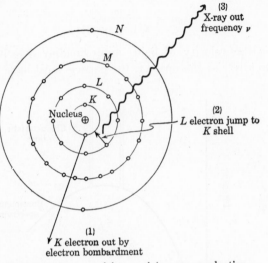

(3)
X-ray out
frequency ν

(2)
L electron jump to
K shell

Nucleus

(1)
K electron out by
electron bombardment

Fig. 1.7. Atom model to explain x-ray production.

trons are to the nucleus; if a space in an orbit is available, an L-shell electron is prompted to "jump" to the K shell. Radiation of frequency ν appropriate to the difference in energy of the two levels is emitted, which constitutes the characteristic x-ray lines of Fig. 1.8. (The background light of continuously varying wavelength that is also observed is attributed to the radiation by accelerated incoming electrons.) Although the wavelengths of the lines are measured by use of the diffraction principle, a wave phenomenon, it is interesting to note that the collisions of x-rays with electrons in matter must be explained on a particle collision basis. This process, called the Compton effect, is also of importance in shielding from nuclear radiations. A résumé of the consequences of the theory of relativity is needed before the mechanism can be quantitatively understood. Albert Einstein, in 1905, made two assumptions on which his famous theory of relativity is founded: (a) That the laws of physics may be expressed in the same form in the coordinates of any reference system; (b) That the velocity of light will be found to be the same by all observers, regardless of the motions of their frames of reference. An important consequence of these postulates is that *an object in motion has a greater mass than when at rest*. If the rest mass is m_0, the mass at speed v is

$$m = \frac{m_0}{\sqrt{1 - (v/c)^2}}$$

where c is the velocity of light, approximately 3×10^{10} cm/sec. In order to arrive at this speed v, the particle must have been accel-

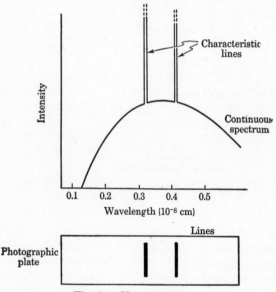

Fig. 1.8. X-ray spectrum.

erated by a force, implying that work was done. The kinetic energy increase is given by the familiar formula

$$T = \int F \, dx$$

By Newton's second law, $F = dp/dt$ where p is the momentum mv. Integration yields the result

$$T = (m - m_0)c^2$$

which shows that kinetic energy and mass increases are synonymous.

It should be noted that for velocities much less than c this formula may be approximated by the usual

$$T \simeq \tfrac{1}{2}m_0v^2$$

At a speed of $0.9\ c = 2.7 \times 10^9$ cm/sec, a particle is 2.3 times as heavy as expected. Machines such as the betatron are capable of accelerating electrons to energies of 100 mev, at which the particle speed is $0.99999c$, and the electron mass is *194* times the rest value. It should be emphasized that the formulas above refer to *all* moving objects, not just to electrons. Now consider a collision between a light quantum of energy $E = h\nu$ and an electron of rest mass m_0. The electron will recoil with kinetic energy supplied by the quantum; the latter now has a new lower energy $E' = h\nu'$ implying a new frequency ν'. Both momentum and energy must be conserved in the interaction. For the electron, momentum is given by mv, using the actual mass; for the quantum, momentum is given by $h\nu/c$. If the collision is of the head-on type, with maximum photon energy loss, the equations are simply

$$h\nu/c = -h\nu'/c + mv \qquad \text{(momentum)}$$
$$h\nu = h\nu' + (m - m_0)c^2 \qquad \text{(energy)}$$

Eliminating v between the equations yields the *maximum* change in wavelength,

$$\lambda' - \lambda = 2h/m_0c = 0.048 \text{ Å}$$

For collisions in which the quantum is deflected through any general angle ϕ from the original motion, one finds the relation

$$\lambda' - \lambda = (h/m_0c)(1 - \cos \phi)$$

Let us estimate the *maximum* change of energy for a 50-kev x-ray. The original energy is $(0.050 \text{ mev})(1.6 \times 10^{-6} \text{ erg/mev}) = 8.0 \times 10^{-8}$ erg. Thus $\nu = E/h = (8.0 \times 10^{-8} \text{ erg})/(6.62 \times 10^{-27} \text{ erg-sec}) = 1.21 \times 10^{19}$/sec, $\lambda = c/\nu = (3 \times 10^{10} \text{ cm/sec})/(1.21 \times 10^{19}/\text{sec}) = 0.248 \times 10^{-8}$ cm. Thus $\lambda' = 0.248 + 0.048 = 0.296$ Å. Working back, we find the new energy E' is 42 kev.

1.3 Nuclear structure

Experimental apparatus very similar to that used to measure the charge to mass ratio of the electron was adapted for the study of the heavy residual ion or nucleus. In the first work of Thomson, the roles of cathode and anode were reversed. "Positive rays" coming through a hole in the cathode were again analyzed by combined electric and magnetic fields. Improvements were made later in the resolution of the patterns the high speed ions made on a fluorescent screen or a photographic plate. With such equipment, the existence of isotopes, nuclei of the element having different masses, was discovered. A typical example is the pattern observed with the element neon, atomic number 10, atomic weight 20.2. Instead of one line on the photographic plate, two were found, corresponding to atomic weights 20 and *22*. The relative intensity of darkening was such that it was clear that neon consisted of these two components, in such proportions that the observed atomic weight of the natural *element* was duplicated. This discovery explained the reason that some elements had atomic weights very close to a multiple of the integer nearest the atomic weight of hydrogen, 1.008, while others had weights lying between integers. For example, the atomic weight of carbon was 12.01, and uranium 238.07, but those for chlorine and cadmium were 35.46 and 112.41 respectively. We now know that the chlorine is made up of two isotopes, $_{17}Cl^{35}$ and $_{17}Cl^{37}$ in proportions 75 and 25 per cent. The superscripts denote mass number A, the nearest whole number to the actual relative weight. The symbol A for mass number is distinguished from M for actual mass (relative to oxygen). The subscripts refer to the atomic number, Z. The two components of chlorine were never detected chemically since they react almost identically in combination with other elements. Some elements have as many as ten isotopes spread over a range of many units of atomic weight. Although uranium appears to have only one isotope, three occur in nature: U^{238} (99.29%), U^{235} (0.71%) and U^{234}, in insignificant amounts. Systematic study of the hundreds of isotopes reveals that all are without doubt composed of integral multiples of a weight that is close to that of the hydrogen atom. (We shall reserve discussion of the important small discrepancies until later.) If nuclei, in which almost the entire weight of the atom resides, were actually composed of ions of the hydrogen atom (protons), the nuclear charge would be A rather than Z. The conclusion was first reached that there were enough electrons in the nucleus to neutralize the positive charge of the protons from A down to the actual value Z. With the experimental discovery of the *neutron* (*n*), a particle of mass very close to that of the proton, but having no charge, the theory of electrons in the nucleus was abandoned.

The present picture is that an atom has Z electrons, surrounding a nucleus composed of Z protons and $A - Z = N$ neutrons. Figure 1.9 shows the "construction" of several of the lighter elements and isotopes. Many improvements in the simple apparatus that first showed the existence of isotopes were made over the course of years.

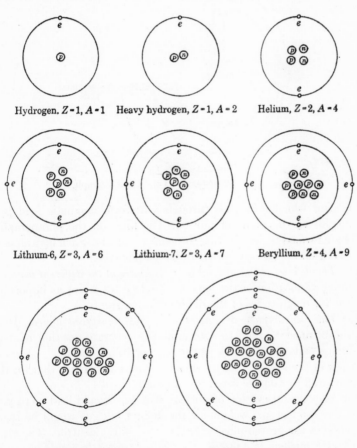

Fig. 1.9. Atomic and nuclear structure for light elements and isotopes. These representations are not to scale, since nuclear dimensions are of the order of 10^{-12} cm, while those of atoms are 10^{-8} cm.

Various mass spectrographs or spectrometers making use of combined electric and magnetic fields were developed. Figure 1.10 shows the basic components of the Dempster-type mass spectrograph. Positive ions are accelerated through the slit system S into the radial electric

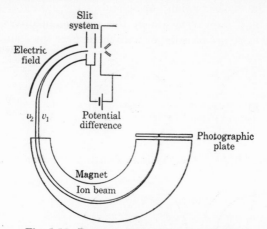

Fig. 1.10. Dempster-type mass spectrograph.

field, after which they pass through a uniform magnetic field perpendicular to the plane of motion. The lines on the photographic plate are formed by ions having the same e/m ratio. Such instruments may be used for two somewhat different purposes:

(1) *The determination of relative abundances of the different isotopes.* Accuracy of location of the ions on the detector is not as important as that for magnitudes of the different ion currents.

(2) *The measurement of masses to several significant figures.* Here resolution must be high to determine the accurate position relative to some standard mass such as the oxygen-16 isotope.

A few of the isotopic masses thus measured along with that for the neutron and proton are listed in Table 1.2.

Our previous discussion of nuclear structure would lead us to predict that the isotopic weight for the helium nucleus would be twice the mass of the proton plus twice the mass of the neutron. The mass of the He nucleus is 4.00277 (the isotopic mass less two electrons each contributing 0.00055 units). Checking our prediction, by subtraction we find

$$2(1.00759) + 2(1.00898) - 4.00277 = 0.03037$$

TABLE 1.2

REPRESENTATIVE ISOTOPIC WEIGHTS

Isotope	Weight, M *	Isotope	Weight, M *
$_1H^1$	1.00814	$_3Li^7$	7.01822
proton	1.00759	$_8O^{16}$	16.0000 ...
neutron	1.00898	$_{26}Fe^{56}$	55.9571
$_1H^2$	2.01473	$_{47}Ag^{107}$	106.950
$_2He^4$	4.00387	$_{82}Pb^{208}$	208.048

* On physical scale, with O^{16} as a standard, in contrast with the chemical scale where the element oxygen has a mass of exactly 16. See articles by C W. LI, et al., *Phys. Rev.*, *83*, 512 (1951); *Phys. Rev.*, *88*, 1040 (1952).

This discrepancy is far greater than the possible instrument error. The explanation is based on the principle of equivalence of mass and energy of Einstein, which had been presented many years before the above data were available. This fundamental law of nature states that matter and energy are forms of the same entity. This is a more general statement of the principle of relativity that describes the fact that kinetic energy is associated with an increase of the mass of a particle, as discussed in Section 1.2. Numerical correspondence in the cgs system of units is expressed by the relation

$$E \text{ (ergs)} = m \text{ (grams)}(c \text{ cm/sec})^2$$

where c is the velocity of light, 2.99790×10^{10} cm/sec. Under proper conditions matter may be converted into energy and vice versa. In place of the former separate laws of conservation of matter and conservation of energy the new law of conservation of mass-energy is substituted. The physical meaning of the defect in masses above thus becomes the following: at the time the helium nucleus was formed in nature from the elementary protons and neutrons, the extra mass was liberated as radiant or heat energy; to disrupt the helium nucleus completely, one would have to supply the same amount of energy. Now the energy equivalent of one unit of atomic weight (amu) is

$$E = (1.66^- \times 10^{-24} \text{ g})(3^- \times 10^{10} \text{ cm/sec})^2$$

or
$$= 14.916 \times 10^{-4} \text{ erg}$$

$$E = (14.916 \times 10^{-4} \text{ erg})/(1.60186 \times 10^{-6} \text{ erg/mev})$$

$$= 931.15 \text{ mev}$$

The energy defect for the He nucleus is thus $(931.15)(0.03037) = 28.2$ mev. The process of forming new elements from lighter particles, called fusion, is the basis of the "hydrogen bomb." For such purposes the use of reactions such as

$$_1H^2 + {}_1H^2 \rightarrow {}_2He^3 + {}_0n^1 + \text{energy}$$
$$_1H^3 + {}_1H^1 \rightarrow {}_2He^4 + \text{energy}$$

would be more practical than the attempt to combine four separate particles. The energy that must be supplied to disrupt the helium nucleus is a measure of the attractive forces between the protons and neutrons. Hence the mass defect may alternatively be called binding energy. Formally,

$$\text{binding energy} = 931.15 \left[Zm_H + (A - Z)m_n - M \right] \text{mev}$$

where M is the isotopic mass, including its Z electrons, m_n is the neutron mass and m_H is the mass of the hydrogen atom. Each atom in the above relation has one electron mass included with the proton mass. The total binding energy increases with mass number of the

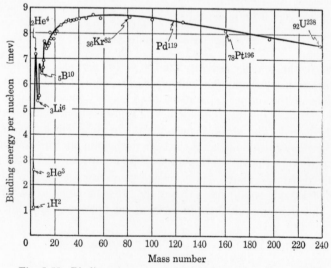

Fig. 1.11. Binding energy per particle in nuclei. [From R. E. Lapp and H. L. Andrews, *Nuclear Radiation Physics*, 2d Ed. Prentice-Hall, Inc., 1954.]

nucleus simply because there are more particles to attract each other. The binding energy *per nucleon* (proton or neutron) rises rapidly in the light element region to a maximum of almost 9 mev, near mass 60, then falls slowly to about 7 mev at the top of the periodic table, as shown in Fig. 1.11. This trend may be explained on the basis of the different forces and resultant potential energies that are present:

(1) *Attraction of nucleons for each other.* This is a cohesion effect, as in a drop of liquid. The energy of attraction is proportional to the number of pairs of nucleons and thus to the total number A. Since the particles are visualized as fitting compactly together, A is proportional to the nuclear volume.

(2) *Coulomb repulsion of protons.* Each pair of charges exerts a force e^2/r^2 on each other and the total electrostatic energy of a sphere with Z protons is $3Z^2e^2/5R$ where R is the nuclear radius (approximately $1.4 \times 10^{-13} A^{1/3}$).

(3) *Surface effects.* Particles lying on the surface of the nucleus are not as tightly bound as those surrounded with other nucleons. The binding goes up as the ratio of surface to volume decreases. This energy contribution is proportional to the surface area, i.e. to $A^{2/3}$.

(4) *Excess of neutrons.* The most stable nucleus, excluding charge and surface effects, would be one in which the numbers of neutrons and protons were equal, i.e., $N = A$ or $A/2 = Z$. An excess of one or the other results in a tendency toward instability or a weakening of the binding. A contribution to the total binding energy proportional to $(A/2 - Z)^2/A$ is assumed to describe this effect. For heavy elements there is a neutron excess with $A/2$ considerably greater than Z. This arrangement is more stable, however, than if there were an equality of neutrons and protons, since the coulomb repulsion is smaller.

1.4 Properties of rays and particles from radioactive materials

The three most important products of radioactive decay are alpha particles, beta particles, and gamma rays. The first of these is a helium nucleus, the second is an electron and the third consists of electromagnetic radiations usually in excess of x-ray energies. Their properties are described below.

Alpha particles. Many of the heavy radioactive elements spontaneously eject these ions, of mass 4, charge 2, to become a new element. The example reaction equation

$$_{92}U^{238} \rightarrow \ _2He^4 + \ _{90}Th^{234}$$

shows how the mass number is reduced by four while the atomic number goes down by two units. The nucleus of a heavy element such as U^{238} can be visualized as a closely bound group of protons, neutrons and alpha particles, in constant motion, contained within a radius of about 10^{-12} cm. The competition of two entirely different types of force determines whether an alpha particle gets out of a nucleus. The first type of force is the electrostatic repulsion. The second is the nuclear force which has no counterpart in familiar large scale phenomena. The latter has the property of being essentially zero except for very short distances of separation ($\simeq 10^{-13}$ cm) of two particles. The relation of these two forces is usually described by a

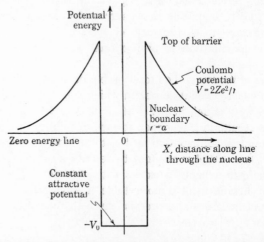

Fig. 1.12. Potential energy diagram for alpha particle and radioactive nucleus.

potential energy diagram as shown in Fig. 1.12. When the alpha particle is in the nucleus, its energy corresponds to the level near the bottom of the well. If by some means it gains sufficient energy from other nuclear particles, it can surmount the barrier and be accelerated "down hill" or out of the nucleus. One of the unusual predictions of quantum mechanics is that the particle can escape even if it does not have this amount of energy. There is a finite but small chance that the alpha particle can be anywhere in space, including out of the well. This process is often described by the phrase "tunneling through the barrier," which helps visualize a phenomenon of a class that, as stated before, transcends physical models. The theory is verified by experimental measurements of the rate of decay of the heavy nuclei and the emitted alpha particle energy. As would be expected, the more energetic alpha particles are, the more likely is their escape.

Although alpha particles are heavy and energetic, they are able to penetrate only short distances in matter. Two rough rules are: (a) Most alphas are stopped by a sheet of paper; (b) The range in air is 1 cm for each 2 mev of energy. They are stopped by the interaction of their charge with that of the electrons in the material they pass through. As the positive ion passes by an atom, the attractive force e^2/r^2 builds up to a maximum as the alpha approaches and falls away as the alpha recedes. Electrons may be torn away from the atom; the energy to achieve this ionization must come from the alpha particles. If the alpha particles have a very high speed, they do not remain near the atom long enough to give the necessary impulse. As their speed is reduced, however, the electrons have time to adjust themselves to the passing effect and eventually the helium ion captures its normal complement of two electrons. A typical rate of ionization in air as a function of distance from the alpha source is shown in Fig. 1.13.

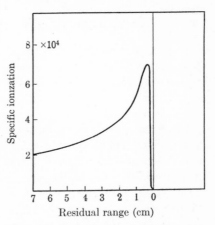

Fig. 1.13. Ionization per centimeter of air by alpha particles.

Beta particles. Electrons emitted by radioactive nuclei are called beta particles, a name given before they were identified as electrons. In a previous section, we pointed out that there were no electrons in the nuclei as such. This apparent paradox may be explained by assuming that the source of electrons is the following transformation of a neutron within the nucleus

$$_0n^1 \rightarrow {}_1H^1 + {}_{-1}e^0$$

which converts the parent element into one with Z greater by one, but with no change in A. An example is

$$_{82}Pb^{214} \rightarrow {}_{83}Bi^{214} + {}_{-1}e^0$$

Accompanying each beta particle is a new type of particle, the *neutrino*, having a very small mass and no charge, but carrying, on the average, around two-thirds of the total energy released in the beta disintegration. The neutrino penetrates matter very readily, and apparently plays no important role in reactor technology or radiation safety.

The penetration of matter by the beta particles is generally much higher than that by alphas. Only a few millimeters of metal such as aluminum are required to stop these electrons. A rough range-energy relation applicable for beta energies above about 0.8 mev is Feather's formula:

$$\text{range (g/cm}^2) \simeq 0.546E \text{ (mev)} - 0.16$$

Their reaction with the electrons of the atoms is similar to that for alpha particles, since both are energetic charged particles. The difference is in degree, associated with the fact that the electron has a much lower mass than the alpha particle.

Gamma rays. The origin of x-rays was described in a previous section as due to the changes in energy of the electrons in atoms. Gamma rays, which are physically the same as x-rays in that they are quanta or electromagnetic radiations, originate from energy changes within the *nucleus*. When an alpha particle is emitted from a heavy nucleus, the energy it takes with it may be less than the normal value for the new nucleus, i.e. the nucleus is left in an excited energy state. This energy is released in the form of a gamma ray of energy $h\nu$. Whereas x-rays have energies of the order of thousands of ev, most gammas are in the mev region. A phenomenon labeled *internal conversion* is an alternative to the emission of a gamma ray by the nucleus. The energy of nuclear excitation may be transmitted to an electron in the K shell of the atom. The electron is ejected, and the usual x-ray emission follows. Internal conversion is sometimes incorrectly visualized as the emission of a gamma ray that knocks out the electron.

Gamma rays penetrate great thicknesses of matter in comparison with alphas and betas, with the further difference that there is no true range. The diminution of intensity of a stream of gammas incident on a slab of material such as lead is described by the exponential function. The fraction of gammas that still remains in the beam, such that the rays retain their original direction and energy, on traversing a distance x into a medium is given by

$$I/I_0 = e^{-\mu x}$$

where μ is the "linear absorption coefficient," a function of the gamma energy and the medium. The thickness of matter needed to reduce the intensity by a factor of two can be computed from this exponential formula

$$I/I_0 = \tfrac{1}{2} = e^{-\mu x_{1/2}}$$

or
$$x_{1/2} = \log_e 2/\mu = 0.693/\mu$$

In each successive layer, the beam is attenuated by an additional factor of two. The term "half-value layer" is often used as a convenient description of a substance. For 1-mev gamma rays in lead, $x_{1/2}$ is about 1 cm. It follows that the thickness needed to reduce the intensity to the fraction $1/32 = (\tfrac{1}{2})^5$, is around 5 cm. Three processes serve to use up the gamma ray energy. The first is ionization or the photo-electric effect in which the gamma ray ejects an electron from the element bombarded. This is dominant at low energies, up to 1 mev. The second is the Compton effect, described earlier in relation to x-rays. It decreases with frequency (i.e. gamma energy) but is appreciable up to 5 mev or higher. The third process is called *pair production*. The energy of the quantum is converted into mass. The particles created are an electron and a positron, which has a mass equal to that of an electron but is a positively charged particle. This effect sets in at 1 mev and increases indefinitely with energy. The threshold for positron-electron pair production can be verified by noting that the energy corresponding to two electron masses is

$$2m_0c^2 = (2)(9.1 \times 10^{-28})(3 \times 10^{10})^2$$
$$= 1.64 \times 10^{-6} \text{ erg } or \text{ 1.02 mev}$$

For completeness in our outline of physical effects that occur in radioactivity, the process of K capture is included. In some nuclei, such as $_{29}Cu^{64}$, one of the K-shell electrons is captured by the nucleus.

which becomes an element of lower atomic number, here $_{28}Ni^{64}$. The nucleus emits a gamma ray to rid itself of the resulting excess energy. This particular parent element may decay by a competing reaction, positron emission. In either case a neutrino is also emitted.

1.5 Radioactive decay calculations

We have described the individual radioactive processes that yield alphas, betas, and gammas without reference to the *rate* at which these events occur. First, it must be recognized that the decay process is of a statistical nature. In an accumulation of radioactive atoms, there is no way of predicting which nucleus will disintegrate in a given time interval. All that can be said is that a certain *fraction* will decay during each time interval of one second. This fraction, labeled λ, the decay constant, is independent of the number of nuclei under consideration, whether it is 10 or ten billion. The mathematical analysis we shall now apply has a wide variety of applications in the nuclear engineering field, and thus deserves detailed attention at this point.

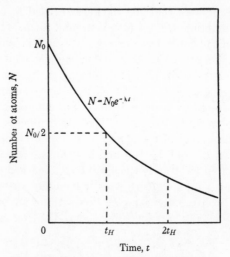

Fig. 1.14. Decay of a radioactive substance.

Let the number of radioactive nuclei present at any time t be N. After an infinitesimal time interval dt the number will drop to $N - dN$. If the fraction that decays each second is λ, the fraction lost in dt seconds is $\lambda\,dt$. However this is also equal to $-dN/N$, where the negative sign indicates the reduction. Thus we have the differential equation

$$-dN/N = \lambda\,dt$$

which is to be solved for N as it depends on t. Integrating both sides, we find $\log_e N = -\lambda t + C$, where C is a constant to be determined. If we had N_0 atoms at the start ($t = 0$), then to satisfy the equation just obtained, C must be $\log_e N_0$. Substituting and simplifying,

$$N = N_0 e^{-\lambda t}$$

A plot of N as a function of time is shown in Fig. 1.14. The *half-life t_H* of a radioactive substance is defined as the time that must elapse for the initial number of atoms to be reduced by a factor of two. Thus $N/N_0 = \frac{1}{2} = e^{-\lambda t_H}$, which on taking logarithms of both sides leads to the relation

$$t_H = 0.693/\lambda$$

where 0.693 is $\log_e 2$. Let us compute the number of disintegrations per second (d/sec) for a gram of the radioactive element radium, atomic weight 226, half-life 1620 years. The rate of decay, called *activity*, is

$$A = |dN/dt| = \lambda N = \lambda N_0 e^{-\lambda t}$$

The half-life of radium in seconds is

$$t_H = (1620 \text{ yr})(365 \text{ days/yr})(86{,}400 \text{ sec/day})$$

$$= 5.11 \times 10^{10} \text{ sec}$$

and the decay constant is

$$\lambda = 0.693/t_H = 1.356 \times 10^{-11} \text{ sec}^{-1}$$

The number of atoms per gram is

$$N = [6.023 \times 10^{23} \text{ (atoms/mole)}]/[226 \text{ (g/mole)}]$$

$$= 2.665 \times 10^{21}$$

Thus the activity is

$$A = \lambda N = (1.356 \times 10^{-11})(2.665 \times 10^{21})$$

$$= 3.61 \times 10^{10} \text{ d/sec}$$

Earlier measurements were found to yield a disintegration rate for radium of about 3.7×10^{10}. For convenience this rate was taken as a standard for activity and called the curie. This definition has been retained even though the correlation with radium is no longer exact:

$$1 \text{ curie} = 3.7 \times 10^{10} \text{ d/sec}$$

Another useful calculation concerns the *growth* of a radioactive sample, as in a target bombarded by high-energy charged particles in a cyclotron, by neutron bombardment in a reactor, or by the process of fission. Assume that the constant rate of generation of atoms is g per second, while the rate of radioactive decay is $-\lambda N$. The *net* rate of accumulation of particles is thus

$$dN/dt = g - \lambda N$$

The standard method of solution of this differential equation is to multiply both sides of the equation by the integrating factor $e^{\lambda t}$, and rearrange to the for n

$$\frac{d}{dt} (Ne^{\lambda t}) = ge^{\lambda t}$$

If the number of particles at $t = 0$ is zero, we may integrate to obtain the number at any later time t

$$N = e^{-\lambda t} \int_0^t ge^{\lambda t} \, dt$$

(It should be noted that this method is also applicable to a case in which the generation rate g is not constant with time, for instance when a radioactive parent element decays to form the new isotope.) The integration is straightforward for constant g, yielding

$$N = (g/\lambda) (1 - e^{-\lambda t})$$

Three regions on the curve can be identified at once. When $t = 0$, N reduces to zero, as was put in the problem originally. For short generation times, i.e., t much smaller than the half-life of the product ($\lambda t \ll 1$), we approximate by using the first two terms of the Maclaurin series expansion of the exponential function

$$e^x = 1 + x + x^2/2! + \ldots$$

thus
$$e^{-\lambda t} \simeq 1 - \lambda t$$

For these times, N is

$$N \simeq (g/\lambda) [1 - (1 - \lambda t)] = gt$$

Qualitatively, this means that the product accumulates linearly with time until its decay begins to make itself felt. For times much longer than the half-life, the accumulation approaches the horizontal line g/λ, as may be seen by letting $t \to \infty$ in the original equation for N,

$$N \simeq (g/\lambda)(1 - e^{-\infty}) = g/\lambda$$

The activity of the number collected after a long period of time is

$$A_\infty \simeq N\lambda \simeq g$$

which is to be expected: the rate of production and the rate of decay are the same at equilibrium. The activity in curies at equilibrium is

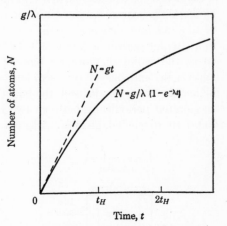

Fig. 1.15. Growth of a radioactive product.

of course $g/(3.7 \times 10^{10})$. Figure 1.15 shows the number of atoms present as a function of time.

1.6 Nuclear reactions and artificial radioactivity

Rutherford first discovered in 1919 that high-speed charged particles were capable of transmuting the nuclei of elements. The effect on nitrogen by bombardment by alpha particles may be written

$$_2\text{He}^4 + {}_7\text{N}^{14} \rightarrow {}_8\text{O}^{17} + {}_1\text{H}^1$$

or in abbreviated notation

$$\text{N}^{14}(\alpha,p)\text{O}^{17}$$

where α and p stand for the alpha particle and proton. The product element in this reaction already exists in nature as a stable isotope of oxygen. Many transmutations however, yield radioactive substances. For example, the reaction

$$_2\text{H}^4 + {}_5\text{B}^{10} \rightarrow {}_7\text{N}^{13} + {}_0n^1$$

yields the radioactive isotope N^{13}. This product in turn emits a positron with the half-life of the radioactive decay, 10.1 min. During the period 1930–40, great strides were made in the study of nuclear reactions and artificial radioactivity because of the development of accelerators for charged particles, in particular the cyclotron, devised by E. O. Lawrence at the University of California. The operation of this machine depends on the fact that a charged particle moves in a circular path in a magnetic field. If the field intensity is H oersteds, the radius of motion r (cm) of a particle of charge q (esu), mass m (g) and speed v (cm/sec) is $r = v/\omega$ where $\omega = qH/mc$. The higher the energy and speed, the larger is the circular orbit. Ions are accelerated periodically between two hollow electrodes, called dees, Fig. 1.16, to which high alternating potentials are applied. Resonance

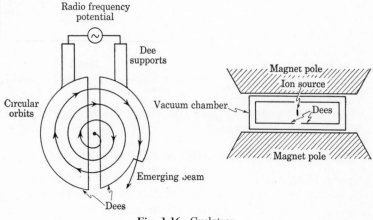

Fig. 1.16. Cyclotron.

between the potential and the ion motion may be established, since the time required for the ion to execute a half-circle is independent of speed. The ions move on larger and larger circles until the desired kinetic energy has been gained, at which point the particles are made to strike a target. The main projectiles used are protons, deuterons (ionized deuterium atoms) and alpha particles. Almost any element in the periodic table may be used as the target. In contrast with the use of particles emitted in radioactive decay for bombardment, the cyclotron has the great advantage that the particle energy can be adjusted to the best value for a reaction, and can be raised to hundreds of mev. A few illustrative reactions obtained by the use of high-energy charged particles are listed in Table 1.3. The new abbreviations are γ for gamma rays, and d for deuterons.

TABLE 1.3

CHARGED PARTICLE REACTIONS

Reaction	Radioactivity of product	Half-life	Particle energy (mev)
Proton:			
(p,γ) $_6C^{12} + _1H^1 \rightarrow _7N^{13} + \gamma$	positron	10.1 min	1.24
(p,n) $_8O^{18} + _1H^1 \rightarrow _9F^{18} + _0n^1$	positron	1.87 hr	0.64
(p,α) $_9F^{19} + _1H^1 \rightarrow _8O^{16} + _2He^4$	stable	...	...
(p,d) $_4Be^9 + _1H^1 \rightarrow _4Be^8 + _1H^2$	2 α particles	10^{-16} sec	0.1
Deuteron:			
(d,p) $_{15}P^{31} + _1H^2 \rightarrow _{15}P^{32} + _1H^1$	electron	14.3 days	1.71
(d,n) $_4Be^9 + _1H^2 \rightarrow _5B^{10} + _0n^1$	stable	...	...
(d,α) $_{13}Al^{27} + _1H^2 \rightarrow _{12}Mg^{25} + _2He^4$	stable	...	...
Alpha particle:			
(α,n) $_{13}Al^{27} + _2He^4 \rightarrow _{15}P^{30} + _0n^1$	positron	2.18 min	3.5
(α,p) $_7N^{14} + _2He^4 \rightarrow _8O^{17} + _1H^1$	stable	...	...

The neutrons and gamma rays from the charged particle reactions may also be used as projectiles. Examples of the secondary reactions that they produce are given in Table 1.4.

TABLE 1.4

REACTIONS WITH NEUTRON AND GAMMA RAY BOMBARDMENT

Reaction	Radioactivity of product	Half-life	Particle energy (mev)
Neutrons:			
(n,γ) $_{48}Cd^{113} + _0n^1 \rightarrow _{48}Cd^{114} + \gamma$	stable	...	...
(n,p) $_7N^{14} + _0n^1 \rightarrow _6C^{14} + _1H^1$	electron	5700 yr	0.155
(n,α) $_3Li^6 + _0n^1 \rightarrow _2He^4 + _1H^3$ (tritium)	electron	12.5 yr	0.189
Gamma rays:			
(γ,n) $_{35}Br^{81} + \gamma \rightarrow _{35}Br^{80} + _0n^1$	2 γ rays	4.4 hr	0.049; 0.037
	electron	18.5 min	2.0
(γ,p) $_1H^2 + \gamma \rightarrow _0n^1 + _1H^1$	stable	..	...

The reactions of principal interest in nuclear engineering are of two types, those that yield neutrons, such as the fission process, and the (n,γ) or radiative capture reactions. The latter are significant for two reasons: (a) The neutrons that one wishes to use in the chain reaction may be lost by absorption; (b) The radioactive products of neutron absorption provide a hazard to personnel working with irradiated equipment. We shall therefore not discuss further the charged particle reactions, but examine instead in the next chapter the properties of neutrons.

Problems

1.1 What is the approximate mass in grams of a uranium atom?

1.2 Find the quantity of electricity needed to deposit 100 g of zinc, which has a valence of $+2$.

1.3 Calculate the electric field intensity between parallel plates with a potential difference of 45 v, separated by 2 cm. What relationship must exist between the electric field intensity ε and the magnetic field intensity H that are applied to an electron stream of speed v in order to obtain zero deflection?

1.4 Calculate the energy, in ev, of a 5-g mass that has fallen from rest under the gravity force through 10 cm. Compare this result with the energy of a hydrogen molecule falling through the same distance. What is the energy of a hydrogen molecule ion $H_2{}^+$ accelerated through 10 cm with a potential difference of 100 v?

1.5 Find the energy in ergs and in ev of a quantum of sodium light, $\lambda = 5890 \times 10^{-8}$ cm.

1.6 What is the magnitude of the force between an electron and a proton separated by 0.5×10^{-8} cm (the radius of the smallest Bohr orbit)?

1.7 Using the condition that the electron angular momentum must be an integer times $h/2\pi$, find the electron speed in the first Bohr orbit.

1.8 What potential difference must be applied to an x-ray tube to excite radiation of 0.1×10^{-8} cm wavelength or longer?

1.9 Estimate the proportions of B^{10} and B^{11} in natural boron, atomic weight 10.82.

1.10 What equivalent energy in ev does an electron have, mass 9.11×10^{-28} gram?

1.11 Calculate the energy release in the reaction $_1H^2 + {}_1H^2 \rightarrow {}_2He^4$.

1.12 What is the binding energy of the isotope $_{82}Pb^{208}$? What is the binding energy per nucleon?

1.13 What contribution to the binding energy of $_{82}Pb^{208}$ does the positive charge in the nucleus make?

1.14 From any nuclear physics text available make a chart of the radioactive series involving U^{235} and Th^{232}.

1.15 Calculate the decay constant λ for U^{235}, half-life 8.5×10^8 yr. How many disintegrations occur each second in a 0.2-g sample of U^{235}? What number of curies is this?

1.16 One milligram of polonium-210, half-life 140 days, is allowed to decay for 1 yr. What is its activity at the end of that time?

1.17 Derive a formula for the number of daughter atoms present at any time t after observations are started with a radioactive parent.

1.18 Show that the number of atoms produced at a constant rate g in a cyclotron is half the equilibrium value by the end of a time t_H from the start of bombardment.

1.19 Calculate the number of atoms of the isotope Co^{60}, half-life 5.3 yr, that will accumulate in 2 yr with a generation rate of 10^{12} atoms per second. What number of grams does this comprise? What error is incurred in using the linear approximation $N \simeq gt$?

1.20 What energy in mev do protons have moving on a 25-in. radius in a uniform cyclotron magnetic field of 10,000 oersteds?

1.21 Calculate the fractional increase in mass of a 20-mev proton.

References*

SHORTLEY, GEORGE and DUDLEY WILLIAMS, *Elements of Physics.* New York: Prentice-Hall, Inc., 1953.

VAN NAME, F. W., JR., *Modern Physics.* New York: Prentice-Hall, Inc., 1952.

SEMAT, HENRY, *Introduction to Atomic Physics.* New York: Rinehart & Co., 1946.

RICHTMYER, F. K. and E. H. KENNARD, *Introduction to Modern Physics.* New York: McGraw-Hill Book Co., 1947.

LAPP, R. E. and H. L. ANDREWS, *Nuclear Radiation Physics*, 2d Ed. New York: Prentice-Hall, Inc., 1954.

POLLARD, E. C. and W. L. DAVIDSON, *Applied Nuclear Physics.* New York: John Wiley & Sons, 1951.

* This list is by no means complete; however, bibliographies in these references will lead the reader to more specialized books.

STRANATHAN, J. D., *The "Particles" of Modern Physics.* Philadelphia: The Blakiston Co., 1945.

HALLIDAY, DAVID, *Introductory Nuclear Physics.* New York: John Wiley & Sons, 1950.

PERSICO, E., *Fundamentals of Quantum Mechanics.* New York: Prentice-Hall, Inc., 1950.

SMITH, LLOYD P., *Mathematical Methods for Scientists and Engineers.* New York: Prentice-Hall, Inc., 1953.

SALVADORI, M. G., and R. J. SCHWARZ, *Differential Equations in Engineering Problems.* New York: Prentice-Hall, Inc., 1954.

FREY, P. R., *College Chemistry.* New York: Prentice-Hall, Inc., 1952.

CHAPTER 2

NEUTRONS

The first experimental verification of the existence of the neutron was in Chadwick's bombardment of beryllium by high-speed alpha particles, giving the reaction

$$_4Be^9 + {_2}He^4 \rightarrow {_6}C^{12} + {_0}n^1$$

The neutrons proceeded to strike hydrogen atoms in a paraffin target. The atoms were dislodged in the form of protons, which were then detected by virtue of their charge. This historic experiment still has practical importance in two ways: (a) The nuclear reaction takes place in artificial "sources" of neutrons used in reactor testing; and (b) The proton recoil technique for indirect observation of neutrons is commonly used in neutron instrumentation.

2.1 General properties of neutrons

The penetration of matter by charged particles such as alpha particles or protons, produced from radioactivity or by electrical acceleration, is relatively slight because of the electrostatic force between the incident particle and the electrons of the target atoms. On the other hand, neutrons, having no charge, can move through matter for long distances without being stopped. Only by collisions with nuclei, which are exceedingly small in size, can neutrons eventually lose energy and be absorbed. Externally applied electrical fields or magnetic fields have no effect on their motion; the influence of gravity on neutrons, although demonstrable, is too small to require accounting. The electron-volt energy unit is used universally to describe a neutron in motion. As an important example, consider the neutrons that have lost energy by collisions with nuclei to the extent that they have no more energy than the moving molecules in the medium they find themselves. Their velocity in a substance such as heavy water at room temperature is approximately 2200 m/sec. The kinetic energy of a typical neutron of mass 1.66×10^{-24} gram will be

$$E = \tfrac{1}{2}mv^2 = \tfrac{1}{2}(1.66 \times 10^{-24})(2.2 \times 10^5)^2$$
$$= 4.0 \times 10^{-14} \text{ erg} = 0.025 \text{ ev}$$

This result coincides with that obtained in Section 1.1, since the masses of hydrogen atoms and neutrons are indistinguishable, within the degree of accuracy of the above computation.

2.2 Neutron temperature

One finds frequent reference in the literature of reactors and neutron experiments to the term "neutron temperature." The basis of this alternative description of neutron energy is that the neutrons behave very much like a molecular gas, for which the temperature is an experimentally measurable quantity. Visualize a container filled with

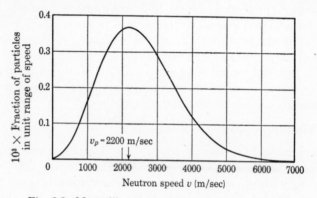

Fig. 2.1. Maxwellian distribution of neutrons at 25°C.

a gas such as hydrogen, with a source of neutrons in the center. The neutrons will lose energy to the molecules as they move about, and will eventually slow down to the point where they have an equal chance of picking up or losing energy by collision with gas particles. In this special case, they effectively become a part of the gas and have the same average velocities and energy as do the gas molecules. The kinetic theory of gases tells us that the molecules of a gas, under conditions where the temperature is steady, have a variety of different velocities, ranging from zero to thousands of meters per second. The distribution among the speeds of the gas particles is described by the mathematical formula below. The number of molecules in a range dv at the speed v is

$$dn = n_0 A v^2 e^{-mv^2/2kT} \, dv$$

where n_0 is the total number of particles per unit volume. A is a constant independent of velocity, m is the particle mass, T is the absolute temperature (°K), and k is Boltzmann's constant, 1.38×10^{-16} erg/deg (k is merely R, the general gas constant per mole, divided by the number of particles per mole, N_a). Figure 2.1 shows the shape of this "maxwellian distribution function." The peak of the curve occurs at the *most probable velocity* v_p, near which there are more molecules than at any other speed. The value of v_p can be found by taking the derivative of $v^2 e^{-mv^2/2kT}$ with respect to v, letting it equal zero, and solving for v. The most probable velocity is found to be

$$v_p = \sqrt{2kT/m}$$

and the energy associated with v_p is $E_p = \frac{1}{2}mv_p{}^2 = kT$. (This is *not* the most probable energy, but is the energy corresponding to the most probable velocity.) The relations above may now be used to describe a group of "thermal" neutrons, those sharing the thermal energy of the medium. The neutrons are said to have a maxwellian distribution in velocity like that of a gas, with some most probable velocity v_p. The energy of those characteristic neutrons is kT, so we may use the word "temperature" interchangeably with the word energy. It should be clear however, that a single neutron cannot truly have a temperature, although it is often convenient to imagine that it does. Let us check the statement made earlier that the velocity of thermal neutrons is 2200 m/sec. Substituting 298°K, corresponding to a room temperature of 25°C, in the most probable velocity relation:

$$v_p = \sqrt{(2)(1.38 \times 10^{-16})(298)/(1.66 \times 10^{-24})}$$
$$= 2.2 \times 10^5 \text{ cm/sec}$$

2.3 Cross sections for neutron-nucleus interactions

The chance of a collision between a neutron and the nucleus of an atom is measured by the nuclear "cross section." Because of the frequent use of the term in reactor literature, we shall devote particular attention to it. Suppose that we have a single neutron or a group of neutrons moving about through a nuclear reactor, and wish to find out the number that collide with nuclei each second. This collision rate will determine the energy loss and the rate of absorption into nuclei by radiative capture reactions such as

$$_0n^1 + {}_1H^1 \rightarrow {}_1H^2 + \gamma$$
$$_0n^1 + {}_6C^{12} \rightarrow {}_6C^{13} + \gamma$$

We may simplify the problem by picturing a single neutron entering anywhere in one face of a cubic centimeter of material, moving normally to the face, as shown in Fig. 2.2. To the oncoming neutron each nucleus presents a certain area, which we denote by the symbol

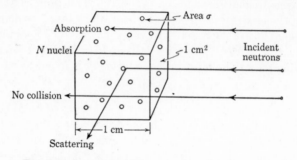

Fig. 2.2. Geometrical interpretation of cross section.

σ and call *cross section*, by analogy with the familiar "cross-sectional area." The total area exposed by the nuclei in the cube is simply $N\sigma$, where N is the number of atoms per unit volume, as computed earlier. If the neutron enters within the face area of 1 cm², then the *chance* of making a collision is just the ratio of target area to total area or $N\sigma$, If we knew the dimensions of nuclei accurately, and if the geometric areas presented completely determined the collision process, we could easily compute the chance of collision. It turns out, however, that the *effective* cross sections, particularly for thermal neutrons, do not agree with expectations based on nuclear size data. For example, recalling that the diameters of nuclei were quoted to be about 10^{-12} cm, one would predict that the area of a U^{235} nucleus would be about 2×10^{-24} cm². Experimentally, it is found that the cross section for thermal neutrons is 650×10^{-24} cm². The geometrical concept clearly must be abandoned with a discrepancy of this size, except for saying that the uranium behaves *as if* the nuclei had these large areas. With some ingenuity, it is possible experimentally to distinguish between collisions that merely change the direction of motion of the neutron and those in which the neutron is absorbed. The relative number of cases in which these two different events take place on collision are expressed by cross sections σ_s for *scattering*, and σ_a for *absorption*. Use of the geometrical picture is even less meaningful than it was before since one cannot visualize a part of the area that scatters neutrons and another part that absorbs them. Cross section thus becomes a measure of *probability* of different events. The total chance of collision σ, sometimes written σ_t, is the sum of the chances of separate processes. Thus we write

$$\sigma = \sigma_s + \sigma_a$$

Scattering cross sections of nuclei for thermal neutrons do not vary greatly from element to element, in contrast with the case for absorption cross sections. Table 2.1 shows values for some of the elements

TABLE 2.1

THERMAL NEUTRON CROSS SECTIONS

Element (or isotope)	σ_s	Cross sections (barns) σ_a	σ_f
H	38	0.33	
Be	7	0.010	
B	4	750	
C	4.8	0.0045	
O	4.2	$< 0.2 \times 10^{-3}$	
Fe	11	2.43	
Cd	7	2400	
Xe^{135}	> 4.3	3.5×10^6	
U (natural)	8.2	7.42	3.92
U^{235}	8.2	650	549
U^{238}	8.2	2.80	0
Pu^{239}	. . .	1025	664

of interest to the nuclear engineer. A complete table of neutron cross sections for all elements and many isotopes is given in the Appendix.

Instead of carrying along the cumbersome units 10^{-24} cm², it is standard practice to substitute the term *barn*, coined by Los Alamos scientists Holloway and Baker to suggest how large neutron cross sections actually are. Thus, we say that the absorption cross section of U^{235} is 650 barns, but for numerical calculations remember that it is actually 650×10^{-24} cm². Note the column in Table 2.1 headed σ_f which refers to the chance of fission. Absorption cross sections, in addition to the dependence on element, are usually strongly dependent on energy. Two types of variation are found. The first is called "$1/v$" dependence, in which σ_a varies according to the relation

$$\sigma_a = (\sigma_a)_0 v_0 / v$$

where σ_a is the absorption cross section at velocity v and $(\sigma_a)_0$ is that at the thermal velocity $v_0 = 2200$ m/sec. The other, "resonance" absorption, has sharp rises at one or more particular energies. As examples, the cross sections for boron and cadmium are shown in Fig. 2.3. The use of logarithmic scales on the cross-section axis and

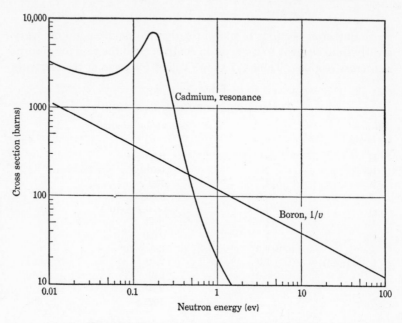

Fig. 2.3. Cross sections for boron and cadmium.

the energy axis is convenient for the following reason. Take the logarithm of both sides of the $1/v$ equation above. The result is log $\sigma_a = \log [(\sigma_a)_0 v_0] - \log v$, but since $v = \sqrt{2E/m}$, the equation reduces to $\log \sigma_a = -\frac{1}{2}\log E + b$, where b is a constant. This expression can be compared with the familiar equation for a straight line $y = mx + b$ by identifying $\log \sigma_a$ with the variable y, $\log E$ with x. The slope of the line m is $-\frac{1}{2}$ and b is the intercept on the vertical axis. Absorption that obeys the $1/v$ law is described by a straight line with these changes of scale. A full explanation of the reasons for the above two types of variation of cross section with energy or neutron speed is beyond the scope of this book. It is convenient, however, to use qualitative concepts to visualize the trends. First, it seems reasonable that the chance of capture is greatest if the neutron energy coincides with some natural energy of the composite nucleus formed by the neutron and target, just as large vibrations of a mechanical system are set up by the application of impulses near its natural frequency. In Section 12.6 we shall discuss the Breit-Wigner formula which describes resonance cross sections. Second, if the neutron energy is far from any resonance value, one might expect the available time of interaction between neutron and nucleus would determine the cross section. The slower the neutron, the longer it remains in the vicinity of the nucleus, and the higher the chance of absorption. Thus the proportionality of σ to $1/v$ is made plausible.

2.4 Neutron flux

The term "neutron flux" refers to the rate of flow of neutrons within a reactor. Consider first a stream of neutrons having a common direction and speed v. If there are n neutrons in each cubic centimeter of the stream, then the number that cross a square centimeter area perpendicular to the stream is the product nv, since all neutrons in a cylinder of length v get across the area in a second. See Fig. 2.4.

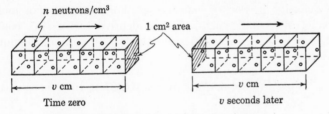

Fig. 2.4. Relation of neutron density and flux.

This flow rate we may call a neutron flux (actually flux density). Now neutrons in a reactor are not moving in uniform streams, but at random directions. It is convenient however, to retain the term flux, symbolized by ϕ, to describe the product of the speed and the number of neutrons having that speed.

$$\phi\left(\frac{\text{number}}{\text{cm}^2\text{-sec}}\right) = n\left(\frac{\text{number}}{\text{cm}^3}\right) v\left(\frac{\text{cm}}{\text{sec}}\right)$$

The reason is that the occurrence of nuclear reactions does not depend on the directions from which the neutrons arrive at the nuclei. In this extended viewpoint, one can no longer visualize the square centimeter across which the neutrons flow—each neutron would require its own normal surface.

For numerical illustration, let us compute the neutron "density" n from a typical reactor flux of 10^{12}. The thermal velocity being 2200 m/sec, we have

$$n = \frac{\phi}{v} = \frac{10^{12} \ (\text{cm}^{-2} \ \text{sec}^{-1})}{2.2 \times 10^5 \ (\text{cm} \ \text{sec}^{-1})} = 4.5 \times 10^6 \ (\text{cm}^{-3})$$

Although this is a large number, it corresponds to a very good vacuum, since 1 cm³ of a gas at standard conditions contains 2.7×10^{19} particles as computed in Section 1.1.

2.5 Macroscopic cross sections and mean free paths

The product $N\sigma$, the total area of nuclei per cubic centimeter, is commonly labeled Σ and called "macroscopic cross section," meaning large scale, referring to bulk area, as contrasted with the "microscopic cross section," σ, having to do with the individual small scale collisions with nuclei. With Avogadro's number and the density of any substance, we may calculate N and thence Σ, which is an indispensable quantity in reactor calculations. For example, if a mole of carbon of molecular weight 12.01 g, density 1.65 g/cm³, contains 6.023×10^{23} atoms, then 1.65 g contains, by proportion, the number of atoms

$$N = \frac{1.65}{12.01} \times 6.023 \times 10^{23} = 0.0827 \times 10^{24} \ (\text{cm}^{-3})$$

The virtue in expressing the number of atoms or nuclei as a multiple of 10^{24} will be seen shortly. The general relation to remember is that the number of nuclei per cubic centimeter is

$$N = \rho N_a / M$$

where ρ is the density, N_a is Avogadro's number and M is the atomic (or molecular) weight. To illustrate the calculation of Σ, let us find the microscopic and macroscopic cross sections of boron, density 2.5 g/cm³, at thermal energy and at 0.04 ev. From Table 2.1, σ_a is 750 barns at 0.025 ev. The number of boron nuclei per unit volume is

$$N = \rho N_a / M = (2.5)(6.023 \times 10^{23})/10.82$$
$$= 0.139 \times 10^{24} \ \text{cm}^{-3}$$

Thus the macroscopic thermal cross section is

$$\Sigma_a = N\sigma_a$$
$$= (0.139 \times 10^{24} \text{ cm}^{-3})(750 \times 10^{-24} \text{ cm}^2) = 104 \text{ cm}^{-1}$$

Note that the factors 10^{24} and 10^{-24} "cancel out" to unity. Many decimal point errors can be avoided by expressing N as a multiple of 10^{24}. Since boron is a $1/v$ absorber, the cross section at 0.04 ev will be lower than the thermal value by a factor

$$v_0/v = \sqrt{E_0/E} = \sqrt{0.025/0.04} = 0.79$$

The relation between macroscopic cross section and the progress of a beam of neutrons through a medium is now derived. Suppose that the substance scatters neutrons but does not absorb them appreciably. The total target area presented by a slab of material of thickness dx to a beam of n particles passing through a square centimeter is $\Sigma_s \, dx$. The fraction scattered out in that distance is $dn/n = -\Sigma_s \, dx$ since the chance of collision is the ratio of target area to beam area. The integration parallels that for radioactive decay. The limits are: n_0 initial particles at the surface of the slab, $x = 0$ and n remaining at a distance x into the medium. Thus we obtain

$$n = n_0 e^{-\Sigma_s x}$$

or

$$dn = -n_0 \Sigma_s \, e^{-\Sigma_s x} \, dx$$

We should now like to compute the *average distance* one of the particles goes before making a collision.* The number leaving the beam

---

* The problem would be simple if we had to find the average weight of a group of n people. If n_1 had weights near w_1, n_2 had weights near w_2, etc., the average would be

$$\bar{w} = \frac{n_1 w_1 + n_2 w_2 + n_3 w_3 + \ldots}{n_1 + n_2 + n_3 + \ldots = n}$$

For a large population, the number of people in each group could be made very small, or even infinitesimal in relation to the whole population. A more accurate average would be

$$\bar{w} = \frac{\int w \, dn}{\int dn = n}$$

where dn is the number in each group, and the integral is taken over all the people, or if dn is known as a function of w, over all weights. We may apply this general method of averaging to the scattering of particles.

near a point x is $dn = n_0 \Sigma_s e^{-\Sigma_s x} dx$, the average coordinate at which they leave is

$$\bar{x} = \frac{\int x \, dn}{\int dn} = \frac{\int_0^\infty x \, n_0 \Sigma_s e^{-\Sigma_s x} \, dx}{\int_0^\infty n_0 \Sigma_s e^{-\Sigma_s x} \, dx}$$

The integrals are readily evaluated from tables, yielding the result $\bar{x} = 1/\Sigma_s$. This characteristic distance is called the "mean free path," for scattering, and labeled λ_s. It is also the average distance a single particle travels *between* collisions, as one can see by imagining that the 1-particle "beam" starts its motion into the medium on the instant of its last collision. As an illustration, we may compute the scattering mean free path for thermal neutrons in graphite. σ_s from Table 2.2 is 4.8×10^{-24}, N is 0.0827×10^{24} and $\Sigma_s = N\sigma_s = 0.397$ cm^{-1}. Thus $\lambda_s = 1/\Sigma_s = 2.5$ cm. Similar averages may be made for absorption processes, yielding the absorption mean free path, $\lambda_a = 1/\Sigma_a$. The total mean free path is $\lambda = 1/\Sigma = 1/(\Sigma_a + \Sigma_s)$. It should be noted that λ is not the sum of the separate mean free paths.

It is useful to find out the effective microscopic cross section $\bar{\sigma}$ of a $1/v$ absorber placed in a reactor in which the speed distribution of neutrons is maxwellian, most probable speed v_v, and temperature T. Let us define the effective or average *macroscopic* absorption cross section $\bar{\Sigma} = N\bar{\sigma}$ as the ratio of total absorption occurring each second to the total neutron flux, i.e.

$$\bar{\Sigma} = N\bar{\sigma} = \frac{\int v \, dn \, N\sigma_a}{\int v \, dn}$$

The use of the integral method for finding averages is applied again. This time n refers to the number in a velocity range given by the maxwellian distribution formula instead of the number in a beam.

$$\bar{\sigma} = \frac{\int v \, dn \, (\sigma_a)_0 v_0 / v}{\int v \, dn} = \frac{(\sigma_a)_0 v_0 \int dn}{\int v \, dn}$$

The numerator is simply the total number of neutrons n_0, the denominator is n_0 times the *average* speed of the neutrons. Thus $\bar{\sigma} = (\sigma_a)_0 v_0 / \bar{v}$. The average speed is somewhat higher than the most probable speed from which the temperature is computed, i.e.,

$\bar{v}/v_p = 2/\sqrt{\pi} = 1.128$. Thus the effective cross section of $1/v$ absorber for a maxwellian distribution of neutrons is given by

$$\bar{\sigma} = \frac{(\sigma_a)_0 v_0}{1.128 v_p} = \frac{\sigma_p}{1.128}$$

2.6 Energy losses on collision

Since the neutron is neutral, it can lose appreciable energy on collisions only by interaction with the nucleus of an atom. The energy of the neutron may be absorbed to excite the nucleus, with subsequent gamma ray emission, a process termed *inelastic scattering*. This is analogous to the collision of a bullet and a target, in which much energy goes into heat. A more common process is *elastic collision*,

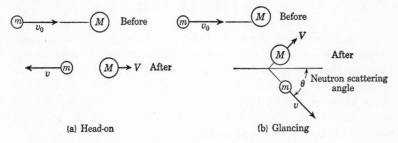

(a) Head-on   (b) Glancing

Fig. 2.5. Collisions of neutron with nucleus.

as approximated by the reaction of a golf ball and a club, or better, by two billiard balls. The calculation of neutron energy loss for elastic scattering is simple in that only the rules of conservation of kinetic energy and momentum must be applied. Let M be the mass of target nucleus, and m that of the neutron. In the special instance of a head-on collision, the neutron speed changes from v_0 to v, as in Fig. 2.5. The nucleus, originally at rest gains a speed V. We may write

$$\tfrac{1}{2}mv_0^2 = \tfrac{1}{2}MV^2 + \tfrac{1}{2}mv^2 \qquad \text{(conservation of energy)} \qquad (1)$$

$$mv_0 = MV + mv \qquad \text{(conservation of momentum)} \qquad (2)$$

or $\qquad v_0^2 - v^2 = (M/m)V^2 \qquad\qquad\qquad\qquad\qquad (1a)$

$$v_0 - v = (M/m)V \qquad\qquad\qquad\qquad\qquad (2a)$$

Dividing Eq. (1a) by (2a) yields

$$v_0 + v = V \qquad\qquad\qquad\qquad\qquad\qquad (3)$$

Solving Eqs. (2) and (3) simultaneously, one obtains

$$v = -v_0 \frac{M - m}{M + m}$$

from which the ratio of final to initial energy is

$$E/E_0 = [(M - m)/(M + m)]^2$$

and the change in energy is

$$\Delta E = E_0 - E = [4mM/(M + m)^2]E_0$$

For the example of a head-on collision of a neutron with a carbon nucleus, this ratio is

$$\frac{E}{E_0} = \left(\frac{12 - 1}{12 + 1}\right)^2 = 0.72$$

implying a loss of 28 per cent of the initial energy. For a neutron-hydrogen collision, the ratio is zero (approximately equal masses), meaning that the projectile neutron can lose all of its energy in one collision. The energy loss in a head-on collision (180° scattering of the neutron) is greater than a collision at any other angle. The extreme case of a "complete miss," (0° scattering of the neutron) clearly results in zero loss of energy.

The slowing of neutrons in a nuclear reactor is described in terms of *average* energy losses, considering the variety of angles at which neutrons collide with the "moderating" nuclei. The most useful quantity is the average change in the natural logarithm of the energy, symbolized by

$$\xi = \overline{\Delta \log_e E} = \overline{\log_e E_0 - \log_e E}$$

A rigorous expression for ξ is

$$\xi = 1 + \frac{r \log_e r}{1 - r}$$

where r is the ratio $[(M - m)/(M + m)]^2$ found in the previous calculation. For quick approximate calculations we may use the relation

$$\xi \simeq 2/(M + 1)$$

This formula tells us that the energy loss is large for collisions with light nuclei, and small for collisions with heavy nuclei.

The average number of collisions C needed to reduce a neutron

from high energy (as produced by fission, $E_f = 2$ mev) to thermal
energy ($E_t = 1/40$ ev) may be calculated by the use of ξ. We shall
illustrate with the case of graphite. The value of ξ is 0.159 for a carbon nucleus. Thus

$$C = \frac{\log_e E_f - \log_e E_t}{\Delta \log_e E} = \frac{\log_e (E_f/E_t)}{\xi} = \frac{\log_e \left(\dfrac{2 \times 10^6}{1/40}\right)}{0.159} = 114$$

The necessary number of collisions with the hydrogen atoms ($\xi = 1$)
in water is much smaller, namely 18. It is interesting to contrast
this result with the conclusion reached earlier, that a single collision
may be all that is necessary to reduce the energy to thermal. It follows that few collisions are of the "head-on" type.

2.7 Slowing down and thermal diffusion lengths

The number of neutron-nucleus collisions required to bring a neutron
from fission energy to thermal is only a part of the complete description of the slowing down process. We should like to know also how
far away from the starting point the neutrons are when they become
thermal. It is clear that there is no unique distance, since some by
chance may wander about through the medium and finally slow
down very near the source, while others, perhaps, may progress in
essentially a straight line. The conventional way to resolve this
ambiguity is to determine an effective *average* distance from the
neutron origin labeled L_f the "fast diffusion length" or by some
authors L_s, the "slowing down length." In one theory L_f^2 is called
"age." Let us attempt to analyze what L_f might depend on. The
total zigzag path length may be computed at once. The scattering
mean free path was shown in a previous section to be $\lambda_s = 1/\Sigma_s$. If
Σ_s were constant with neutron energy or if a good average value
could be found, the distance traveled from fission energy to thermal
would be merely $C\lambda_s$ where C is the number of collisions $\log_e (E_f/E_t)/\xi$.
The true path must include these factors. Even though the neutron
may bounce off at any angle from the nucleus, there is a tendency·
for the motion to be in the same general direction as it was traveling
originally. A measure of this trend is the average angle of scattering
or more precisely the average cosine of the angle. Since the angle θ
is more often acute than obtuse, the particles migrate away from the
starting point more rapidly than if the angles were equally distributed.

The "transport mean free path" $\lambda_t = \lambda_s/(1 - \overline{\cos\theta})$ may be used to represent the *effective* distance neutrons move between collisions, so far as transfer is concerned. (One may also define a macroscopic transport cross section $\Sigma_t = 1/\lambda_t$). The relation of $\overline{\cos\theta}$ to nuclear mass labeled M, is simply $\overline{\cos\theta} = 2/(3M)$. The "age" theory of Fermi, based on the statistical analysis of particle motion, shows that all the preceding quantities are related by

$$L_f^2 = \lambda_t\lambda_s C/3$$

where the λ's are appropriate averages of the transport and scattering mean free paths over the energy range. The usual expression found in the literature is

$$\tau = L_f^2 = \int_{E_t}^{E_0} \frac{\lambda_t}{3\,\Sigma_s}\frac{dE}{\xi E}$$

Note that if λ_t and λ_s did not depend on energy or were replaced by average values this expression would reduce to the previous one. Derivation of this formula appears in the Appendix.

The average distance neutrons move between the time they arrive at thermal energy and the time they are absorbed is called the "thermal diffusion length," L. The factors that make up L can be deduced by a logic similar to that applied to the age in the previous paragraph. Competition exists between scattering and absorption collisions: the measure of flight between such events are the mean free paths λ_s and λ_a evaluated at thermal neutron energy. The correction of λ_s by the factor $1/(1 - \overline{\cos\theta})$ to form λ_t again must be made. The statistical formula for diffusion length is

$$L = \sqrt{\frac{\lambda_t\,\lambda_a}{3}} = \frac{1}{\sqrt{3\,\Sigma_t\,\Sigma_a}}$$

The theoretical results above have been presented to assist in arriving at some idea of the physical factors in neutron slowing and diffusion. In practice, the experimentally determined values for τ and L are preferable to those obtained from theory and fundamental nuclear constants. The formulas are useful however for cases in which no data are available or if the effects such as density changes are of interest. We shall reserve discussion of numerical values of the constants until Chapter 6 where there is need for them in reactor calculations.

Problems

2.1 The average energy of neutrons released by the fission process in uranium is 2 mev. Calculate the neutron velocity that corresponds to this energy.

2.2 Verify that setting the derivative of the maxwellian distribution equal to zero leads to the formula for the most probable velocity $v_p = \sqrt{2kT/m}$.

2.3 What temperature of a block of graphite containing neutrons in equilibrium will yield a most-probable neutron velocity of 3000 m/sec?

2.4 Show that the constant A in the maxwellian distribution depends on particle mass and temperature according to $4\pi(m/2\pi kT)^{3/2}$. HINT: the total area under the distribution curve must equal n_0, the total number of particles in a unit volume.

2.5 What neutron temperature corresponds to 7 ev, the first uranium resonance?

2.6 Show that the number of uranium atoms per cubic centimeter is 0.0473×10^{24}, with the metal density taken as 18.7 g/cm³.

2.7 Calculate the number of hydrogen atoms per cubic centimeter of ordinary water. Repeat for heavy water, density 1.1 g/cm³.

2.8 What is the total cross section for natural uranium? For U^{235}?

2.9 What is the particle density for a flux of 10^5 neutrons per cm²-sec of 1.5-mev energy?

2.10 Find the mean free path for absorption of thermal neutrons in water.

2.11 Find the mean free path for thermal absorption in boron.

2.12 Compute the macroscopic thermal cross section of pure U^{235}. NOTE: make use of the assumption that the density of U^{235} and U bear the same ratio as do their mass numbers. What justification is there for this?

2.13 Calculate the effective cross section in boron for maxwellian neutrons of temperature 400°K.

2.14 Compare ξ by the rigorous and approximate formulas for collisions of neutrons with beryllium. NOTE: it is necessary to carry along several significant figures in the use of the rigorous formula.

2.15 Calculate ξ for U^{238} by the two methods as in Problem 2.14.

2.16 How many collisions are needed to bring 2-mev neutrons to thermal energies in U^{238}?

2.17 Determine the transport mean free path λ_t and the absorption mean free path λ_a for thermal neutrons in carbon. Recall that the scattering mean free path λ_s is 2.5 cm.

2.18 Calculate the thermal diffusion length of neutrons in graphite from the results obtained in Problem 2.17.

References

LOEB, L. B., *Kinetic Theory of Gases*, 2d Ed. New York: McGraw-Hill Book Co., 1934.

THE AEC NEUTRON CROSS SECTION ADVISORY GROUP, *Neutron Cross Sections*, AECU-2040. Washington, D. C.: Office of Technical Services, U. S. Department of Commerce, 1952. Graphs of total cross sections as a function of energy. Tables of thermal neutron cross sections for elements and isotopes.

LAPP, R. E. and H. L. ANDREWS, *Nuclear Radiation Physics*, 2d Ed. New York: Prentice-Hall, Inc., 1954, Chap. 12.

SOODAK, HARRY and E. C. CAMPBELL, *Elementary Pile Theory*. New York: John Wiley & Sons, 1950.

CHAPTER 3

FISSION AND THE CHAIN REACTION

The year 1939 is notable for the discovery that the nuclei of uranium would split into two fragments upon bombardment by neutrons, with an accompanying release of a large amount of energy.* The first public suggestion of the effect by Meitner and Frisch was based on their work and that of Hahn and Strassmann in Germany. Radioactivity observed after the exposure of uranium to a neutron beam was found to be attributable to barium, of mass number 138, rather than the expected heavier element radium. As soon as the Danish physicist Niels Bohr brought word of the new process to the United States, scientists set about to verify the effect. At the same time they conjectured as to the possibility that new neutrons would be ejected at the same time. If such were the case, a chain reaction might be induced, in which the original neutrons give rise to several more neutrons by fission, which in turn can induce further fissions, and so on. Von Halban, F. Joliot and Kowarski of France shortly thereafter reported verification of the hypothesis that neutrons were emitted in fission.

3.1 Uranium fission

It was quickly shown that the isotope of uranium that was principally responsible for fission was U^{235}, and that neutrons of low kinetic energy were more effective than were fast neutrons. The nuclear reaction can be written in two steps:

$$_0n^1 + {}_{92}U^{235} \rightarrow {}_{92}U^{236}$$

$$_{92}U^{236} \rightarrow {}_{Z_1}F^{A_1} + {}_{Z_2}F^{A_2} + 2.5 \, _0n^1$$

with several gamma rays and beta particles also released, along with energy. The symbols ${}_{Z_1}F^{A_1}$ and ${}_{Z_2}F^{A_2}$ refer to product nuclei called fission fragments. The subscripts and superscripts to denote atomic

---

* For the history of this period see H. D. SMYTH, *Military Applications of Atomic Energy*. Princeton: Princeton University Press, 1945, p. 22; and L. A. TURNER *Rev. Mod. Phys.*, *12*, 1 (1940).

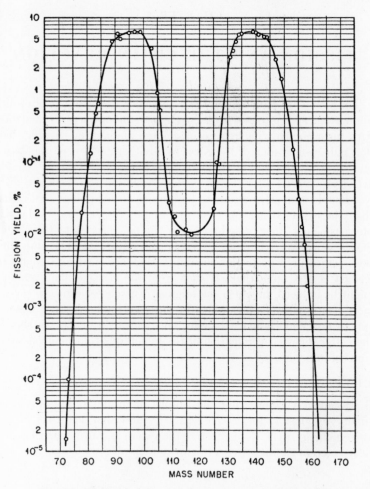

Fig. 3.1. Yield of fission products by mass number. [From C. Coryell and N. Sugarman, Eds., *Radiochemical Studies: The Fission Products,* Vol. 9. McGraw-Hill Book Co., 1952. Copyright, 1951, by McGraw-Hill Book Co., Inc.]

number and mass number are in general terms because of the large variety of possible combinations. A portion of the U^{236} nuclei formed by the absorption of the neutrons remains stable, at least in the sense that fission does not take place. The remainder of nuclei give the two fragments of mass consistent (a) with the total at the start (236), and (b) with the number of neutrons emitted, usually two or three. On the *average*, 2.5 ± 0.1 neutrons are released. Of these, the majority are released at the instant of fission; a fraction 0.00755 is the result of radioactive decay of fission fragments. These *delayed neutrons*, emitted with an average half-life of around 10 sec, play a significant role in the control of nuclear reactors, as we shall see in Section 8.1. Since the two fragments have a variety of masses and nuclear charges, many elements are represented in the fission products of nuclear reactor operation. Further, the split is generally asymmetric—the most likely ratio of masses is three to two. Figure 3.1 shows the distribution of fission products by mass number. As illustration of the use of the graph, note the ordinate 4.9 per cent at $A = 133$. This means that the number of atoms of mass 133 is 4.9 per cent of the number of *fissions* (*not* of the number of fission fragments). The most likely products, corresponding to the peaks of the curve, are elements with mass 95 or 139, the sum of which is 234, which is 236 less two neutrons. Any combination adding to 234 or 233 is possible, however, in the range of masses 70 to 160. As a typical example, assume that two neutrons are released. The sum of the mass numbers of fragments $A_1 + A_2$ must be 234, and the total charge of the two fragments, $Z_1 + Z_2$ must be 92. Assume that both the mass and charge divide in the ratio three to two, so that the original fragments are $Z_1 = 55$, $A_1 = 140$, and $Z_2 = 37$, $A_2 = 94$. The heaviest stable isotope of the element of atomic number 55, cesium, has a mass number 133, while the heaviest of the element rubidium $Z = 37$ has an A of 87. In the terminology of nuclear physics the fission fragments have "too much mass for their charge," a condition that leads to radioactive instability. One mode of disintegration that would reduce the mass to normal, neutron emission, occurs rarely. The usual process is beta emission, without change in mass number, but with an increase in one unit in atomic number with each electron emitted. Several electrons are released in sequence by each fragment, with increasing half-lives, before stability is achieved. Herein lies the danger from fission products. Each nucleus produced has its characteristic radioactive "chain." The many beta particles and gamma rays given off by millions of fragments can seriously damage human tissue exposed to them. Several typical sequences that are of importance in the operation of nuclear reactors or in the production of useful isotopes are listed below:

$$_{51}Sb^{133} \xrightarrow[10 \text{ min}]{} {}_{52}Te^{133} \xrightarrow[60 \text{ min}]{} {}_{53}I^{133} \xrightarrow[22 \text{ hr}]{} {}_{54}Xe^{133} \xrightarrow[5.3 \text{ days}]{} {}_{55}Cs^{133} \text{ (stable)}$$

$$_{52}Te^{135} \xrightarrow[2 \text{ min}]{} {}_{53}I^{135} \xrightarrow[6.7 \text{ hr}]{} {}_{54}Xe^{135} \xrightarrow[9.2 \text{ hr}]{} {}_{55}Cs^{135} \xrightarrow[2.1 \times 10^6 \text{ yr}]{} {}_{56}Ba^{135} \text{ (stable)}$$

$$_{36}Kr^{90} \xrightarrow[33 \text{ sec}]{} {}_{37}Rb^{90} \xrightarrow[\text{(short)}]{} {}_{38}Sr^{90} \xrightarrow[25 \text{ yr}]{} {}_{39}Y^{90} \xrightarrow[65 \text{ hr}]{} {}_{40}Zr^{90} \text{ (stable)}$$

The half-lives of each member of the chain are listed below the transition arrows, in hours, minutes or days, as the case may be. Each decay is one nucleus emitting a beta particle, as may be seen from the changes in atomic number.

The most important byproduct of fission is the *energy*. In addition to the physical particles, a total of around 200 mev of energy is released, disposed in the following way—fast neutrons, each having around 2 mev, making a total of 5 mev on the average; gamma rays of 2 mev each, totaling 10 mev more; beta particles and the neutrinos that accompany them, 18 mev more, and finally the heavy fission fragments, carrying 83 mev each. The latter separate from each other at high speeds, and lose energy as heat to the medium in which they are formed. It is this energy that makes the atomic bomb explosive, and which engineers and scientists will put to useful purposes in running electrical generators or propelling vehicles of various kinds. Several computations. that illustrate the magnitudes of possible available energy and that will be useful for future estimates can be made. First, let us find the energy in kilowatt-hours resulting from the fission of 1 g. of U^{235}. In this mass there are $(1/235)$ 6.023×10^{23} nuclei, each releasing 200 mev, or 320×10^{-6} erg. The product of these two numbers is 8.2×10^{17} ergs, or 8.2×10^{10} joules. Now since 1 joule = 1 watt-sec = $1/(3.6 \times 10^6)$ kwhr, the energy yield is 2.3×10^4 kwhr per gram. This is the same as

$$(2.3 \times 10^4 \text{ kwhr/g})(454 \text{ g/lb}) = 10^7 \text{ kwhr/lb}$$

At standard power costs of around $\frac{1}{2}$¢/kwhr, the ultimate value of U^{235} amounts to $50,000/lb.

3.2 The theory of fission

The explanation of the fission event that is currently accepted is based on the "liquid drop" model of the nucleus. In a drop of water, the attractions of the molecules for each other result in a spherical shape that tends to resist deformation. The same effect is assumed to be true in the nucleus by virtue of the nuclear forces. If sufficient energy is supplied, either the water drop or the nucleus can be split in two smaller parts. The interesting theory of fission by Bohr and Wheeler* is now reviewed in a qualitative way. Two of the contributions to the binding energy, as stated in Section 1.3, were the coulomb repulsion, and surface effects. If the nuclear "drop" is distorted, the magnitudes of these energies only are affected. Write their sum as

$$E = E_c + E_s = \frac{3Z^2e^2}{5r} + (C)(4\pi r^2)$$

where r is the nuclear radius, $4\pi r^2$ is the surface area and C is a constant. Let the nucleus be flattened as in Fig. 3.2. The effective r

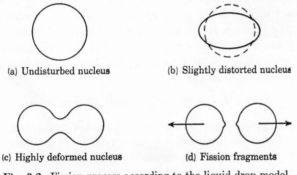

(a) Undisturbed nucleus   (b) Slightly distorted nucleus

(c) Highly deformed nucleus   (d) Fission fragments

Fig. 3.2. Fission process according to the liquid drop model.

increases. From the formula above, the electrostatic energy is reduced, as one would expect because the charges are farther apart. The surface energy becomes increased, however, because the original sphere had the least surface area. For small oscillatory distortions, there is a net energy increase. Since binding energy is a measure of the forces holding nuclei together, a restoring force to the original stable sphere is implied. Certain special distortions, such as into a

* N. Bohr and J. A. Wheeler, *Phys. Rev.*, *56*, 426 (1939).

dumbbell shape shown also in Fig. 3.2, can cause the energy to rise to a maximum and then fall, meaning that the system is more stable as separate parts than as a sphere. Geometric analysis of the binding energy formula above yields two conditions on fission:

(1) If Z^2/A is greater than 45, the nucleus will split spontaneously. Now this ratio for $_{92}U^{235}$ is only 36, which shows that some energy must be supplied for fission to occur. An incoming neutron may supply the lack.

(2) The *activation energy* E_a, the amount that must be added to bring the nucleus to the point of fission, is dependent on the nuclear surface area and to the electrostatic energy. Calculations yield the typical E_a values below for the nuclei that are products of neutron absorption.

Nucleus	U^{236}	U^{239}	Pu^{240}
E_a (mev)	6.8	7.1	5.1

In the previous section we pointed out that fission takes place in U^{235} with neutrons of zero kinetic energy. The question that arises is: How is the necessary activation energy supplied by a neutron? The answer is that the additional neutron upsets the neutron-proton balance and changes the binding energy, which results in an excess of energy available in the compound nucleus U^{236}. We may estimate this *excitation energy* E_e by subtracting the mass of U^{236} from the sum of the U^{235} and neutron masses.

$$E_e = (M_{235} + M_n - M_{236})(931.15 \text{ mev/amu})$$

The semi-empirical mass formula of Weizsacker and Fermi* may be used to compute isotopic masses. They may be in absolute error by about 0.01 mass units in the region of heavy elements but the differences of adjacent masses are probably much more accurate than this. The mass difference $M_{236} - M_{235}$ is computed to be 1.00168 amu by this relation. Combining this result with the neutron mass, 1.00898 yields $E_e = (0.00730)(931.15) = 6.80$ mev. This result is almost exactly equal to the needed excitation energy, and within the accuracy of the Bohr-Wheeler theory would "prove" that fission in U^{235} is possible. A repetition of the calculation with the heavier uranium isotope U^{238} plus a neutron, and U^{239} yields a value of E_e of about

---

* Quoted in one useful form by M. O. STERN, "The Masses of the Heavy Isotopes." *Rev. Mod. Phys., 21*, 316 (1949).

5.3 mev, which is less than the required $E_a = 7.1$ mev. The difference in the energies (1.8 mev) must be supplied by the kinetic energy of the neutron. The important conclusion for our purposes is that U^{235} will fission with thermal neutrons but that U^{238} will not. The neutron energy at which U^{238} fission starts is found experimentally to be close to 1 mev.

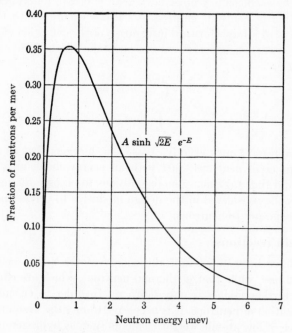

Fraction of neutrons per mev

$A \sinh \sqrt{2E}\ e^{-E}$

Neutron energy (mev)

Fig. 3.3. Fission neutron energy distribution.

Several careful studies* of fission neutron energies have shown that there is a wide spread of energy values around the 2-mev figure that is commonly quoted as the average. The methods in general consist of observing the effects of inserting a piece of pure U^{235} in a beam of thermal neutrons from a reactor. The fission neutrons are allowed to knock protons from a hydrogenous foil. The energy of the protons is then measured by a cloud chamber or other suitable detector.

* T. W. BONNER, R. A. FERRELL, and M. C. RINEHART, *Phys. Rev.*, 87, 1032 (1952); D. L. HILL, *Phys. Rev.*, 87, 1034 (1952); B. E. WATT, *Phys. Rev.*, 87, 1037 (1952).

The data in the range 0.05 to 17 mev fit rather closely the theoretical relation

$$n(E) = A \sinh \sqrt{2E} \, e^{-E}$$

where E is in mev. It is convenient to plot the distribution "normalized to one neutron," i.e. such that the area under the curve is unity. The coefficient A must be $\sqrt{2/\pi e} = 0.484$. Figure 3.3 shows the fraction of neutrons emitted at various energies with this normalization. A straightforward integration of the definition of average neutron energy using $n(E)$ above and the method described in Section 2.5,

$$\overline{E} = \frac{\displaystyle\int_0^\infty E \, n(E) \, dE}{\displaystyle\int_0^\infty n(E) \, dE}$$

yields the result 2 mev exactly. It is clear, however that an appreciable number of neutrons start with an energy much greater than 2 mev, and thus take many more collisions to become thermal. This fact must be considered in the design of shields to protect personnel against exposure to neutrons.

3.3 Chain reactions

It will have been noted that the energy of the fission neutrons is around 2 mev, while that of thermal neutrons, which are effective in causing further fission, is only 0.025 ev. In order to encourage the multiplication of neutrons, it is necessary to mix the uranium with a substance of low atomic weight elements such as hydrogen in water, beryllium, or carbon, whose nuclei are able to slow the neutrons down to thermal energy. These elements, however, compete with the uranium for the available neutrons. A rather delicate balance of constituents is required to achieve a steady chain reaction. In the two diagrams of Fig. 3.4, the multiplication process is reproduced. A single neutron causes fission in U^{235}, giving for example, three more neutrons. In the absence of any other material, these proceed to split three other nuclei, giving rise to two, two, and three neutrons respectively. Thus after only two steps in the chain, we have seven neutrons where there was but one originally. If, however, there is present an absorbing substance, the moderator, that slows the neutrons down, fewer than seven will be available. If the right proportions of uranium and moderator are chosen, the net number left over after many cycles will be exactly one neutron, which defines the steady reactor. In a reactor composed of natural uranium, with its principal component U^{238}, other effects take place. The first of these occurs during the

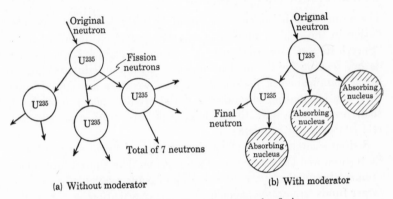

(a) Without moderator   (b) With moderator

Fig. 3.4. Multiplication of neutrons by fission.

slowing down history of a neutron. It has a chance of being captured by U^{238} at one of its strong resonance peaks in the cross-section curve. Thermal neutrons also are absorbed by the heavy isotope without fission resulting. In the more detailed study to follow in later chapters, the relation of the above effects to the way in which the material is disposed in the reactor will be discussed.

A measure of the fractions of thermal neutrons absorbed in uranium and nuclei of the moderator is provided by the cross sections. Consider a single neutron finding itself in a mass of graphite that has been impregnated with U^{235} in such a way that there are 10,000 carbon atoms for each uranium atom. The total target area that the neutron sees, looking at a cubic centimeter volume with its face normal to its direction of motion, is the sum of $N\sigma_a$ of the carbon and $N\sigma_a$ of the U^{235}. Let us compute the chance that the neutron will be absorbed in that cubic centimeter from the data on number of nuclei and cross sections. As calculated earlier, N_C is 0.0827×10^{24} and $(\sigma_a)_C$ is 0.0045×10^{-24} cm^2, so that $\Sigma_C = N_C(\sigma_a)_C$ is 3.72×10^{-4}. With the 10,000:1 atom ratio, N_U is 8.27×10^{18}, and with the tabulated $(\sigma_a)_U$ of 650×10^{-24}, the product is $N_U(\sigma_a)_U$ or 5.4×10^{-3}. It is clear that less than 10 per cent of the total absorption is due to the carbon, even though there are 10,000 times as many atoms as of U^{235}. Thus effects are not proportional to the amounts of material present as in most problems.

3.4 The atomic energy program

The sequence of historical events leading to the present status of the nation in the field of nuclear energy has been well described in the "Smyth Report" (see references in Section 3.5), which is almost mandatory reading for the nuclear engineer. In it the industrial and political significance of fission and atomic weapons are stated, along with the fascinating chronology of the atomic energy project. We shall review here only the highlights of this story, and only as it relates to current problems.

Serious contemplation of the importance of fission to the United States followed the discovery of the process. The United States Government became actively interested, and made available increasingly larger funds to various agencies for the investigation of military use of the new phenomenon. Nuclear theory also suggested that fission would occur in elements of higher atomic number than uranium, if they could be formed by the absorption of neutrons in uranium. This was found to be the case, with the production of the new "transuranic" element plutonium (Pu). The set of reactions involved is now known to be

$$_{92}U^{238} + {_0}n^1 \rightarrow {_{92}}U^{239}$$

$$_{92}U^{239} \underset{23 \text{ min}}{\rightarrow} {_{93}}Np^{239} + {_{-1}}e^0$$

$$_{93}Np^{239} \underset{2.3 \text{ days}}{\rightarrow} {_{94}}Pu^{239} + {_{-1}}e^0$$

The intermediate step involves another new element, neptunium, which is of such short half-life as to be useless. The final fissionable product Pu^{239} has a relatively long half-life. A second fact of great importance was that U^{235} was the principal fissionable isotope. Thus, two choices were open for the direction of development: (a) the production of plutonium by a chain reaction in natural uranium, if such were possible, or (b) the separation of the uranium isotopes, again if it could be done. Serious unknowns were immediately recognized in each problem. In the case of the plutonium, it appeared that a chain reaction could take place profitably only if the uranium were mixed with a moderator, such as graphite or heavy water. Graphite was not available in pure enough form and heavy water was not available in large enough quantities. After it had been shown at the University of Chicago that a chain reaction with uranium and graphite was actually possible, it still remained to make great extensions from the rudimentary experimental equipment to the design of the production plants. These successful machines are located at the Hanford Engineering Works, in the state of Washington. It is remarkable to note that the theoretical calculations on the final design came within less than 1 per cent of the actual performance, even though there was not enough time to perform all of the necessary experimental measurements of cross sections of important elements or of the motion properties of neutrons. The air cooled reactor at Oak Ridge was intended to serve as a pilot plant, but since the production unit used water as a coolant, little guidance in design was provided. The eventual use of the Oak Ridge reactor was for the accumulation of plutonium for chemistry studies.

Two independent methods of uranium isotope separation evolved from consideration and testing of many methods. The first was the *electromagnetic*, based on the Dempster-type mass spectrograph. A beam of ionized uranium atoms is shot into a uniform magnetic field by properly arranged electrodes. After traveling through a half-circle, there is a small spatial separation of the ions of U^{235} and U^{238}. No previous models of spectrographs had been able to achieve the current of ions of the order of milliamperes that was necessary to give measurable quantities of the isotopes. The degree of separation was inherently limited because of the small fractional mass difference. Through the efforts of the group at the University of California Radiation Laboratory at Berkeley, equipment was improved to the extent that it could be recommended for duplication on a large scale in the production plant (Y-12) at Oak Ridge, Tennessee. The atomic bomb dropped at Hiroshima, Japan was composed of U^{235} obtained by this method.

The other approach to isotope separation was by *gaseous diffusion*, studied by the SAM Laboratory at Columbia University. Uranium in the form of a gaseous compound, uranium hexafluoride, UF_6, is forced through noncorrosive permeable "barriers," such as silver-zinc alloy. The lighter isotope passes through with greater facility, leaving the remainder depleted in U^{235}. The separation achieved in a single

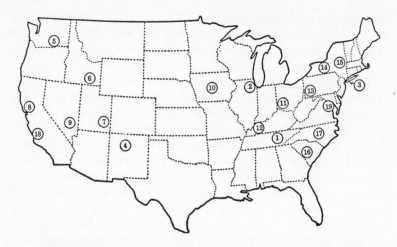

Fig. 3.5. (a) Geographic distribution of the United States atomic energy program. Circled numbers correspond to the following list of centers:

1 *Oak Ridge, Tennessee:*
Gaseous Diffusion Plant,
Oak Ridge National Laboratory
(Carbide and Chemicals Corp.);
Oak Ridge Institute of Nuclear
Studies.

2 *Chicago, Illinois:*
Argonne National Laboratory
(University of Chicago).

3 *Upton, Long Island, New York:*
Brookhaven National Laboratory
(Associated Universities, Inc.).

4. *Los Alamos, New Mexico:*
Los Alamos Scientific Laboratory
(University of California);
Albuquerque, New Mexico:
Sandia Laboratory, Sandia Base
(Western Electric Co.).

5. *Hanford, Washington:*
Hanford Plutonium Works
(General Electric Co.).

6. *Arco, Idaho:*
Reactor Testing Station
(U.S. Atomic Energy Commission).

7. *Monticello, Utah:*
Ore refineries.

8. *Berkeley, California:*
Radiation Laboratory
(University of California).

9. *Nevada:*
Weapons testing area.

10. *Ames, Iowa:*
Ames Laboratory
(Iowa State College).

11. *Miamisburg, Ohio:*
Mound Laboratory
(Monsanto Chemical Co.).

12. *Paducah, Kentucky:*
Gaseous Diffusion Plant.

13. *Pittsburgh, Pennsylvania:*
Bettis Plant (Westinghouse Electric
Co., Atomic Power Division).

14. *Rochester, New York:*
Rochester Atomic Energy Project
(University of Rochester).

15. *Schenectady, New York:*
Knolls Atomic Power Laboratory
(General Electric Co.).

16. *Aiken, South Carolina:*
Production Center (duPont Co.).

17. *Raleigh, North Carolina:*
Raleigh Research Reactor
(North Carolina State College).

18. *Los Angeles, California:*
Atomic Energy Project
(University of California).

19. *Washington, D.C.:*
U.S. Atomic Energy Commission.

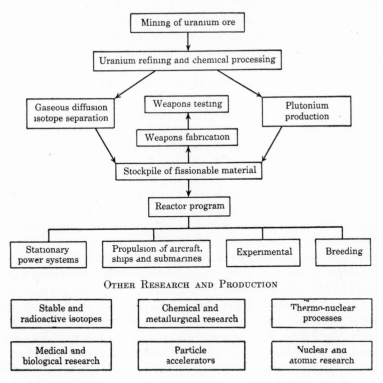

Fig. 3.5. (b) Functional distribution of the United States atomic energy program.

stage of the system is only a fractional per cent, so that a series of thousands of stages was found necessary. By the middle of 1945 a production plant called K-25, located also at Oak Ridge, was put into production. Because of the continuous nature of this essentially chemical process, it has been found economically preferable to the electromagnetic method, in which operations have now been suspended.

Long before material in appreciable quantities issued from the production plants, theoretical calculations and plans for utilization of fissionable masses in a weapon were being made at Los Alamos Laboratory in New Mexico. As quickly as a kilogram of U^{235} was made, critical mass tests were performed, using the "water boiler" arrangement, in which a uranium salt is dissolved in a spherical vessel of water. Considerations of the proper way to assemble the subcritical parts of the bomb, the necessary containment of material to achieve maximum power release, and the mechanism of detonation were studied thoroughly.

Since the end of World War II, no let-up in the production of fissionable materials has been permitted. In fact, expansion of diffusion plant and plutonium plant facilities has resulted in a marked increase in the rate of accumulation of a material stockpile. More attention however, has been devoted to possible peacetime applications of nuclear energy. In particular, the Atomic Energy Commission has actively encouraged the use of radioactive isotopes made within nuclear reactors by making available production time and facilities in the Oak Ridge, Argonne, and Brookhaven National Laboratory machines. The study of the propulsion of aircraft and submarines by nuclear energy, while primarily of military importance, serves to determine the possibilities of commercial use. Studies or designs of power producing reactors by industrial concerns have also been sponsored by the Atomic Energy Commission.

Figure 3.5(a) shows a map of the United States with atomic energy installations and a schematic "flow chart" of the atomic energy program, Fig. 3.5(b). The sequence starts with the raw material, uranium ore, and ends with a stockpile of fissionable material. Research and development activities stem from the available new materials and byproducts but they also supply new methods and improvements in the cycle.

Sources of uranium ore available to this country include the Belgian Congo, the Great Bear Lake region of Canada, and limited deposits in the western part of the United States, principally in Utah and Colorado. These last two locations produce carnotite ore, assaying less than 1 per cent uranium. Prior to World War II, the carnotite ore was processed for vanadium; a considerable part of the uranium supply came at one time from the reprocessed wastes of earlier operations. In order to be processed in the gaseous diffusion plant or the plutonium plant, the uranium has to be highly purified chemically, and put in the form of UF_6 for the gaseous diffusion plant, or the metal for the plutonium plant.

The only phase of the program shown in Fig. 3.5 that probably is not self-evident is the research on the regeneration of fissionable material, called breeding. It was found that the element thorium, on absorbing neutrons, is changed into another fissionable isotope of uranium, U^{233}, in a manner analogous to the creation of plutonium. Thus there is a good possibility that two nonfissionable materials may be made useful by converting them into fissionable form.

3.5 General references in the nuclear energy field

Although applicable references will be collected at the end of each chapter, at this point it is advisable to list and describe reading material useful throughout the book:

SMYTH, H. D., *Atomic Energy for Military Purposes.* Princeton: Princeton University Press, 1945. This book, known also as the "Smyth Report," is highly recommended for history and foundations of the atomic energy project. It is also published in an inexpensive paper-back edition by the U. S. Government Printing Office, Washington, D. C.

GLASSTONE, S., *Sourcebook of Atomic Energy.* New York: D. Van Nostrand Co., 1950. Brief but clearly written semi-technical descriptions of nuclear energy processes, facilities and uses, this book is sponsored by the Atomic Energy Commission.

SOODAK, H. and E. C. CAMPBELL, *Elementary Reactor Theory.* New York: John Wiley & Sons, 1950. Brief but comprehensive mathematical treatment of the homogeneous-type reactor. It provides the justification for many of the reactor formulas assumed in the present book.

GOODMAN, CLARK, Ed., *The Science and Engineering of Nuclear Power.* Cambridge, Mass.: Addison-Wesley Press, Vol. I, 1947; Vol. II, 1949. This two-volume collection of M.I.T. lectures on reactor theory and design, and many other aspects, is a useful reference for tabular data and an exhaustive treatment of their specialties by a number of authorities.

GLASSTONE, S. and M. C. EDLUND, *The Elements of Nuclear Reactor Theory.* New York: D. Van Nostrand Co., 1952. The theory of reactors is clearly and thoroughly described, and correct declassified nuclear constants are used consistently.

The Semi-Annual Reports of the Atomic Energy Commission to Congress. Washington, D. C.: U. S. Government Printing Office. These volumes serve to bring the "Smyth Report" up to date, and each is usually devoted to a specific portion of atomic energy development. Typical titles: "Atomic Energy and the Life Sciences" (sixth); "Atomic Energy and the Physical Sciences" (seventh); "Control of Radiation Hazards in the Atomic Energy Program" (eighth).

The research and development in the atomic energy program differs from that in the pre-war science and engineering in that the individual's prerogative to publish findings in the established literature must be suspended in the interests of national security.* Despite this handicap, the Technical Information Division of the Atomic Energy Commission, located at Oak Ridge, Tennessee, has performed a very valuable service to universities and industry by publishing thousands of "declassified documents" on almost all aspects of the program. These are available in about 30 libraries throughout the country designated as authorized repositories (see list in Appendix), or may be purchased at nominal rates from the issuing division.

Nuclear Science Abstracts. Oak Ridge, Tenn.: Technical Information Division, Atomic Energy Commission. This magazine appears twice monthly, listing all publications and abstracts relevant to the field, including technical periodicals as well as those of AEC National Laboratories or AEC sub-contractors. Cumulative indexes are released each year.

National Nuclear Energy Series. New York: McGraw-Hill Book Co. These books cover most aspects of work done during 1941–46. The AEC has sponsored this series as a large-scale reference book publishing program.

---

* The result is that many of the interesting useful details of processes remain sealed in the minds and files of those performing the restricted work. All too much of that which has been declassified consists of descriptions of general principles and mathematical methods from which one can, with sufficient effort and ingenuity, design equipment that would be equivalent to the classified version, or consists of reviews which acquaint an uninformed reader with the past and possible future overall progress in the field, but which reveal no details, or consists of isolated reports on special topics that are out of context.

These footnote comments are a statement of fact rather than a criticism, since the policy set down in the Atomic Energy Act of 1946 is quite explicit: "Restricted data" means all data "concerning the manufacture or utilization of atomic weapons, the production of fissionable material, or the use of fissionable material in the production of power, but shall not include any data which the Commission from time to time determines may be published without adversely affecting the common defense and security."

Nucleonics. New York: McGraw-Hill Publishing Co. This independent monthly magazine features review articles, new developments in the reactor field, nuclear instruments, and descriptions of many practical experimental apparatus. A nuclear engineer will find a subscription well worth while.

Problems

3.1 What are the particular fission fragments resulting from an *even* split of U^{235}, with 4 neutrons and 2 beta particles emitted instantaneously?

3.2 Show that a fission rate of 3×10^{10} per sec will result in approximately 1 watt of power. NOTE: this useful conversion factor is easily remembered as the same as the velocity of light in cm/sec.

3.3 In a homogeneous solution of water and natural uranium with a chemical concentration of 5 per cent by weight, what fraction of thermal neutrons are absorbed in uranium?

CHAPTER 4

THE SEPARATION OF ISOTOPES

The principles of isotope separation will be discussed in this chapter with particular attention to the extraction of U^{235} from uranium by the gaseous diffusion process. A brief description will also be given of the electromagnetic separation method, which serves as a principal source of stable isotopes. The separation of deuterium from hydrogen will be included because of its importance in the production of heavy water for reactor moderators. Since the isotopes of elements differ by virtue of their mass and not appreciably because of their chemical properties, it is necessary to employ processes in which forces produce different responses of the isotopes on the basis of mass.

Fig. 4.1. Gaseous diffusion plant at Oak Ridge, Tennessee. [Photograph by J. E. Westcott, courtesy U.S. Atomic Energy Commission.]

4.1 Gaseous diffusion separation

The main plant for the separation of U^{235} from U^{238} at Oak Ridge, Tennessee has been described as a U-shaped building, 1 mile in total length and 400 ft across. The "K-25" area, Fig. 4.1, will give some idea of the magnitude of the operations. In such buildings, a sequence of individual separators accept natural uranium "feed" and discharge the enriched "product" and the depleted "waste." We shall discuss the theoretical properties of the barrier through which the UF_6 gas passes, and the arrangement of stages in cascade. The principal sources of our theory are the declassified writings of Cohen and of Schacter and Garrett. The analysis we shall use will not be rigorous, but will be much easier to understand than the exact approach.

The most rudimentary type of gaseous diffusion separator would consist of a container with a porous membrane separating it into two halves, as shown in Fig. 4.2. A gas such as UF_6 is supplied at slight

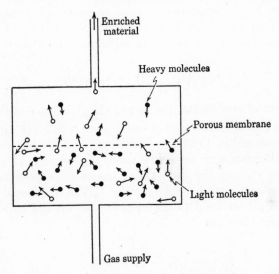

Fig. 4.2. Separation of molecules by barrier.

pressure on one side and a vacuum is maintained on the other. The two molecules present have masses 349 and 352 (six times 19, the mass of fluorine, plus 235 or 238). The average energies of the molecules of mass 349 and 352 are the same, according to the principle of equipartition of energy of kinetic gas theory. If we let the subscript L denote the light molecule and H the heavy, then

$$\tfrac{1}{2}m_H v_H{}^2 = \tfrac{1}{2}m_L v_L{}^2$$

where the v's are effective average velocities. From this equation it may be seen that the velocity of the light molecules is higher than that of the heavy, according to

$$v_L = \sqrt{m_H/m_L}\, v_H$$

Thus the frequency of collision with the porous barrier will be higher for the light molecules, and a slightly higher proportion of them will pass through. After a very short time has elapsed, the material on the low pressure side of the barrier will have a different ratio of numbers of the two isotopes than the original mixture had. The ratio $(n'_L/n'_H)/(n_L/n_H)$ comparing the particle ratio after processing to that before in any separation process, regardless of elapsed time is called the *separation factor*, r. In this special case of a small (approximately zero) take-off, or "cut," the separation factor is

$$r_0 = \left(\frac{n'_L/n'_H}{n_L/n_H}\right)_0 = \sqrt{m_H/m_L}$$

The amount of enrichment, the increase in abundance of the lighter isotope, is almost imperceptibly small, since $\sqrt{352/349}$ differs very slightly from unity, 1.0043. A simple proof of the above relation between abundance ratios can be made. The number of each type of molecule striking the barrier each second is proportional to the number present n, and to the velocity v. The number n' that get through, is proportional to the number that hit the barrier. Thus we may form the ratio

$$\frac{n'_L}{n'_H} = \frac{n_L v_L}{n_H v_H}$$

which can be rearranged to give the formula quoted.

If instead of the idealized situation above, one allows an appreciable fraction of the original gas to pass through, the separation will not be as perfect. A logical argument can be applied to show that the separation factor should be smaller. As the diffusion proceeds, the high pressure side becomes depleted in the light isotope. This has the effect of reducing the ratio of the collision rates of light and heavy molecules with the barrier. A somewhat higher fraction of heavy molecules gets through the barrier than at the start and effectively "contaminates" the mixture on the low pressure side. The separation factor r will no longer be given simply by the ratio of the square roots of the masses. For instance, in the lower container of the apparatus sketched in Fig. 4.3, if half of the original gas on the bottom side of the barrier has penetrated

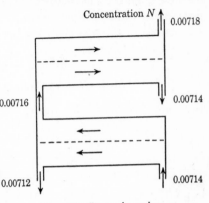

Fig. 4.3. Stages in series.

the barrier and been pumped off, the effective separation factor is

$$r = \frac{n'_L/n'_H}{n_L/n_H} = 1 + 0.693(\sqrt{m_H/m_L} - 1)$$

For uranium this theoretical separation factor is computed to be 1.0030. At this point it is necessary to define two new terms used in separation calculations. The first is the *concentration* N, which is the fraction by numbers of atoms of a given isotope in the mixture. The concentration of the *light* isotope is

$$N = \frac{n_L}{n_L + n_H}$$

This is also called "mole fraction" by some writers. It is often convenient to quote this as a percentage. The isotopic concentration of U^{235} in natural uranium is 0.00714 or 0.714 per cent. Another useful variable is the *abundance ratio*, given by

$$R = n_L/n_H$$

The quantities N and R are related by the formulas

$$N = \frac{R}{R + 1} \quad \text{and} \quad R = \frac{N}{1 - N}$$

The abundance ratio of natural uranium is $R = 0.00714/(1 - 0.00714) = 0.00719$. We may now estimate the effect of a separation process on these quantities, letting primed and unprimed symbols refer to the material after and before separation respectively. If half of a UF_6 sample passes through a perfect barrier, the abundance ratio in the product would be

$$n'_L/n'_H = r(n_L/n_H)$$

or

$$R' = rR = (1.0030)(0.00719) = 0.00721$$

In terms of concentration this is

$$N' = R'/(R' + 1) = 0.00721/1.00721 = 0.00716$$

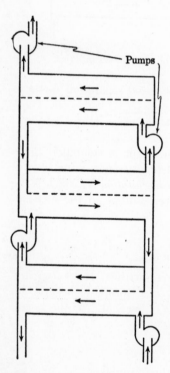

A convenient approximation for processes having the separation factor very nearly unity is the expression

$$N' \simeq rN$$

As a test of its accuracy note that

$$N' \simeq (1.0030)(0.00714) = 0.00716$$

agrees with the more rigorous result. The error is entirely negligible in this case. For separation factors close to unity, it may be shown that the rise in N for the enriched material is the same as the drop in N for the depleted. Thus we would estimate that the depleted material will have a concentration of 0.00712. When several *stages* are connected in sequence, the successive change in N can be estimated easily. It is clear that the resulting amounts of enriched material left after passage through many such stages is impractically low. Further we note that the depleted concentration at each stage matches the feed of the stage below, which suggests that the material be recirculated. The arrangement shown in Fig. 4.4, called a *cascade*, takes

Fig. 4.4. Elementary cascade.

advantage of these facts. Under the condition that the two mixing flows have the same concentration, as we have assumed, the system is called an *ideal cascade*. Thousands of stages are linked together in the gaseous diffusion plant to raise the concentration from 0.00714 to the order of 0.8 or 0.9. Figure 4.5 shows a schematic ar-

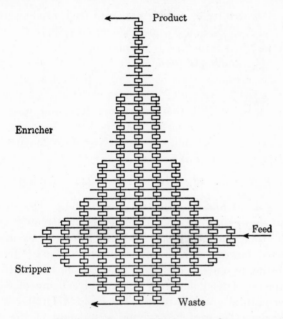

Fig. 4.5. Gaseous diffusion cascade.

rangement of the complete system. The tapering of the pattern is intended to show how the amount of material circulated becomes smaller as the material is enriched. Because the depleted material from the first stage of the cascade still contains 99.7 per cent of the initial amount of U^{235}, it is necessary to add the "stripping" section to reduce the waste concentration. In this section the U^{235} migrates upward, the U^{238} downward. There must be points in the system for withdrawal of final product and for the waste, as well as a feed stage. Since the process is inherently inefficient, the weight of material that goes out the bottom is much greater than that out the top. For this reason, the flow capacity, separator size and pump power in the stages may be reduced as one goes up in the system. The input of uranium must equal the output, and similarly for each isotopic component, except for holdup of material in the system, which we shall neglect. The equations giving the balance of uranium and U^{235} may be readily written as

$$F = P + W, \qquad N_F F = N_P P + N_W W$$

where F, P, and W refer to the masses of feed, product and waste *uranium*, and N_F, N_P, and N_W are the concentrations of U^{235} in each of the streams. The term $N_F F$ is the mass of U^{235} being fed in, $N_P P$ is the product U^{235} and $N_W W$ is the waste U^{235}. A simple example of the use of balance formulas is given. Take a hypothetical diffusion plant designed to yield 1 mole of U^{235} per day, with an isotopic concentration of 0.8. It is supplied with natural uranium, and must discharge the waste at a concentration of 0.006 in U^{235}. The main unknown quantity is the daily uranium feed, F. Now $P = 235/0.8 = 294$ g. The two equations are thus

$$F = 294 + W, \qquad 0.00714F = 235 + 0.006W$$

Eliminating W, we find $F = 204,600$ g, or 204.6 kg. This surprisingly large result shows that the refined product is an extremely small fraction of the total material processed (0.14% for this example). The U^{235} extracted, however, is a reasonable portion of the U^{235} feed (16%). We may estimate roughly the part of the cost of U^{235} that is related to the expense of feed material, using Zinn's figure of \$35/lb* or \$77/kg for natural uranium metal. The cost, (\$77)(205) = \$15,800, goes to produce 235 g of U^{235}, giving a unit cost of \$67/g for the light isotope. The assumption is made that the term "waste" is literally correct in that the material is not reused.

4.2 Cascade parameters

Let us determine the number of stages needed to carry feed material at concentration N_F to a product concentration N_P under the condition that the two flows entering each stage from above and from below have the same concentration. The abundance ratio of the feed to each stage is always r times that for the product of the preceding stage. Letting the feed stage be numbered 0, the first stage 1, etc. on up to any higher stage S

---

* ZINN, W. H., "Basic Problems in Central Station Nuclear Power." *Nucleonics*, September (1952).

$$R_1 = rR_0 = rR_F$$
$$R_2 = rR_1$$
$$R_3 = rR_2$$
$$\cdots\cdots\cdots$$
$$R_S = rR_{S-1}$$

Combining these equations by repeated substitution,

$$R_S = r^S R_F$$

or taking logarithms,

$$\log_e R_S = \log_e r^S + \log_e R_F$$

or

$$S = \frac{\log_e R_S/R_F}{\log_e r}$$

Since r is very close to 1, $\log_e r$ is approximately $r - 1$, and the total number of stages in the enricher is

$$S \simeq \frac{1}{r - 1} \log_e \frac{R_S}{R_F}$$

This relation may be used to calculate the number of stages between the feed point and one at higher concentration, including the withdrawal point. Let us find how many stages are needed to carry natural uranium to a concentration of 0.8. Now $r - 1 = 0.0030$, $R_F = 0.00719$ and $R_P = 0.8/(1 - 0.8) = 4.0$. Therefore

$$S = (1/0.003) \log_e (4.0/0.00719) = 2107$$

The stage number expression above holds for the stripper as well as the enricher. Since R_S/R_F is now less than unity, S comes out to be a negative number. The stripper stages can thus be numbered -1, -2, -3 on down to the waste outlet. Figure 4.6 shows how the concentration increases with stage number for a hypothetical case with $N_F = 0.00714$, $N_P = 0.8$ and $N_W = 0.006$.

Another factor of practical interest is the amount of material that must be circulated at one level in the cascade. Each stage has its "interstage flow" L, which is proportional to the pumping power. This is not to be confused with any of the three flows from and to the outside, feed, product or waste, since the system could conceivably be shut off from the outside and still have a tremendous circulating flow. By the application of flow balance and enrichment theory, a formula may be derived for L, the interstage flow associated with a stage at which the concentration is N,

$$L = \frac{2P}{r-1} \frac{N_P - N}{N(1-N)}$$

This formula as it stands applies to the enricher, but if P is replaced by W and N_P by N_W, it will yield the interstage flow for the stripper.

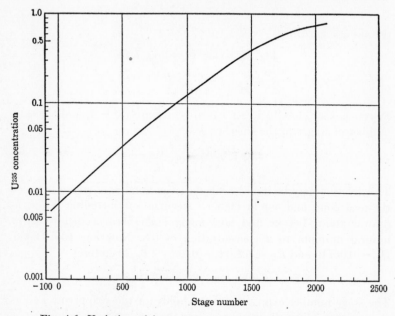

Fig. 4.6. Variation of isotopic concentration with stage number.

As an example, let us compute L for the $N = 0.05$ level, with a U[235] product of 0.235 kg per day at a concentration N_P of 0.80. Thus $P = 0.294$ kg and

$$L = \frac{(2)(0.294)}{0.003} \cdot \frac{0.80 - 0.05}{(0.05)(1 - 0.05)} = 3100 \text{ kg/day}$$

The general formula above may be used to calculate values of L and the pumping power capacity needed at all concentration levels in the plant. Figure 4.7 is a plot of interstage flow as a function of concentration, based on a cascade with these characteristics:

U^{235} *in product:* 0.235 kg/day, concentration 0.8
Uranium feed: 205 kg/day, concentration 0.00714
Waste concentration: 0.006
Number of stages: enricher 2107, stripper 58.

A relatively straightforward integration of the interstage flow for-

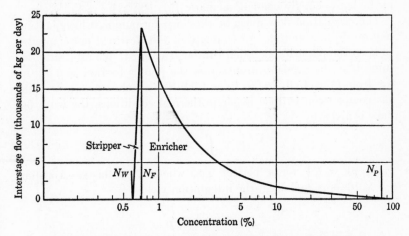

Fig. 4.7. Interstage flow in cascade as it depends on concentration.

mula over the whole cascade can be made using the assumption that the concentration varies continuously with the stage number S according to the approximate condition

$$dN/dS \simeq (r - 1)(1 - N)N$$

The result is

$$L_{\text{total}} = 2/(r - 1)[S_S W(1 - 2N_W) + S_E P(2N_P - 1)]$$

where S_S and S_E are the numbers of stages in the stripper and enricher and the other symbols have been used before. The total interstage flow for our example cascade is easily computed to be 1.03×10^7 kg/day, about 4.3×10^7 moles/day of UF_6, molecular weight 0.352 kg. The circulating material in the thousands of stages far exceeds the daily input and output. It follows that in the start-up of a diffusion plant a considerable time is needed to build up an inventory.

In the cascades described above, we assumed that exactly half of the gas in each stage passed through the barrier, and that the rise in concentration in one stage was equal to the drop in the part sent down to the stage below. If the amount taken out to send upward is small, however, the depleted material coming down is of higher concentration than the feed with which it blends, and in effect enriches it. It turns out that fewer stages are required to achieve the desired concentration by use of this *non-ideal* cascading technique, in the limit, exactly one-half as many.

The circulation flow must be provided by pumps, which in turn require driving motors. An estimate of the electrical power needed to keep the plant in operation can be attempted. We arbitrarily assume that the pressure drop across the porous barriers is 0.9 atm, e.g. from $P_a = 15$ lb/in.^{2} to $P_b = 1.5$ lb/in.^{2} absolute pressure. If the gas compression is done under isothermal conditions, the work per mole is given by

$$w = \int_{V_a}^{V_b} p \, dV$$

Since $pV = RT$ for a perfect gas, where R is the gas constant 8.3×10^7 ergs/mole-deg, the integration yields

$$w = RT \log_e \frac{P_a}{P_b}$$

Assume the gas temperature to be 100°C which is somewhat above the boiling point of UF_6, 56.2°C. Thus $T = 373$°K and

$$w = (8.3 \times 10^7)(373)(\log_e 10)$$
$$= 7.10 \times 10^{10} \text{ ergs/mole}$$
$$= 7.10 \times 10^3 \text{ watt-sec/mole}$$

With an interstage flow of 4.3×10^7 moles/day or $(4.3 \times 10^7)/(8.64 \times 10^4) = 0.500 \times 10^3$ moles/sec, the power is

$$P = wL = (7.10 \times 10^3)(0.500 \times 10^3) = 3.55 \times 10^6 \text{ watts}$$

The pumps probably have an efficiency of no higher than 10 per cent, which would give us the estimate of about 35 mw power for circulating the process gas. This result is probably a *lower* limit on the total power needed for the system.

A few of the research problems that were attacked during World War II, or which have been solved satisfactorily since, may be listed to give a little more insight into the diffusion process operations.

(1) *Development of resistant materials.* The process gas UF_6 is cor-

rosive, as are many fluorine compounds. A plastic that withstands UF_6 corrosion (fluorothene) has wide use in pumps, valve seats, and piping.

(2) *Development of barrier.* The requirements on this material are very stringent, in that it must be thin and thus delicate, with billions of holes per square inch, each about 10^{-7} in. in diameter.

(3) *Barrier cleaning.* Methods of preventing or removing deposits of uranium compounds on the interior surfaces of the separators have been found.

(4) *Control.* Automatic control of the cascade system by electrical devices is possible, with continuous mass-spectrographic sampling of the process gas.

4.3 Electromagnetic separation

The production separators that isolated U^{235} for the first atomic weapons consisted of large scale versions of the mass spectrograph

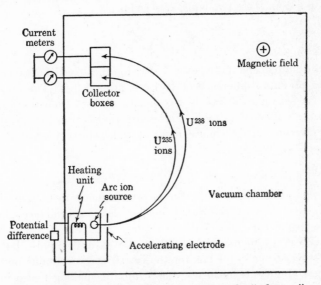

Fig. 4.8. Electromagnetic isotope separator—the "calutron."

devised by Dempster. The machines were labeled "calutrons," after the University of California, where they were developed. The basic principle of operation is that high-speed charged particles of different mass travel in different paths in a uniform magnetic field. A compound of uranium, such as UCl_4 or UBr_4, is vaporized in a furnace and a stream of electrons from a heated filament is allowed to bombard the molecules. Among the ions created is the particle U^+. By a system of electrodes at high negative potential relative to the source of ions, these ions are drawn into a vacuum chamber pervaded by a uniform magnetic field. The ions of the heavy isotope (U^{238}) travel in semi-circles of radius slightly larger than that for the light ions (U^{235}), as shown in Fig. 4.8. They may be collected separately in boxes halfway around the circle, at 180°, from the starting point. The electric current associated with each type of ion serves as a measure of the resolution and output during operation. A particle of mass m (g) bearing a charge e (statcoulombs) will be accelerated to a speed v in a potential drop V (statvolts) given by $Ve = \frac{1}{2}mv^2$. Its radius r (cm) in a magnetic field of intensity H (oersteds) is obtained from the equality of centripetal and magnetic forces $mv^2/r = Hev/c$. Eliminating v from these two equations yields

$$r = \frac{c}{H}\sqrt{\frac{2mV}{e}}$$

As an example, the radius of a (U^{238})$^+$ ion in a field of 2000 oersteds with a potential difference of 10 kv is around 3 ft. The maximum distance between the foci of two beams at 180° from the source is twice the difference in radii. This separation is thus proportional to the difference in the square roots of the isotope masses, all other factors being constant,

$$\Delta x \sim (\sqrt{m_H} - \sqrt{m_L})$$

The separation factor r for the electromagnetic method is infinite in principle, since two extremely fine pencils of ions will be completely isolated from each other. If the ratio of numbers of atoms of U^{235} and U^{238} is approximately 1/139 in the natural supply, but after processing the collector box for the light isotope contains pure U^{235}, the new abundance ratio n'_L/n'_H is infinite, making r also infinite. It is incompatible to achieve a resolution approximating the fine pencil needed for perfect separation and at the same time transfer large quantities of material. An overlap of two finite beams will set in if for any reason their widths become equal to the natural separation at the 180° point. There is a spread of the ions at the collector if the ions emerge from the source at any angle from the normal, as one can show by drawing a few circles, (see Fig. 4.9). Any scattering of ions by air that remains in the vacuum chamber or the effect of mutual repulsion of the positively charged ions as they execute their paths serves also to distort the ideal pattern. The separation factor even with all these effects is much larger than the 1.003 of the diffusion process. Only a few stages are needed to reach the desired U^{235} purity; the capacity, however, is limited. The electrical energy needed to accelerate the required currents is large.

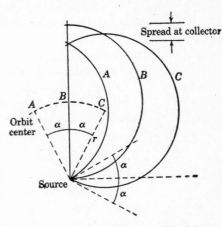

Fig. 4.9. Natural focussing at 180° of diverging ion beam.

Costs of batch handling, cleaning, and replacement parts of the electrical source and associated equipment are prohibitive for continued large-scale U^{235} separation.

The process is very practical, however, for the separation of special isotopes, for which it would be too expensive to set up a many-stage diffusion plant. The electromagnetic equipment has served as the principal source of stable isotopes for research use for a number of years. Table 4.1 is a list of a few separated isotopes indicating how proficient the electromagnetic separation process is for special elements. In Chapter 18 we shall take up the uses of stable isotopes.

4.4 Separation of deuterium

The heavier isotope of hydrogen, called deuterium (H^2), was first discovered around 1930. Its abundance in nature is 0.02 per cent. Pure heavy water formed from deuterium has slightly different physical properties from ordinary water:

Density: 1.108 g/cm³
Freezing point: 3.82°C
Boiling point: 101.42°C

One of the early methods of separation was unsuspected. The concentration of mass two was discovered to be higher than normal in the residual solution from commercial electrolytic cells that had been producing hydrogen and oxygen gases for many years. The reason for the effect was that there was a slight preference for dissociation of the light water by an electric current. Two additional methods were made successful on a large scale in America.

The first of these is *fractional distillation*. Since the boiling point of heavy water is about 1° higher than that for light water, the condensate from evaporation is slightly enriched in deuterium. One may draw a very close analogy between the separation factor r as defined for gaseous diffusion and the relative volatility, which is the ratio

TABLE 4.1

TYPICAL ELECTROMAGNETICALLY SEPARATED ISOTOPES*

Element	Isotope Mass	Natural Abundance (%)	Enriched Abundance (%)
Lithium	6	7.39	99.4
	7	92.61	99.91
Carbon	12	98.90	99.99
	13	1.10	7.52
Potassium	39	93.30	99.94
	41	6.70	98.94
Calcium	40	96.96	99.97
	42	0.64	61.40
	43	0.15	59.90
	44	2.06	96.20
	46	0.0033	7.30
	48	0.19	83.90
Iron	54	5.81	93.27
	56	91.64	99.70
	57	2.21	87.29
	58	0.34	79.80
Gallium	69	60.20	98.42
	71	39.80	98.08
Zirconium	90	51.46	98.00
	91	11.23	86.89
	92	17.11	95.38
	94	17.40	92.80
	96	2.80	89.48

* Selected from a more complete list; see C. P. KE M. *Nucleonics*, August (1951).

of vapor pressures of the two constituents at the operating temperature. A plant based on this principle was started by the duPont Company in January, 1943 and put into operation by January, 1944.

The second alternative method is *catalytic exchange*. When hydrogen gas containing deuterium in the form of the mixed molecule HD is passed through water, some of the deuterium becomes part of the water molecule. The reaction may be written

$$H_2O + HD \rightleftarrows HDO + H_2$$

In this process, water fed into a tower flows down counter currently to hydrogen and steam. At the bottom of the tower, the water is converted to H_2 and O_2 by electrolytic cells. The deuterium concentrates in the steam, and is transferred to the water again. It was found that a catalyst was needed to promote the forward reaction. Thus the tower is constructed in such a way that the steam-hydrogen mixture passes over beds of catalyst. A plant using this principle was built by Consolidated Mining and Smelting Company at Trail, British Columbia, where facilities for electrolysis were available.

Problems

4.1 Compute the ideal separation factor r for the isotopes N^{14} and N^{15} using the compound nitric oxide, NO. Comment on the relative ease of separating isotopes of light and heavy elements.

4.2 Find the uranium isotope abundance ratio corresponding to a concentration of 4 per cent.

4.3 What is the waste concentration in a diffusion plant that is fed a ton of natural uranium per day, and produces $\frac{1}{2}$ lb of uranium per day with a U^{235} concentration of 0.25? What is the effect on waste concentration of raising the product concentration to 0.5, all the other quantities being the same?

4.4 How many stages in the enriching section are required to bring natural uranium to a concentration of 0.25 with $r = 1.003$? How many to 0.99?

4.5 If the separation factor could be improved from 1.0030 to 1.0035, how many stages could be eliminated? Would this change the total equipment cost appreciably? Explain.

4.6 How many stripper stages will yield a waste concentration of 0.002? Assume $r = 1.003$.

4.7 Calculate the interstage flow L at the feed point of a diffusion plant yielding 2 lb of uranium per day at 0.75 U^{235} concentration. Repeat for the level 0.6.

4.8 Calculate the proper distance between collector openings in an electromagnetic separator operating under the following conditions: $V = 10,000$ v (practical), $H = 2000$ oersteds, $(U^{238})^+$ ion mass 3.95×10^{-22} g, $e = 4.80 \times 10^{-10}$ statcoulomb.

4.9 What must be the total U^+ current in amps in order to collect U^{235} at the rate of 1 kg per day? Assume perfect separation, with natural uranium feed. What electrical power must be expended in the process if the acceleration potential is 10,000 v?

4.10 Calculate the separation factor in a heavy-water fractional distillation system. Assume that the operating temperature is 101.42°C and that the vapor pressure of light water in the range is given by the following data:

Vapor pressure (lb/in.²)	14.696	15.228	15.776
Temperature (°C)	100	101	102

4.11 With the separation factor computed in Problem 4.10, how many stages would be needed to obtain heavy water containing only 0.23 per cent water?

References

SMYTH, H. D., *Atomic Energy for Military Purposes*. Princeton: Princeton University Press, 1945, Chaps. IX, X, XI.

"Atomic Energy Development." *The Fifth Semi-Annual Report to Congress, 1947–1948*. Washington, D. C.: Atomic Energy Commission, U. S. Government Printing Office, p. 15. General description of diffusion process.

SCHACTER, J. and G. A. GARRETT, *Analogies between Gaseous Diffusion and Fractional Distillation*, AECD-1940. Carbide and Carbon Chemicals Corp., K-25 Plant, June 5, 1948.

COHEN, KARL, "Fundamentals of Isotope Separation." *Nucleonics*, June (1948).

COHEN, KARL, (GEORGE M. MURPHY, Ed.), *The Theory of Isotope Separation as Applied to the Large-Scale Production of U^{235}*. New York: McGraw-Hill Book Co., 1951. Advanced analysis.

BENEDICT, M., "Diffusion Separation Methods," *Encyclopedia of Chemical Technology*. New York: The Interscience Encyclopedia, Inc., 1950, Vol. 5, p. 76.

STEWART, D. W., "The Separation of Stable Isotopes." *Nucleonics,* October (1947).

KEIM, C. P., "Enriched Stable Isotopes: Five Years of Production and Use." *Nucleonics,* August (1951).

BROWN, W. G., "Plant for Production of Heavy Water," *J. Chem. Phys., 3,* 216 (1935). Electrolytic method.

RANDALL, M. and W. A. WEBB, "Separation of Isotopes by Fractional Distillation of Water," *Ind. Eng. Chem., 31,* 227 (1939).

McCORKLE, W. H., "Heavy Water in Nuclear Reactors." *Nucleonics,* May (1953), p. 21.

CHAPTER 5

PLUTONIUM PRODUCTION

The new element plutonium is formed by the absorption of a neutron in U^{238} according to the reaction

$$_{92}U^{238} + {_0}n^1 \ \underset{\beta}{\rightarrow} \ _{92}U^{239} \ \underset{\beta}{\rightarrow} \ _{93}Np^{239} \ \rightarrow \ _{94}Pu^{239}$$

A period of only five years elapsed between the discovery of the element and the explosion of an atomic bomb composed of it. In this chapter we shall describe the machines that convert U^{238} to Pu^{239} and shall perform some elementary calculations on plant production.

5.1 The Hanford works

The plutonium production equipment is considered to be the most remarkable outgrowth of scientific work during World War II.

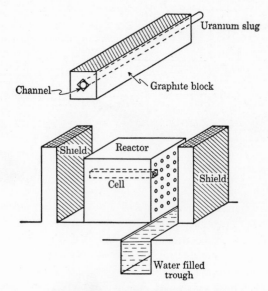

Fig. 5.1. Schematic view of the Hanford reactor system.

As mentioned earlier, its design was an extrapolation from a much simpler model. Smyth remarks "The plant was built without the benefit of a true pilot plant, much as if the hydro-electric generators had been designed merely from experience gained with a generator of quite different type and of a small fraction of the power." One can obtain a qualitative picture of the apparatus at Hanford, Washington, from a study of the "Smyth Report," the reports of the Atomic Energy Commission to Congress, and by the information released on the reactor at Oak Ridge, Tennessee, which was built to allow the study of chemical processes relating to the Hanford process.

Fig. 5.2. Loading face of the Oak Ridge Laboratory reactor. [Photograph by J. E. Westcott; courtesy U.S. Atomic Energy Commission.]

The crucial part of the Hanford system is the nuclear reactor, a large cube of graphite pierced completely through in one direction by ducts of a size to accommodate cylinders of natural uranium metal. A space in the form of an annulus to allow for a flow of cooling water is left between the cylinders and the duct. Figure 5.1 is a diagram of the reactor and associated equipment. The individual cylinders are called "slugs." They are "canned" in aluminum jackets in order to prevent the fission product radioactivity from being washed from the surface by the flowing water. In the case of the Oak Ridge National Laboratory reactor (see Fig. 5.2), the individual carbon blocks that are stacked up to form one "cell" are 4 in. wide, 4 in. high and about 4 ft long. The fuel channels are located in the center of each block making them 8 in. apart on centers. The slugs are 1.1 in. in diameter, 4 in. in length, and weigh 2.57 lb apiece. The channels are diamond shaped, with sides of 1.75 in., presumably arranged in such a way that the slug is held symmetrically within the diamond. The cooling for the Oak Ridge reactor is air, drawn through the system at a rate of 100,000 ft³/min. From the total number of channels,

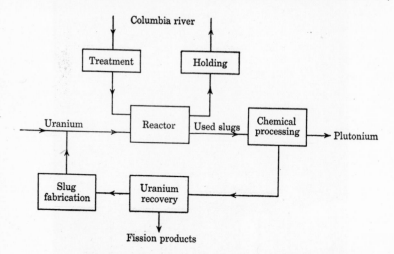

Fig. 5.3. Material cycle in the plutonium plant.

1248, we can estimate that the array of slugs fills the 24-ft cube except for about 1½ ft extra graphite on the sides. An air space and then a 7-ft thick concrete shield surround the cube, giving these overall dimensions: 47 ft long, 38 ft wide, and 32 ft high. Other pertinent data include the power level, 3800 kw; maximum slug temperature, 245°C; and the average graphite temperature, 130°C. We would expect the Hanford system to be built in about the same way, except perhaps larger in every dimension. The official statement that "A reactor using slow neutrons . . . such as the one at Oak Ridge and those at Hanford, Washington, may be as high as a 5-story building" suggests that such is the case. As the plutonium content is built up in the slugs by exposure to the neutrons of the chain reaction, the slugs are pushed along, end to end, until they drop out of the reactor. A large basin or trough filled with water is located below this side of the reactor. The slugs drop into the trough for storage, to let the fission product radioactivity die down, to serve as shielding, and as a channel for conveying the uranium to the chemical separation plant. In the chemical area, plutonium is removed from the solution formed by the dissolving of slugs, fission products are taken out and the residual uranium reclaimed. Because of the high radiation level around the reactor and in the chemical processing stage, it is necessary to perform all manipulations by remote control, and behind thick concrete shields. Figure 5.3 indicates the flow diagram of materials. In order to convert the U^{238} into plutonium in the desired quantities (Smyth quotes the minimum need of somewhere between 1 kg per month and 1 kg per day), a tremendous number of neutrons must be released and thus a great deal of energy is evolved. Almost all of this heat must be removed by the cooling water. The source is the nearby Columbia River, from which the water is pumped, filtered and treated. After passage through the machine, the water is held in basins for further decay of induced radioactivity, to levels safe enough for discharge back into the river.

5.2 Neutron economy

We may gain an understanding of the magnitudes involved in the production problem by simple considerations of the way in which neutrons are utilized. Let us attempt to estimate the number of plutonium atoms formed per U^{235} atom used up, or "burned." For each absorption of neutrons in U^{235}, a net production of 2.1 neutrons is realized, according to the following argument. Every *fission* gives 2.5 neutrons; but not all absorptions result in fission. The competing process is simple *capture* to form U^{236}, the measure of probability of which is the capture cross section of 101 barns. This, plus the fission cross section of 549 barns, makes up the total absorption cross section of 650 barns. The number of neutrons per *absorption* is evidently only a fraction, $549/650 = 0.845$ of 2.5, or 2.1. There is a loss of neutrons by absorption in the graphite blocks: the water that flows through the reactor is a fairly good absorber also. Let us make the convenient assumption that these materials take up on the average

0.1 neutron, leaving exactly 2 neutrons. To perpetuate the chain reaction 1 neutron is certainly needed, so that exactly 1 neutron is left for absorption in U^{238} to give the desired plutonium. We thus conclude that about one plutonium atom is produced per U^{235} burned. Later on, we shall find this result to be somewhat optimistic.

The thought that immediately comes to mind is that the plutonium itself may be used as a fuel to sustain the chain reaction. This is true, except for the fact that it is not economical to leave the slugs in the equipment for a long period.

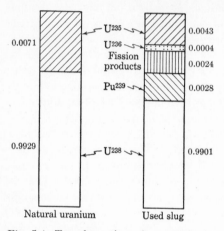

Fig. 5.4. Transformation of materials in uranium slug.

Thus the exposure time is not long enough to give a conversion that plays an important role in the fission process. One may make crude estimates on the appropriate degree of conversion of U^{238} to plutonium. The starting concentrations of the two isotopes of uranium are, in decimal fractions, approximately 0.0071 and 0.9929. The first block diagram of Fig. 5.4 represents the initial fuel. Both of these materials are used in obtaining the plutonium. We may write a simple relation for the net production rate of plutonium as follows:

$$\begin{pmatrix} \text{net rate of Pu} \\ \text{accumulation} \end{pmatrix} = \begin{pmatrix} \text{rate of } n \text{ absorp-} \\ \text{tion in 238} \end{pmatrix} - \begin{pmatrix} \text{rate of } n \text{ absorp-} \\ \text{tion in Pu} \end{pmatrix}$$

The last term on the right is the burn-up of plutonium. In mathematical form this may be written as a differential equation,

$$dN/dt = \phi N_{238}\sigma_{238} - \phi N\sigma$$

where N is the number of plutonium atoms per cubic centimeter at any time t, N_{238} is the number of U^{238} atoms per cubic centimeter, the σ's are the corresponding absorption cross sections, and the ϕ is the average value of the neutron flux to which the materials are exposed. To a good approximation for short exposure times we may

think of N_{238} as being constant. This differential equation then has
the same form as that describing the charging of a condenser or the
growth of a radioactive element
on bombardment with nuclear
particles. Its solution, given in
Section 1.5, allows a plot of N
as a function of time, as shown
in Fig. 5.5. The "saturation"
level is that for the situation
where the production is exactly
equal to the burn-up; the maximum number of plutonium
atoms is the horizontal line,
which we may compute merely
by setting $dN/dt = 0$ in the original equation. Thus we obtain

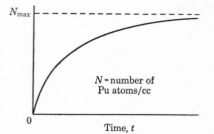

Fig. 5.5. Growth of plutonium in reactor
with time.

$$N_{\max} = N_{238}\sigma_{238}/\sigma$$

Our first choice of σ_{238} would be the thermal neutron cross section of
2.80 barns found in Table 2.1. Account must be taken, however,
of the resonance absorption at energies above thermal, which amounts
to about the same magnitude as low energy absorption. As an estimate, then, we merely double the 2.80 thermal value, to give an effective 5.6 barns. Taking the cross section of plutonium to be roughly
1000 barns gives the result $N_{\max}/N_{238} = 0.0056$. It is clear that it is
not desirable to approach this level very closely, or the desired plutonium would be used up. Let us assume that a reasonable time lapse
before removal of the slugs is such that about half of this amount of
plutonium, or 0.0028 is accumulated. We may now draw a new distribution chart of various materials as in Fig. 5.4. A fraction, 0.0028,
of the U^{235} has been burned, leaving 0.0043 as the final concentration.
Of the 0.0028, 84.5 per cent or 0.0024 is now in the form of fission
products, the rest, 15.5 per cent or 0.0004 is U^{236}; the U^{238} content is
dropped only slightly to 0.990.

The method of loading the power reactor is presumably the same
as that used in the Oak Ridge reactor—a new slug is introduced,
pushing out a used slug on the other side of the system. As slugs go
through the reactor, they are exposed to a variable flux. The neutron
density and flux in any reactor is found to be higher in the center
than at the edges, as will be shown later. The flux density varies

according to a sine curve along any axis. In particular, at a point x along the central axis of the reactor, ϕ is given by

$$\phi = \phi_c \sin \pi x / L$$

where ϕ_c is the peak flux in the system and L is the length of side of the reactor. It will not be much in error to assume that the slugs are pushed through continuously at a uniform speed so that $x = (t/T)L$, where T is the total exposure or "cycle" time. Thus when the slug is at a point x, it is immersed in a flux $\phi = \phi_c \sin \pi t/T$. The rate of thermal absorption in U^{235} at any time is

$$dN_{235}/dt = -\phi N_{235}(\sigma_a)_{235} = -\phi_c \sin (\pi t/T) N_{235}(\sigma_a)_{235}$$

Integrating with limits $(N_{235})_0$ at $t = 0$, $(N_{235})_T$ at $t = T$, we find

$$\frac{(N_{235})_T}{(N_{235})_0} = e^{-\frac{2}{\pi}\phi_c(\sigma_a)_{235}T}$$

Now $(2/\pi)\phi_c$ is merely the space average flux along the slug channel $\bar{\phi}$, as proved below, using the definition of averages given in Section 2.5.

$$\bar{\phi} = \frac{\int \phi \, dx}{\int dx} = \frac{1}{L}\int_0^L \phi_c \sin \frac{\pi x}{L} \, dx = \frac{2}{\pi}\phi_c$$

The rate of burn-up is the same as if the slug did not move but was kept in a constant flux at some level $\bar{\phi}$. Inserting this flux and taking natural logarithms

$$T = \frac{-\log_e \left[(N_{235})_T/(N_{235})_0\right]}{\bar{\phi}(\sigma_a)_{235}}$$

As an example, we may find the proper cycle time to reduce the U^{235} concentration from 0.0071 to some nominal value such as 0.0050. In an average flux $\bar{\phi}$ of 10^{13} with $(\sigma_a)_{235} = 650$ barns,

$$T = \frac{-\log_e \left[0.005/0.0071\right]}{(10^{13})650 \times 10^{-24}} = 5.4 \times 10^7 \text{ sec}$$

$$= 620 \text{ days}$$

We cannot judge the accuracy of this result since data on the neutron flux in the Hanford reactor are not available.

5.3 Operation problems

A reactor is a completely new type of machine for processing materials, since it is based on nuclear transmutations rather than chemical reactions. The main factor that distinguishes the Hanford Works from conventional chemical plants, however, is the radioactivity and radiation. There are many aspects to the problem.

(1) The stray neutrons and gamma rays from the reactor proper require that the control, loading and observation be done behind thick shielding.

(2) The discharged slugs are highly radioactive, giving off gamma rays that penetrate the aluminum cans.

(3) Direct handling is impossible: all materials of construction of the reactor and auxiliaries such as cooling water pipes become radioactive by the absorption of neutrons leaking from the reactor.

(4) Even the air in the vicinity of the machine constitutes a danger because of absorptive constituents and impurities.

(5) The cooling water is active, requiring that piping be specially shielded.

(6) The plutonium that must be recovered is toxic, independently of its emanations. Adding the effect of its alpha radioactivity, with a half-life of 24,000 yr, plutonium becomes a deadly poison in the body even at levels of the order of a few micrograms.

In order to guarantee protection of operators from external exposure, advantage is taken of shielding, distance between operator and source of danger, and time limits on exposure. For protection against internal exposure due to the accumulation of radioactive substances in the body, rigid control of air and surface contamination is maintained. Ingenious mechanisms have been developed for remote handling of radioactive equipment. For example, a robot "tool dolly," controlled by an operator at a switchboard some distance away, can operate machinery, open and close doors, turn valves, move objects and even handle a fire hose. The robot is equipped with electric "feelers" to determine whether it is grasping an object properly.

In some portions of the plant it may be necessary to remove a heavy piece of equipment for repair. A remote control crane capable of supporting more than 36 tons is directed to the spot by means of remote viewing and magnifying apparatus. It can be made to detach the piece of equipment, remove it and erect necessary shielding for subsequent work.

A few characteristic problems that concern workers in the plutonium process are now listed:

Properties of uranium metal. Methods of obtaining the purest possible slugs are sought. The one obvious reason for such a need is that every neutron that is lost to an impurity reduces the number of plutonium atoms by one. Much remains to be known about the metallurgical properties of uranium—especially the changes due to stress, temperature, radiation or a combination of these influences.

Separation of uranium from fission products. Throughout World War II, the waste from the reactor was set aside in huge storage containers. This waste contained uranium somewhat depleted in U^{235}, with the plutonium removed, but the whole collection of fission products present. Chemical separation of the still useful uranium with a minimum of cost is the ultimate goal.

Deterioration of reactors. The possibility of failure of some component is continually increased upon use at maximum production over a period of years, with high local temperatures, erosion by water flow, and neutron bombardment.

Problems

5.1 At what power level must the Hanford reactor be operated to yield 1 kg/day of Pu^{239}? Assume that each fission of a U^{235} nucleus eventually results in the production of one plutonium atom.

5.2 From the answer in Problem 5.1 estimate the flow rate of water at 20°C necessary to prevent boiling in the reactor.

5.3 What would the initial supply of uranium for the Oak Ridge reactor cost, using data from Section 4.1 on the value of the metal?

5.4 How many pounds of uranium metal must be supplied and discharged from the Hanford-type reactor if the number of atoms of plutonium per U^{235} burned is 0.75 and the plutonium production goal is 0.5 kg/day?

5.5 How accurate is the assumption of Section 5.2 that N_{238} is constant for exposure times of the order of one year? HINT: solve the exact differential equation for the number of plutonium atoms as a function of time.

5.6 Plot a graph of U^{235} burn-up per year as a function of neutron flux level in the range $\bar{\phi} = 10^{10}$ to $\bar{\phi} = 10^{14}$.

References

GLASSTONE, S., *Sourcebook of Atomic Energy*. New York: D. Van Nostrand Co., 1950. Chap. XV, "The New Elements," includes the chemical properties of plutonium; Secs. 14.68 and following discuss the Oak Ridge and Hanford reactors.

"How to Load a Reactor." *Nucleonics*, February (1952). Oak Ridge reactor specifications.

"Control of Radiation Hazards in the Atomic Energy Program." *Eighth Report of the Atomic Energy Commission*. Washington, D. C.: U. S. Government Printing Office, July, 1950.

SMYTH, H. D., *Atomic Energy for Military Purposes*. Princeton: Princeton University Press, 1945, Chaps. VI, VII.

CHAPTER 6

NUCLEAR REACTOR PRINCIPLES

In the chapter just completed we reviewed only the general construction of one type of reactor and some of the rudiments of the neutron economy. This constitutes only a start in our understanding of this new machine since we have not yet established its principle of operation. We shall now study the methods for calculating the amounts, arrangement and properties of the materials that go into a chain reactor. Since the types of reactors, the functions of the components, and the theory behind the design formulas are very intimately related, it is difficult to start the description at any point more logical than another. At the risk of leaving questions unanswered in the reader's mind as we proceed, the following order of topics is adopted: (a) the terminology of reactor components and types, citing example reactors; (b) the nature of the neutron multiplication cycle in simple mathematical form; (c) the method of calculating neutron flux, power, overall sizes and shapes; and (d) the procedure for handling more complicated problems in reactor design. There are thus several natural stopping points in the discussion according to the reader's interest and previous background.

6.1 Reactor classification

An individual reactor can be described fully only if the design drawings, the construction plans and the operating procedures are available. Several descriptive categories are used, however, to characterize reactors. These will be listed and defined, and reference will be made to particular machines as examples. First of all we note that the term *reactor* will be used throughout this book in preference to the older word *pile*, although the expressions are synonymous.*

Energy of neutrons that cause fission. Three general prefixes are applied to reactors. A *fast* reactor is one having no moderator to slow down the fission neutrons, hence the chain reaction is based on fission

---

* It is reported that the British use the term pile to distinguish natural uranium from enriched uranium reactors. This usage is not common in the United States.

by absorption of fast neutrons. The atomic bomb is presumably of this type, since the multiplication and energy release must be more rapid than would be obtained if the neutrons took time to slow to thermal energy. The controlled plutonium reactor at Los Alamos also falls in this category. Either plutonium or enriched uranium is necessary to achieve a critical unmoderated assembly. At the other extreme is the *thermal* reactor, which depends on low energy neutrons for fission. The majority of units constructed are thermal reactors, largely because of the safety of operation, and because natural uranium may be used as fuel. The first experimental unit at Chicago was of this type, as are the Hanford plutonium machines. *Intermediate* reactors are those that use neutrons of energies somewhere between the fission and thermal levels. Advantage may be taken of the resonance absorption or of the low cross sections for neutrons of other than thermal energy. The theory of this type of reactor has not been released.

The fast reactor appears to hold great promise for practical power systems. First, the unit is small in comparison with reactors of the Hanford or Oak Ridge type. Second, the absorption of most materials for fast neutrons is much lower than for thermal neutrons, which removes one limiting factor in the choice of materials of construction and cooling medium.

Fissionable material used as fuel. There are four fuels that can serve as active material: *natural uranium*, as it comes from the refined ore; *enriched uranium*, in which the fraction U^{235} has been increased by an isotope separation process; and two artificial elements, plutonium, Pu^{239}, and U^{233}, formed by neutron absorption in thorium. The advantage of using natural uranium over enriched processed material is the lower cost of fuel. The disadvantage is that the overall size must be considerably greater. This stems from the need for a high ratio of moderator volume to uranium volume to thermalize the neutrons. Since the last two artificial elements are reactor produced, the fuel cost in a reactor using them is high.

Arrangement of moderator and fuel. The *heterogeneous* reactor is one in which the fuel is lumped as a metal or a compound in some regular pattern within the moderator. The Oak Ridge reactor described in Chapter 5 is a typical example. If the fuel and moderator are intimately mixed, the system is said to be *homogeneous*. It can be demonstrated by theory that an assembly of natural uranium, no matter how large, will not be chain reacting when mixed uniformly with common moderators, although it can be chain reacting with water composed of the rare isotope deuterium. This is due to the high effective resonance capture cross section when the uranium is in immediate contact with the moderator. Thus a heterogeneous arrangement, with the two media separated is demanded. A homogeneous fluid system, composed of sufficiently enriched uranium or one of the artificial elements, has several advantages. Limitations on the rate of transfer of heat across metal surfaces are minimized, minimum neutron absorption exists (no extraneous jackets or ducts) and chemical processing of the exhausted fuel is simpler, as is the mechanical structure. The Los Alamos "water boiler" is an example of a low-power homogeneous reactor.

Moderator, reflector and coolant. The main materials that have been employed to reduce the neutron energy in thermal reactors are *graphite, light water*, and *heavy water*. *Beryllium* can also be used as a moderator or reflector. The criterion for a good moderator is that neutrons shall lose a large fraction of their energy on collision, and that there should be very little absorption. The active portion or core of the system is usually surrounded with a layer of nonfissionable moderating material, the reflector, to help prevent the escape of neutrons from the multiplication cycle. A *bare* reactor has no reflector, while a *reflected* or "tamped" reactor does. Only a reactor operated at extremely low power levels can dispense with a cooling fluid and depend on ordinary conduction and convection to keep the reactor temperature down. Units may be cooled with *water* or *heavy water* if it does not matter if the exit fluid temperature is below the boiling point of water. At high enough density, steam could presumably be used. *Air* cooling is used in the machines at Brookhaven, Long Island, and in England. The properties of *liquid metals* such as sodium, potassium, a mixture of the sodium and potassium, lead and bismuth have been studied with reactor cooling in mind. Mercury can serve as coolant if there is sufficient U^{235} enrichment to overcome the neutron absorptions.

Purpose of reactor. The Hanford reactor, discussed in Chapter 5, is of the regenerative or converter type, intended to produce new fissionable material from inert elements by the burn-up of another fissionable element. In addition to the U^{235}, U^{238}, Pu^{239} cycle described in Section 3.4, conversion may be achieved by the absorption of neutrons in thorium, by the nuclear reactions

$$_{90}\text{Th}^{232} + {}_{0}n^{1} \rightarrow {}_{90}\text{Th}^{233}$$

$$_{90}\text{Th}^{233} \underset{23.5 \text{ min}}{\rightarrow} {}_{91}\text{Pa}^{233} \underset{27.4 \text{ days}}{\rightarrow} {}_{92}\text{U}^{233}, \qquad t_H = 1.62 \times 10^5 \text{ yr}$$

The new element U^{233} is fissionable, with properties similar to U^{235}. A chart listing all known combinations of fuel, "fertile" material and fissionable product can easily be prepared.

Fuel	U^{235}	U^{235}	Pu^{239}	Pu^{239}	U^{233}	U^{233}
Absorber	U^{238}	Th^{232}	U^{238}	Th^{232}	U^{238}	Th^{232}
Product	Pu^{239}	U^{233}	Pu^{239}	U^{233}	Pu^{239}	U^{233}

The advisability of constructing any one reactor of this list must be estimated from the rate of replacement or gain of fissionable material, as well as from other economic and physical factors. One obvious principle to be kept in mind in considering such machines is that there must be an advantage in substituting one material for another. The advantages may be the achievement of useful power, a gain in material quantity and value, or the conversion of an original fissionable isotope that is in an inaccessible form, e.g., depleted uranium.

Another primary purpose of a reactor is to produce useful power. The fission fragment heat may be removed by a suitable coolant, and an electrical generator or propulsion engine driven by the expanding fluid or by an intermediate medium. The reactor has been proposed as a source of energy for regions lacking water for hydroelectric plants or far from coal supplies to feed steam plants. It makes use of a new natural resource, and thus may provide supplementary power to reduce the rate at which oil and coal are being exhausted. The propulsion of vehicles by nuclear energy will probably be aimed toward large military aircraft and ships for some time to come. There is little chance that nuclear vehicles as small as the automobile will be constructed in the near future, because of the excessive shielding from reactor radiation that is needed. Experimental reactors are designed for one or more of several uses: (a) to make use of the neutrons for research on physical or chemical processes; (b) the measurement of the amount of neutron shielding provided by different

Name and Location	Neutron energy	Arrangement	Fuel	Moderator	Reflector
CP-1,2 (Chicago Pile); Chicago, Illinois.	thermal	heterogeneous	U and UO$_2$ spheres	graphite	graphite
Oak Ridge National Laboratory; Oak Ridge, Tennessee.	thermal	heterogeneous	U slugs 1.1 in. diameter, 8 in. on centers	graphite	graphite
SUPO (Super Power) Water Boiler; Los Alamos, New Mexico.	thermal	homogeneous	enriched U (90% U^{235}) 870 g	H$_2$O	graphite
Los Alamos Fast Reactor (Clementine); New Mexico.	fast	heterogeneous	plutonium	none	...
CP-3 Argonne National Laboratory; Chicago, Illinois.	thermal	heterogeneous	U slugs 1.1 in. diameter, 5$\frac{3}{8}$ in. on centers	D$_2$O	graphite
GLEEP (Graphite Low Energy Experimental Pile); Harwell, England.	thermal	heterogeneous	U slugs 0.9 in. diameter, 7$\frac{1}{4}$ in. on centers	graphite	graphite
Brookhaven National Laboratory; Upton, Long Island, New York.	thermal	heterogeneous	U slugs 1 in. diameter, 8 in. on centers	graphite	graphite
Hanford; Washington.	thermal	heterogeneous	U slugs	graphite	graphite
NRX; Chalk River, Canada.	thermal	heterogeneous	U slugs	D$_2$O	graphite
BEPO (British Experimental Pile 0); Harwell, England.	thermal	heterogeneous	U slugs 0.9 in. diameter, 7$\frac{1}{4}$ in. on centers	graphite	graphite
ZOE (Zero Energy); Chatillon, France	thermal	heterogeneous	UO$_2$ bars	D$_2$O	graphite
JEEP; Kjeller, Norway.	thermal	heterogeneous	U slugs 1 in. diameter, 7 in. on centers	D$_2$O	graphite
Swimming Pool, Oak Ridge National Laboratory; Oak Ridge, Tennessee.	thermal	heterogeneous	enriched U plates, 3.5 kg	H$_2$O	H$_2$O or I
EBR (Experimental Breeder Reactor) Reactor Testing Station; Arco, Idaho.	fast	heterogeneous	enriched U	none	natural "blanke
Raleigh; North Carolina State College.	thermal	homogeneous	enriched U (93% U^{235}) 860 g	H$_2$O	graphite

Coolant	Purpose	Power	Flux	Size and shape	Remarks
ne	experimental	200 watts	...	17-ft cube	First reactor; December 6, 1942.
, 10^5 /min	experimental, isotopes	3800 kw	10^{12}	24-ft cube	
O	experimental	45 kw	1.7×10^{12}	1-ft sphere	Predecessors: LOPO (Low Power), HYPO (High Power).
rcury	experimental	10 kw	5×10^{12}	small, compact	Dismantled.
O 200 /min	experimental	300 kw	10^{12}	cylindrical tank 6 ft diameter, 8 ft 10 in. height	First heavy water reactor; May 15, 1944.
	experimental	100 kw	3×10^{10}	cylinder $9\frac{1}{2}$ ft diameter, 17 ft long	
	experimental, isotopes	28 mw	4×10^{12}	25-ft cube	
)	plutonium production	10^3 mw (estimate)	...	cube	
)	experimental, isotopes	10 mw	6×10^{13}	cylindrical tank 8 ft diameter, 10 ft height	Damaged, late 1952.
	experimental, heat supply	4 mw	10^{12}	cylinder 20 ft diameter, 20 ft long	
)	experimental	10 kw	3×10^{10}	cylinder 6 ft diameter, 7.8 ft long	
)	experimental	300 kw	10^{12}	cylindrical tank 6 ft long, $6\frac{1}{2}$ ft diameter	
) con- tion	experimental shielding studies	100 kw	10^{12}	rectangular 12 in. $\times$ 12 in. $\times$ 24 in. high	
id Na, lloy	experimental, breeding	250 kw	6.5×10^{14}	"size of a football"	First reactor source of practical electrical power.
)	experimental, teaching	10 kw	5×10^{11}	cylindrical tank 11 in. diameter, 10 in. high	First reactor open to public inspection and first university reactor.

TABLE 6.1 (cont'd)

Other reactors (further data still classified):

HRE (Homogeneous Reactor Experiment) Oak Ridge National Laboratory; Oak Ridge, Tennessee.	Thermal, homogeneous, enriched uranium, liquid moderator. Study of power possibilities with fluidized reactor. Fuel circulated. Power = 1000 kw.
MTR (Materials Testing Reactor) Reactor Testing Station; Arco, Idaho.	Thermal, heterogeneous, enriched uranium. High flux for evaluation of effects of neutrons on reactor materials. (Similar to swimming pool type.)
STR (Submarine Thermal Reactor) Reactor Testing Station, Arco, Idaho.	Thermal energy, water coolant, designed for Navy by Westinghouse Corp., Argonne National Laboratory.
SIR (Submarine Intermediate Reactor) Knolls Atomic Power Laboratory; Schenectady, New York.	Intermediate neutron energy, liquid sodium coolant. Purpose, propulsion. Designed by General Electric Co.
ANP (Aircraft Nuclear Propulsion)	Design: engine, General Electric Co., Lockland, Ohio; airplane, Consolidated Vultee Aircraft Corp., Fort Worth, Texas; engine, Pratt & Whitney Division of United Aircraft Corp., E. Hartford, Conn.; airplane, Boeing Aircraft Corp., Seattle, Wash.
Savannah River Project; Aiken, S. Carolina.	duPont Corp., heavy water reactors, production of fissionable material.
LITR (Low Intensity Test Reactor) Oak Ridge National Laboratory; Oak Ridge, Tenn.	Thermal, heterogeneous, enriched uranium, light water moderated. (Similar to MTR.)

materials that are used in large scale design; and (c) for the generation of radioactive isotopes. Except for the fuel cost, a low-power research reactor may be built for less than $100,000, which is considerably less than the cost of some of the charged particle accelerators.

Power level and neutron flux density. Whether or not a reactor is intended for practical power generation, its level of operation may be described by the kilowatt or megawatt rating. There is a close relation between total power and average neutron flux, through the value of the reactor volume, as described in Section 6.4. Both power and flux should be quoted in characterizing a particular unit. Table 6.1 gives the features of a number of reactors that have been or are operating. The list is not intended to be exhaustive, but to give examples illustrating the mode of classification.*

6.2 The "infinite" multiplication constant

We shall now describe the way neutron motion, uranium fission, and neutron generation are brought together in the nuclear reactor. The fundamental requirement of a chain reaction is that on the average, every neutron shall *produce another to replace it*, in spite of possible absorptions by the moderator, by the uranium, or losses by escape from the system.

It is convenient to study first an accumulation of fissionable material and moderator that is so large that relatively few neutrons ever get out or "leak" from the bulk of the material. We ask this question: How many neutrons are produced, on the average, by one neutron, which is at fission energy at the time we start observing? We let the symbol k represent this important number for a particular mixture, or since we have assumed the machine to be of effectively infinite size, k_∞, the "infinite" multiplication constant. The answer clearly depends on the composition of the reactor. If it were composed of pure U^{235}, for example, a maximum of 2.1 neutrons would be made available. The rest of the 2.5 neutrons per fission would go to form U^{236}. An opposite extreme would be a very large block of graphite with only a few grams of uranium in it, for which the number of new neutrons produced would be almost zero. The range of k_∞ from the two cases above is 0 to 2.1. The desired number is unity, for which the accumulation is exactly self-sustaining or "critical." We shall anticipate the fact, of course, that if the reactor is not large enough to neglect the leakage of neutrons, k_∞ should be somewhat higher than unity. Those who first designed reactors broke the multiplication constant down into four factors that described separate processes, as follows:

$$k_\infty = \epsilon p f \eta$$

The *fast fission factor* ϵ tells how many neutrons are available after the contribution of uranium fission by fast neutrons is added in. This is a number around 1.03 for a natural uranium reactor, but

---

* Reference is made to the more complete tabulations by ISBIN in *Nucleonics*, March (1952) and June (1953).

almost exactly 1 for an enriched homogeneous system. If we start with 1 neutron we may conclude that the "fast effect" is small. Physically, the reason is that neutrons are quickly slowed down from their average 2-mev fission energy. Below the 1-mev energy U^{238} will not fission as proved in Section 3.2. For rough calculations the effect may be neglected; ϵ is set equal to 1.0. This is quite accurate for the homogeneous reactor.

The quantity p is called the *resonance escape probability*. In simplest terms it is the fraction of fast neutrons that are not caught in U^{238} while the slowing down process is taking place. Not all are captured because the resonance peaks in the cross-section curve for U^{238} are sharp, i.e. the strong absorption occurs over only a small range of energy. Thus a neutron may lose enough energy on one collision with a moderator nucleus to take it from above the resonance point to below it. The value of p depends on the way in which the moderator and uranium are disposed: the slug arrangement in the Hanford or Oak Ridge reactors is preferable to uniform dispersal through the moderator. A discussion of the method of computing the resonance escape probability will be reserved until Section 6.5. A good value of p in a natural uranium heterogeneous reactor is one in the range 0.85 to 0.95. If the reactor is composed only of U^{235}, p is exactly unity, there being no U^{238}.

The *thermal utilization f* is merely the fraction of the neutrons becoming thermal that are absorbed in uranium, the comparison being made with the total absorption, uranium plus moderator. This quantity may be computed for the case of uniformly mixed materials from the relation

$$f = \frac{\Sigma_U}{\Sigma_U + \Sigma_M} \qquad \text{(homogeneous)}$$

where M refers to the moderator. If instead the material is in a heterogeneous form, with lumps or rods of uranium imbedded in the moderator, it is necessary to *weight* each medium appropriately. Two factors must be included. The first is the volume occupied by each substance, as might be expected. The second is the average neutron flux $\bar{\phi} = nv$. If one of the materials is a strong absorber for thermal neutrons in comparison with the other, as in the case of uranium and graphite, the flux will be low in the medium of high absorption. The steady state distribution of neutrons in such a case may be sketched as in Fig. 6.1. Crudely, we may say that there are few neutrons left to be absorbed in a region that has a high absorption cross section. The thermal utilization must be modified to read

$$f = \frac{V_U \Sigma_U \bar{\phi}_U}{V_U \Sigma_U \bar{\phi}_U + V_M \Sigma_M \bar{\phi}_M} \qquad \text{(heterogeneous)}$$

As an illustration, let us find the thermal utilization in a natural-uranium graphite heterogeneous reactor if the average flux in the

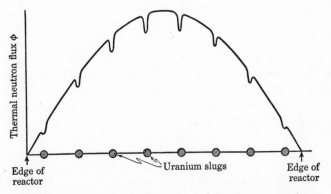

Fig. 6.1. Neutron distribution across a heterogeneous reactor.

moderator is twice that in the uranium. Assume also that the uranium volume is one-fiftieth of the graphite volume. Recalling macroscopic absorption cross sections $\Sigma_C = 3.72 \times 10^{-4}$ and $\Sigma_U = 0.351$, we find

$$f = \frac{1}{1 + (V_C \Sigma_C \bar{\phi}_C / V_U \Sigma_U \bar{\phi}_U)} = \frac{1}{1 + (50)(1.06 \times 10^{-3})(2)}$$
$$= 0.904$$

It is only fair to point out that the calculation of flux values in the two media is more difficult than the reader is led to believe. In Section 6.6 we shall investigate this problem.

The final constant η is the average number of neutrons released per neutron that is absorbed in uranium. If the uranium were pure U^{235}, η would be the familiar number 2.1. If the uranium were of natural or any other U^{235} concentration below 1.0, absorptions in U^{238} that do not cause fission would reduce the average. To prove this, consider the fate of 1 thermal neutron. Its chance of being absorbed in uranium is measured by $(\Sigma_a)_U$, which is the sum $(\Sigma_a)_{235} + (\Sigma_a)_{238}$, or in terms of numbers of nuclei per unit volume and microscopic absorption cross sections,

$$(\Sigma_a)_U = N_{235}(\sigma_a)_{235} + N_{238}(\sigma_a)_{238}$$

where N_{235} and N_{238} are dependent on the isotopic concentration, in general. The chance of causing fission, however, is only $(\Sigma_f)_U = N_{235}(\sigma_f)_{235}$. Each fission gives $\nu = 2.5$ neutrons, therefore the number of neutrons per *absorption* in uranium is

$$\eta = \frac{(\Sigma_f)_U \nu}{(\Sigma_a)_U} = \frac{N_{235}(\sigma_f)_{235}\nu}{N_{235}(\sigma_a)_{235} + N_{238}(\sigma_a)_{238}}$$

The value of η in natural uranium is 1.32 as checked by the substitution of known cross-section values: $(\sigma_a)_{235} = 650$ barns, $(\sigma_f)_{235} = 549$ barns, $(\sigma_a)_{238} = 2.8$ barns. Knowing that the ratio N_{238}/N_{235} is approximately 139,

$$\eta = \frac{(549)(2.5)}{650 + (139)(2.80)} = 1.32$$

In summary, the chain of events is as follows: one fast neutron is released. After fast fission has taken place there are $\epsilon \cdot 1$ neutrons present. Of these, a fraction p get past the resonance capture region, leaving $p \cdot \epsilon \cdot 1$ thermal neutrons. A fraction f are now absorbed in uranium, a total of $f \cdot p \cdot \epsilon \cdot 1$. Each of these gives rise to η fast neutrons, so that the final number after one cycle is $\eta \cdot f \cdot p \cdot \epsilon \cdot 1$; this product is simply k_∞ the number of fast neutrons per cycle. As a numerical example, take values of the separate factors for a typical reactor $\epsilon = 1.03$, $p = 0.9$, $f = 0.9$, and $\eta = 1.32$. Thus

$$k_\infty = \epsilon p f \eta = (1.03)(0.9)(0.9)(1.32) = 1.10$$

Since this is somewhat above unity, it will be chain reacting with a finite volume of material.

The infinite multiplication constant is a property only of the materials that go to make up the reactor; no cognizance is taken of possible leakage that occurs in a realistic reactor. In order to find out whether a machine of definite size will multiply, the effect of escape must be determined, and k_∞ corrected properly.

6.3 Thermal and fast neutron leakage; critical size

The neutrons in the body of a reactor are in incessant motion, interrupted by collisions that result in a change of direction. With the short mean free path for these scattering collisions, e.g. λ_s about 2.5 cm in graphite, and the high speed even at thermal energy, 2.2×10^5 cm/sec, a neutron can cross a given square centimeter as frequently as a 100 thousand times per second. At the edge of the reactor, however, the situation is somewhat different. A neutron that makes its last collision somewhere in the vicinity of an inch from the surface and is directed outward has a good chance of making no more collisions. It escapes from the reactor because the space surrounding the system is either air or a good absorber. A reflector helps to prevent leakage, but eventually a surface will be met at which losses must occur. It is convenient to apply separate correction factors having to do with the leakage of fast neutrons, during the slowing process, and that of thermals. The *effective* multiplication constant is written

$$k_{\text{eff}} = k_\infty \mathfrak{L}_f \mathfrak{L}_t$$

where k_{eff} refers to the net number of neutrons left per original fast neutron after losses have been experienced. The fraction of fast neutrons that do not escape before becoming thermal is $\mathfrak{L}_f$; the fraction of thermals that do not get out before absorption is $\mathfrak{L}_t$. Reactor theory shows how $\mathfrak{L}_f$ and $\mathfrak{L}_t$ may be computed from the shape, size and neutron motion properties of the unit. The results are reported without proof. Reference may be made to the Appendix for derivations of the formulas quoted below.

$$\mathfrak{L}_f = e^{-K^2\tau} \qquad \text{(fast leakage factor)}$$

$$\mathfrak{L}_t = 1/(1 + K^2L^2) \qquad \text{(thermal leakage factor)}$$

The new symbols have the following meanings. K^2 may be called the *size-shape factor* or "buckling." For a spherical reactor of radius R, its value is $(\pi/R)^2$; for a cube of side S it is $3(\pi/S)^2$, for a circular cylinder of radius R and height H it is $(2.405/R)^2 + (\pi/H)^2$. Dimensions must be in centimeters. As pointed out in Section 2.7, τ is the age or square of the "fast diffusion length" and L is the "thermal diffusion length." Physically, τ is one-sixth the average of squares of distances from their origin that fast neutrons become thermal; L^2 is one-sixth the mean square distance between thermalization and absorption. Typical values measured experimentally are listed in Table 6.2. By examining the form of the leakage factors, $\mathcal{L}_f$ and $\mathcal{L}_t$, it may

TABLE 6.2

THERMAL DIFFUSION LENGTHS AND AGES OF VARIOUS REACTOR MODERATORS

Substance	H_2O	D_2O		C	Be
L (cm)	2.88	171 (pure)	100 (0.23% H_2O)	50	24
τ (cm²)	33	120		300	98

be seen that the larger is the reactor dimension, the smaller is the size-shape factor K^2 and the closer $\mathcal{L}_f$ and $\mathcal{L}_t$ are to unity. They go to unity in the limit, of course, and k_{eff} is the same as k_∞. On the other hand, the larger is τ or L^2 (which is the case if the neutrons travel greater distances in the processes of thermalization or absorption) then the closer the $\mathcal{L}$'s are to zero, the no-multiplication situation. By combining these two trends, we may conclude that the longer are the diffusion lengths, the larger the reactor must be to be critical, all other things being equal. For instance, a light-water moderated reactor can be made very much smaller than a heavy-water moderated reactor.

The presence of the absorbing uranium has a marked effect on the thermal diffusion length, as would be expected. The neutrons cannot travel as far before they are absorbed as in pure moderator. To a rather good approximation, one may write

$$L^2 = L_0^2(1 - f)$$

where L_0^2 refers to the pure material, and f is the thermal utilization defined earlier. For example, in a graphite reactor for which f is 0.9, L^2 is $(2500)(1 - 0.9)$ or 250 cm², and L is reduced from 50 to 15.8 cm.

Estimation of effective multiplication constant for reactor. All of the above information may be put together to see if a proposed reactor is critical or not, i.e., if k_{eff} is equal to or greater than unity. As an illustration, let us take a uranium reactor for which k_∞ was computed to be 1.10, and f was 0.9. As a first trial, let the system be a cube of graphite 15 ft on a side. Now S is 15 ft $\times$ 30.5 (cm/ft) = 457 cm, and K^2 is $3(\pi/457)^2$ or 1.42×10^{-4}. From the previous paragraph, L^2 is 250, and we shall assume that the uranium has little effect on the age τ. Thus

$$\mathcal{L}_f = e^{-(1.42 \times 10^{-4})(300)} = e^{-0.0426} = 0.958$$

$$\mathcal{L}_t = \frac{1}{1 + (1.42 \times 10^{-4})250} = 0.966$$

The product of the leakage factors is 0.925. With $k_\infty = 1.10$, k_{eff} is 1.02 which is slightly above critical. It will be necessary to reduce the size of the reactor somewhat to reach $k_{\text{eff}} = 1$. A trial and error approach will quickly yield the correct size.

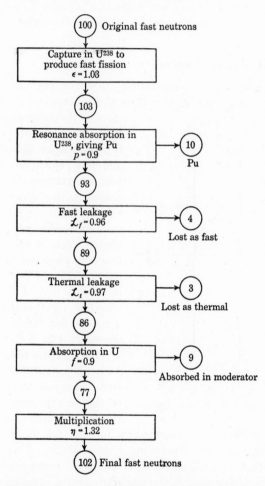

Fig. 6.2. Example of life history of 100 fast neutrons.

The combination of the effects in the "four-factor" k_∞ relation and the leakages may be described graphically as in Fig. 6.2. The chain is applied to a group of 100 neutrons, rather than 1, to make the calculations come out in whole numbers of neutrons instead of fractions. We have used a heterogeneous natural uranium reactor to illustrate the calculations since it displays most of the important features of a thermal unit. The formulas above are applicable to the homogeneous pure U^{235} type and in fact are somewhat simpler to apply. Note that $\epsilon = 1$, $p = 1$, $\eta = 2.1$ and f is obtained from the simple ratio $\Sigma_U/(\Sigma_U + \Sigma_M)$.

6.4 Neutron flux and power

The neutron density (n, number/cm^3) and the flux ($\phi = nv$, number/cm^2 per sec) are not uniform through a reactor because of leakage through the outer surface. With-in the body of the reactor, the neutrons make many collisions and they effectively "pile up" with a maximum density at the center. As they leave the reactor surface, they are moving away at high speed, and thus con-tribute little density. For all practical purposes, one can say that outside the reactor the flux is zero. A plot of the flux dis-tribution for thermal neutrons across a flat "slab" reactor is shown in Fig. 6.3. The shape of the flux distribution curve within the reactor is of interest from the standpoint of heat gen-eration or experimental irradia-tion of samples. One is able to

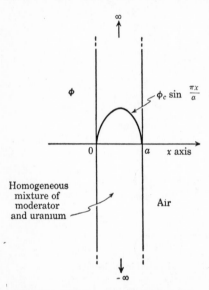

Fig. 6.3. Neutron flux in slab reactor.

derive the mathematical expressions for the flux distributions for various geometries and sizes from reactor theory. The results are shown in Fig. 6.4 including the appropriate K^2 expressions. ϕ_c is the maximum flux, occurring at the geometric center in each case. Most other configurations of interest are special cases of these shapes. The general formulas reduce to simpler forms. For example, in the case of a cube

$$\phi = \phi_c \sin \frac{\pi x}{s} \sin \frac{\pi y}{s} \sin \frac{\pi x}{s}$$

Along a line in the x direction, with y and z constant, this reduces

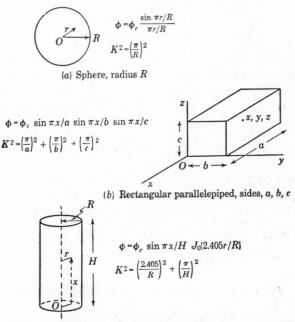

$$\phi = \phi_c \frac{\sin \pi r/R}{\pi r/R}$$

$$K^2 = \left(\frac{\pi}{R}\right)^2$$

(a) Sphere, radius R

$$\phi = \phi_c \sin \pi x/a \sin \pi x/b \sin \pi x/c$$

$$K^2 = \left(\frac{\pi}{a}\right)^2 + \left(\frac{\pi}{b}\right)^2 + \left(\frac{\pi}{c}\right)^2$$

(b) Rectangular parallelepiped, sides, a, b, c

$$\phi = \phi_c \sin \pi x/H \; J_0(2.405r/R)$$

$$K^2 = \left(\frac{2.405}{R}\right)^2 + \left(\frac{\pi}{H}\right)^2$$

(c) Circular cylinder, radius R, height H

Fig. 6.4. Flux distributions in reactors of various shapes. J_0 is the zero-order Bessel function, tabulated in Jahnke and Emde, *Tables of Functions.*

further to a simple sine variation. In a very long pipe where end effects may be neglected,

$$\phi = \phi_c J_0 \left(\frac{2.405r}{R}\right)$$

In a large flat slab with essentially no flux variation in the two dimensions $\phi = \phi_c \sin \pi x/a$.

There is a direct relation between heat generation and flux. The number of fissions per second occurring in 1 cm^3 at a point in the reactor is

$$F = \phi \Sigma_f$$

where Σ_f is the product of the number of fissionable nuclei per unit volume N, and the cross section for fission σ_f. The resulting power can then be found from the equivalence 1 watt $= c$ ($\simeq 3 \times 10^{10}$) fissions/sec

$$P\left(\frac{\text{watts}}{\text{cm}^3}\right) = \frac{F}{c}\left(\frac{\text{fissions/sec-cm}^3}{\text{fissions/watt-sec}}\right) = \frac{\phi \Sigma_f}{c}$$

This computation can be extended to find the power of the whole reactor if instead of the local value of ϕ the *average flux* $\bar{\phi}$ over the system is used, and the result is multiplied with the total volume (in cubic centimeters) of the system containing fissionable material. Thus

$$P_{\text{total}} = \frac{\bar{\phi} \Sigma_f V_f}{c}$$

For example, take a homogeneous mixture of graphite and pure U^{235} with $N_C/N_{U^{235}} = 5000$, of volume 8 m^3 $= 8 \times 10^6$ cm^3, in which $\bar{\phi}$ is 10^{12}/cm^2-sec. As computed earlier, $N_C = 0.0827 \times 10^{24}$, so that

$$N_{U^{235}} = 0.0827 \times 10^{24}/5000 = (1.65 \times 10^{-5})(10^{24})$$

$$\sigma_f = 549 \times 10^{-24}, \quad \text{and} \quad \Sigma_f = 9.06 \times 10^{-3}$$

Thus

$$P_{\text{total}} = (10^{12})(9.06 \times 10^{-3})(8 \times 10^6)/(3 \times 10^{10})$$

$$= 2.4 \times 10^6 \text{ watts or 2.4 mw}$$

As a more complicated case, take a reactor enriched to 5 per cent in U^{235}, consisting of metal slugs of total weight 100 kg, in a suitable moderator with a flux now of 10^{13}/cm^2-sec

$$\Sigma_f = N_{U^{235}}(\sigma_f)_{U^{235}}$$

Recall that U^{238} is not fissionable with thermal neutrons. In the slug,

$$N_{U^{235}} = 0.05 N_U = (0.05)(0.0473 \times 10^{24})$$

$$= 0.00237 \times 10^{24}$$

thus

$$\Sigma_f = (0.00237)(549) = 1.30$$

The total uranium volume is

$$10^5 \text{ (g)}/18.7 \text{ (g/cm}^3) = 5350 \text{ cm}^3$$

The total power is

$$P_T = (10^{13})(1.30)(5350)/(3 \times 10^{10}) = 2.3 \times 10^6 \text{ watts}$$
$$= 2.3 \text{ mw}$$

Note that the reactor size did not come into the problem, since the uranium is the only medium in which heat is generated. It is evident that one can find what the average flux would have to be to achieve a certain power level in a reactor of known size, merely by working the problem backward.

6.5 Resonance escape probability

The calculations of critical size in this chapter were greatly expedited by an assumption of a particular value of the resonance escape probability. We now describe in more detail the method of estimating p, and point out the trends with the relative proportions of the uranium and moderator, and as well with the enrichment of the uranium. We shall accept the theoretical expression as derived in the Appendix for a *homogeneous* mixture

$$p = e^{-"\Sigma_U"/"\Sigma_M"}$$

where "Σ_U" and "Σ_M" are *effective* cross sections for the uranium and moderator for the neutrons of energy in the resonance region. The first of these, "Σ_U", can be written in several ways:

$$"\Sigma_U" = N_U"\sigma_U" = N_U \int \sigma_r \frac{(dE/E)}{5.6}$$

The integral of the resonance capture cross section σ_r is determined empirically; the factor 5.6 is the difference between the natural logarithms of the energies bounding the resonance region. The second factor "Σ_M" is defined by $\xi(\Sigma_s)_M/5.6$ where $(\Sigma_s)_M$ is the average macroscopic scattering cross section of the moderator.

Experimental measurements show that the effective microscopic cross section "σ_U" for uranium dispersed through a moderator is approximately proportional to the 0.415 power of the scattering cross section per uranium atom (up to a value of 1000 barns per atom) with a limiting value of 240/5.6 at great dilution and 9.25/5.6 = 1.652 for the pure metal. Formally, this means

$$"\sigma_U" = \left[\frac{\Sigma_s}{(\Sigma_s)_U} \right]^{0.415} ("\sigma_U")_{\text{metal}}$$

In this relation Σ_s is the sum of the ordinary scattering cross sections of uranium and moderator, $(\Sigma_s)_M + (\Sigma_s)_U$. This is seen to check for the pure metal, for which the scattering is due only to the uranium atoms. The effective resonance cross section for a uranium compound, such as the oxide UO_2, may be determined from the above relation. The microscopic oxygen scattering cross section is 3.8 barns, that for uranium is 8.2 barns, and the atom ratio N_O/N_U is always two. Therefore

$$("\sigma_U") _{UO_2} = \left[\frac{2(3.8) + 8.2}{8.2}\right]^{0.415} (1.652) = 2.15 \text{ barns}$$

Let us compute p for a homogeneous mixture of natural uranium and graphite for which the carbon-uranium atom ratio N_M/N_U is 100. A study of a plot of the graphite cross section* as a function of energy reveals that σ_s is approximately constant at 4.8 barns from the thermal energy 0.025 ev to around 0.1 mev, which we shall assume encompasses the resonance region. The uranium scattering over this region is taken as its thermal value, 8.2 barns. The ratio of total scattering to uranium scattering is

$$\frac{\Sigma_s}{(\Sigma_s)_U} = 1 + \frac{N_M}{N_U} \cdot \frac{(\sigma_s)_M}{(\sigma_s)_U} = 1 + (100)\left(\frac{4.8}{8.2}\right)$$
$$= 59.5$$
$$"\sigma_U" = (59.5)^{0.415} (1.652) = 9.0 \text{ barns}$$

Further,

$$"\sigma_M" = \frac{\xi(\sigma_s)_C}{5.6} = \frac{(0.159)(4.8)}{5.6} = 0.136$$

Thus

$$p = e^{-\frac{N_U}{N_M} \cdot \frac{"\sigma_U"}{"\sigma_M"}} = e^{-\left(\frac{1}{100}\right)\left(\frac{9.0}{0.136}\right)} = 0.516$$

Our answer appears to be very low, in comparison with the figure 0.9 used earlier in the heterogeneous reactor example. This merely demonstrates, however, the difficulty in approaching the necessary $k_\infty \geq 1$ with a *homogeneous* mixture of graphite and natural uranium. Let us continue the problem one step further. Omitting ϵ, but taking $\eta = 1.32$ and the readily computed $f = 0.944$, we find $k_\infty \simeq \eta p f = 0.643$. This is far below critical. Figure 6.5 shows the variation of p, f, and k_∞ for a homogeneous graphite reactor with atom ratio N_M/N_U. The maximum value of k_∞ is seen to be about 0.8, over the range of atom ratios. The empirical variation of "Σ_U" with dilution is of limited accuracy beyond a scattering cross section per uranium atom of around 1000 barns. Thus the calculations just completed, in which $N_M/N_U = 100$ and the total scattering is around 500 are

* For example, *Neutron Cross sections*, AECU-2040.

presumably valid; the extension to N_M/N_U of 1000 is subject to error in magnitude, but not in trend. The situation is considerably more favorable with a pure heavy-water moderator. The multiplication

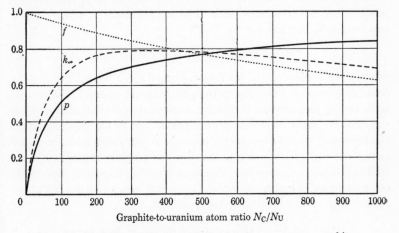

Fig. 6.5. Variation of f, p, and k_∞ for homogeneous graphite-natural uranium mixture.

constant reaches a maximum of 1.2 at a ratio N_{D_2O}/N_U of around 225. In 1942, when the original calculations on reactors were made, sufficient heavy water was not available to build a reactor. The prediction of a maximum k_∞ of 0.8 for a homogeneous graphite-uranium

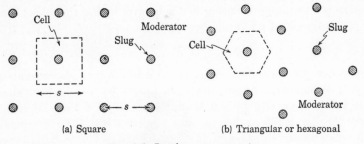

Fig. 6.6. Lattice arrangements.

mixture led to the idea of disposing the uranium as metal or oxide lumps through the graphite moderator.

One of the virtues of the lattice is that many neutrons are slowed through the region of resonance capture (see Fig. 6.6) by moderator atoms, with relatively few encounters with uranium nuclei. A neutron after its last collision may have an energy that coincides with a resonance peak, but is more likely to strike another moderator nucleus than one of uranium. If it does so, the energy is shifted to a point below the resonance peak. The improvement is reflected in a new empirical formula for "σ_U"

$$\text{"}\sigma_U\text{"} = (9.25/5.6)(1 + \mu S/M) \text{ barns}$$

where μ is a constant, 2.67 for metal slugs. S/M is the ratio of surface area (in square centimeters) to the slug mass (in grams). The second term in the parentheses is usually somewhat less than unity. Thus the effective cross section is practically as low as for the metal, but the necessary moderation is still present. As an illustration, we compute "σ_U" for a 0.9-in. slug as used in the graphite-uranium reactor BEPO (British Experimental Pile 0) at Harwell, England. Now S/M for a cylinder of radius r_0 is $2\pi r_0/\pi r_0^2 \rho = 2/r_0\rho$, which for 1.143-cm radius slugs of density 18.7 g/cm³ is 0.0936.

$$\text{"}\sigma\text{"} = \left(\frac{9.25}{5.6}\right)[1 + (2.67)(0.0936)] = 2.06 \text{ barns}$$

It is not quite legitimate to apply the p formula as used for a homogeneous reactor since the scattering occurs in the moderator and the absorption occurs in the slug. We must properly attach weighting factors V_M and V_U and $\bar{\phi}_M$ and $\bar{\phi}_U$ as it was necessary to modify the thermal utilization formula in Section 6.2. To assume that the density of neutrons of the proper energy is exactly the same in the two regions is a first approximation that is in error by less than 2 per cent in p. The modified p formula becomes

$$p = e^{-V_U \text{"}\Sigma_U\text{"}/V_M \text{"}\Sigma_M\text{"}}$$

Let us take the same data for graphite as in the previous calculation of p. The BEPO reactor slugs are $7\frac{1}{4}$ in. apart; the volumes per inch of slug are $V_U = (\pi/4)(0.9)^2 = 0.636$ in.³, $V_M = (7\frac{1}{4})^2 - V_U = 51.92$ in.³ Now "σ_M" = 0.136 as before, and "σ_U" = 2.06. The corresponding macroscopic values are "Σ_M" = (0.0827)(0.136) = 0.0112 and "Σ_U" = (0.0473)(2.06) = 0.0974. Thus

$$p = e^{-\frac{(0.636)(0.0974)}{(51.92)(0.0112)}} = e^{-0.1065}$$

or

$$p = 0.899$$

6.6 Thermal utilization

The thermal utilization f for a homogeneous reactor is very easily calculated, as shown in Section 6.2. The value of f for a heterogeneous reactor, however, must include the flux and volume weighting factors $\bar{\phi}_M$, $\bar{\phi}_U$, and V_M, V_U. From Fig. 6.1 we saw that the flux varies both through the reactor as a whole and locally through an individual slug and surrounding moderator. The mathematical complication that arises from this situation is partly resolved by making a simplifying assumption: *The fraction of thermal neutrons absorbed in uranium for the whole reactor is the same as that for one slug and its associated moderator.* Thus, if we can calculate f for one typical slug, without regard to the others, the infinite multiplication constant for the lattice arrangement under study may immediately be obtained. A question to answer first is: What is the "associated moderator"? Various arrangements of moderator and slug are possible. Figure 6.6 shows the square and triangular configurations. It may be seen that if the centerlines of slugs in a square array are separated by a distance S, the proper area and thus volume accompanying each is S^2. This unit of volume is called a "cell." The solution of the equations that yield the neutron flux is very involved for a geometry that mixes cylindrical shapes (slug) and rectangular boundaries (moderator). An approximate treatment applicable to a lattice in which the slug is small in comparison with the cell is introduced. The neutron distribution is assumed to be unchanged by replacing a square by a circle of the same area, i.e., a rectangular parallelepiped by a circular cylinder. In this process, called "cylindricizing" the cell, one examines the neutron properties in a cylinder of end area πr^2, that is equal to the actual cell area S^2. Several other assumptions must also be made for mathematical convenience in obtaining f. These are listed below to assist in visualizing the effects taking place in the cell; we shall not be concerned here with their mathematical use.

(1) *No thermal neutrons escape from the cell.* This is equivalent to saying that the number of neutrons that leave is just balanced by those that enter from adjacent cells. Only in an infinite reactor would this be true. However, we are computing the infinite multiplication constant k_∞, so this assumption is reasonable. The consequence of this condition is that the neutron flux is flat at the edge of the cell.

(2) *Neutrons become thermal only in the moderator.* The average energy loss of neutrons on a collision with an element was shown in

Section 2.6 to be measured by $\xi = \overline{\Delta \log_e E}$. The value of ξ for uranium is only 0.0084, compared with 0.159 for a light element such as carbon. Further, the moderator-to-uranium volume ratio is usually quite large. The slowing down process thus occurs principally as a result of collisions in the moderator.

(3) *The rate at which thermal neutrons appear in the moderator is uniform throughout the moderator.* The neutrons migrate large distances as they slow down from fission energy to thermal energy in most moderators, and thus "forget" their origin in the slug. The above argument is not incompatible with the idea of an isolated cell if we remember that the same events are occurring in all cells of the reactor.

It is more convenient to calculate the reciprocal of f than f itself. Inverting the formula defining thermal utilization, Section 6.2, we have

$$\frac{1}{f} = 1 + \frac{\Sigma_M V_M \bar{\phi}_M}{\Sigma_U V_U \bar{\phi}_U}$$

A "rigorous" formula of $1/f$ may be obtained by an application of thermal neutron diffusion theory to the cylindrical system. We relegate this derivation to the Appendix on the following grounds: (a) calculations based on the theory require tables of Bessel functions, some of which are not readily available; (b) computing machine accuracy to several significant figures is needed to get 0.5 per cent accuracy; (c) the diffusion theory on which it is based is not strictly applicable. With this apology we adopt the simple, convenient, but reasonably accurate approach described below. Let us rewrite $\bar{\phi}_M$ as $\bar{\phi}_M + \phi_M(r_0) - \phi_M(r_0)$ where $\phi_M(r_0)$ is the height of the flux distribution at r_0, the inside surface of the moderator. See Fig. 6.7. This evidently introduces no change. Substituting in the $1/f$ formula above, we have

$$\frac{1}{f} = 1 + \frac{V_M \Sigma_M \phi_M(r_0)}{V_U \Sigma_U \bar{\phi}_U} + \frac{V_M \Sigma_M [\bar{\phi}_M - \phi_M(r_0)]}{V_U \Sigma_U \bar{\phi}_U}$$

Now if the flux in the moderator turned out to be perfectly flat, i.e., $\bar{\phi}_M = \phi_M(r_0)$, the third term on the right would be zero and the first two terms would yield the result. The flux in the moderator is usually flat enough that the third term can be thought of as a small correction factor, which we will call δ, the "excess absorption" term. Thus

$$\frac{1}{f} = 1 + \frac{V_M \Sigma_M}{V_U \Sigma_U} \cdot \frac{\phi(r_0)}{\bar{\phi}_U} + \delta$$

Note that $\phi_U(r_0) = \phi_M(r_0)$ because the fluxes are assumed to join at the interface of slug and moderator. The volume ratio V_M/V_U and the cross-section ratio Σ_M/Σ_U are easily calculated. The ratio $\phi(r_0)/\bar{\phi}_U$

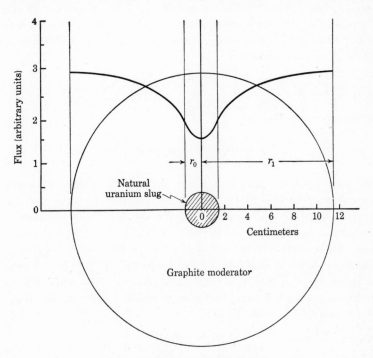

Fig. 6.7. Flux in cylindrical cell.

and δ may also be computed from the dimensions of the slug and moderator and the neutron diffusion properties of the materials of which they are composed. These constants are the reciprocals of the diffusion lengths L of the two substances, $K_U = 1/L_U$ and $K_M = 1/L_M$. Since the L's are effective distances a neutron penetrates a medium before being absorbed, the K's are corresponding absorption coefficients. This relation may be better understood by considering a slab of material on which a beam of thermal neutrons impinges. If the original flux density is ϕ_0, that at any point z within the medium is

$$\phi = \phi_0 e^{-Kz}$$

Experimental or calculated values are available for some materials, e.g., for graphite $L = 50$ cm, $K = 0.02$ cm^{-1}; for pure D_2O, $L = 171$ cm, $K = 0.00585$ cm^{-1}. For natural uranium, K is taken as 0.70 cm^{-1}. Let us adopt the more conventional subscripts 0 for uranium and 1 for moderator. Thus $\bar{\phi}_U \equiv \bar{\phi}_0$. It may be shown (see Appendix) that the flux ratio of interest is

$$\frac{\phi(r_0)}{\bar{\phi}_0} = 1 + \frac{(K_0 r_0)^2}{8} - \frac{(K_0 r_0)^4}{192} + \cdots$$

The correction term is

$$\delta \simeq \frac{(K_1 r_1)^2}{2} \left(\log_e \frac{r_1}{r_0} - \frac{3}{4} \right)$$

We have sufficient information now at hand to estimate f for a particular reactor. The BEPO reactor will continue to serve as our example. Neglecting all cooling channels, the moderator-uranium volume ratio is $V_M/V_U = 51.92/0.636 = 81.64$. The thermal neutron absorption cross sections are $\Sigma_M = 3.72 \times 10^{-4}$, $\Sigma_U = 0.351$. Thus $\Sigma_M/\Sigma_U = 1.060 \times 10^{-3}$ and $V_M \Sigma_M/V_U \Sigma_U = 0.0865$. The cell radius is given by $r_1 = S/\sqrt{\pi} = (7.25)(2.54)/\sqrt{\pi} = 10.39$ while the slug radius is $r_0 = 1.143$ cm. Also $K_0 r_0 = (0.70)(1.43) = 0.800$; $K_1 r_1 = 0.208$ and $r_1/r_0 = 9.09$. Thus

$$\frac{\phi(r_0)}{\bar{\phi}_0} = 1 + \frac{(0.80)^2}{8} - \frac{(0.80)^4}{192} = 1.078$$

$$\delta = \frac{(0.208)^2}{2} (\log_e 9.09 - 0.75) = 0.032$$

$$\frac{1}{f} = 1 + (0.0865)(1.078) + 0.032 = 1.125$$

The thermal utilization is thus $f = 0.889$. As we shall see in Chapter 12, this approximate method can also be applied to the evaluation of the flux ratio for the resonance escape probability.

6.7 The fast fission factor ϵ

The number of neutrons contributed to the chain by fast fission of natural uranium in a slug is small (of the order of 3 per cent), but is of sufficient importance to warrant including the effect in reactor design calculations. Fast neutrons formed in the slug from the fission of U^{235} can escape relatively easily into the moderator, where they are slowed to energies below the 1-mev threshold for fission of U^{238}.

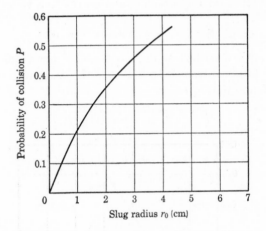

Fig. 6.8. Probability of collision of fast neutrons in natural uranium slugs.

The fast fission factor ϵ is determined in part by the chance of a neutron making a collision in the slug. For one neutron the chance of *escaping* can be represented by $e^{-N\sigma x}$ where σ is the total cross section and x is the linear distance from the point of formation to the surface of the slug. However, the *average* chance of escape for all neutrons depends on the thermal flux density that produces them, the various distances from the edge of the slug, and the original direction of motion. The method of calculation of the chance of collision, labeled P, is far beyond the scope of this book. We shall be content to use the published values of P as a function of radius r_0 of a cylindrical slug, as graphed in Fig. 6.8. In order to represent the different reactions that are the result of a collision, the total cross section σ can be broken down as follows, with numerical values (in barns).

σ	$=$	σ_c	$+$	σ_e	$+$	σ_i	$+$	σ_f
total		capture		elastic scattering		inelastic scattering		fission
4.3		0.04		1.5		2.47		0.29

Each fate has a different effect on the cycle,

σ_c: neutrons are lost,

σ_e: a small loss in energy occurs, of the order of 0.8 per cent, but so small that the neutrons are still fast enough to cause fission,

σ_i: a large drop occurs in the neutron energy to a value below the fission threshold,

σ_f: fission, giving rise to $\nu = 2.55$ new neutrons.

The net effect is described by the fast fission factor ϵ, defined by the ratio of the total neutrons from fission to the neutrons from U^{235} fission. It is found that

$$\epsilon = 1 + \frac{(\nu\sigma_f - \sigma_f - \sigma_c)P}{\sigma - (\nu\sigma_f + \sigma_e)P}$$

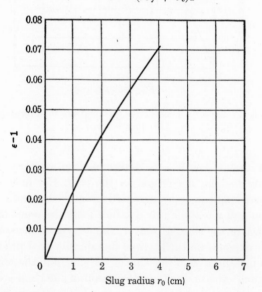

Fig. 6.9. Fast fission factor for natural uranium slugs.

The function $\epsilon - 1$ is plotted in Fig. 6.9 for cylindrical slugs.

The trend is exactly what would be expected. The larger the slug, the greater is the chance that a fast neutron will make a fission collision. For the BEPO slugs, radius 0.9 in. or 1.143 cm, we find $\epsilon - 1$ to be 0.025 or $\epsilon = 1.025$.

6.8 Application of the four-factor formula

We may now complete our calculation of k_∞ for the BEPO reactor. The four factors in k_∞ are:

$$\epsilon = 1.025, \qquad p = 0.899$$
$$f = 0.889, \qquad \eta = 1.32$$

and $k_\infty = \epsilon p f \eta = 1.081$. The above calculation involves an underestimate of p, but also has an overestimate of f because absorption by air cooling ducts has been omitted. The BEPO reactor is described as a cylinder of 10-ft (305 cm) radius, 20-ft (610 cm) high. Let us find out what k_∞ is needed to make this assembly critical with $k_{\text{eff}} = 1$. The size-shape factor for a cylindrical figure is

$$K^2 = \left(\frac{2.405}{R}\right)^2 + \left(\frac{\pi}{H}\right)^2 = \left(\frac{2.405}{305}\right)^2 + \left(\frac{\pi}{610}\right)^2 = 8.87 \times 10^{-5}$$

$$L^2 = L_0^2(1 - f) = (2500)(0.111) = 278 \text{ cm}^2$$

$$\tau = 300 \text{ cm}^2$$

$$k_\infty = \frac{1 + K^2 L^2}{e^{-K^2\tau}} = \frac{1.0247}{0.9738} = 1.052$$

The 3 per cent difference from the expected value may be due to the errors in p and f above, the purity of the graphite used in the BEPO reactor, and the provisions for absorbing control rods.

A study of the data on heterogeneous reactors reveals that most slug diameters are close to 1 in., and cell sizes are around 8 in. A repetition of the above calculation for many different sizes reveals that the above configurations give the optimum k_∞. Figures 6.10, 6.11, and 6.12 show values of p, f and k_∞ for several lattice dimensions in a graphite, natural uranium reactor. Qualitatively, a maximum in k_∞ with rod size is to be expected. For very small slugs, even though the ratio S/M is large, the slug volume is small, resonance capture is low, and p is large. The total thermal neutron absorption in the moderator is large relative to that in the slug and thus f is

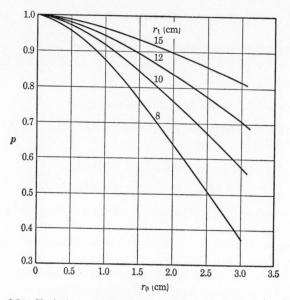

Fig. 6.10. Variation of p with r_0, r_1: graphite-natural uranium heterogeneous reactor.

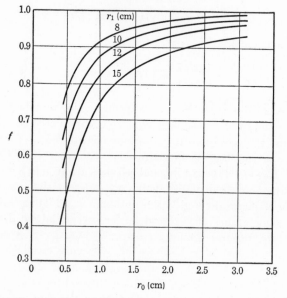

Fig. 6.11. Variation of f with r_0, r_1: graphite-natural uranium heterogeneous reactor.

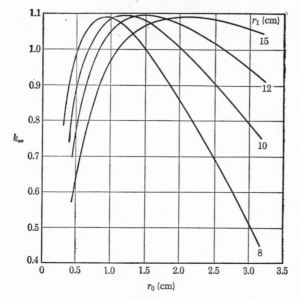

Fig. 6.12. Variation of k_∞ with r_0, r_1: graphite-natural uranium heterogeneous reactor.

small. The reverse situation is found for very large slugs. A compromise that sacrifices both p and f but maximizes k_∞ must be chosen.

6.9 Conversion factor for a heterogeneous reactor

The ratio of plutonium production to U^{235} burn-up will be defined as the conversion factor (CF) or "breeding ratio." When this quantity is equal to one, the reactor exactly replaces the fissionable material as it is used up. The neutron cycle may be adapted to derive a relation for (CF). Since we may start tracing the history of neutrons in any part of the closed cycle, let us consider those starting the slowing down process. The fraction escaping resonance capture is p, the fraction captured is $1 - p$. This serves as the first source of plutonium, which we may label

$$A = 1 - p$$

To a good approximation we may neglect both fast and thermal neutron leakage. Of the neutrons that escape resonance capture, a fraction f are absorbed in uranium. The fraction absorbed in U^{238}, again yielding plutonium is

$$B = pf(\Sigma_{238}/\Sigma_U)$$

The number absorbed or "burned" in U^{235} is the remainder

$$C = pf(\Sigma_{235}/\Sigma_U)$$

The conversion factor is the ratio

$$(CF) = \frac{A + B}{C} = \left(\frac{\text{resonance absorption} + \text{thermal absorption in } U^{238}}{\text{thermal absorption in } U^{235}} \right)$$

or simplified

$$(CF) = \frac{(1 - p)/pf + \Sigma_{238}/\Sigma_U}{\Sigma_{235}/\Sigma_U}$$

From the known cross sections we may find the necessary ratios:

$$\Sigma_{238}/\Sigma_U = N_{238}\sigma_{238}/N_U\sigma_U$$
$$= (0.99286)(2.80/7.42) = 0.375$$
$$\Sigma_{235}/\Sigma_U = N_{235}\sigma_{235}/N_U\sigma_U$$
$$= (0.00714)(650/7.42) = 0.625$$

The conversion factor for the BEPO reactor may be estimated from the data $p = 0.899$ and $f = 0.889$. Then

$$(CF) = \frac{0.126 + 0.375}{0.625} = 0.80$$

The result that 80 per cent of the atoms burned are replaced by more fissionable atoms is somewhat short of the desired unity for exact replacement. One way to improve the (CF) is to change the lattice geometry to effect a reduction in p. There is a limit to such adjustments because of the $k_\infty > 1$ requirement. In general, a drop in p must be compensated by an equal rise in f. A change to a new moderator, e.g. from graphite to D_2O, will be effective, however. The upper limit in (CF) is obtained with a hypothetical reactor with no leakage and no poisoning of any kind. Let f be its maximum of 1 and p its minimum of $1/\eta = 0.758$; thus the term in (CF) containing resonance absorption becomes $\eta - 1 = 1.32 - 1 = 0.32$. Then (CF) is

$$(CF)_{max} = \frac{0.32 + 0.375}{0.625} = 1.1$$

It will be noted that this coincides, as it should, with the maximum number of neutrons available for breeding: (2.1 neutrons/absorption in U^{235}) − (1.0 neutrons to continue the chain) = 1.1. This comparison shows that such proposals as enriching the uranium will not lead to higher ultimate conversion ratios. With uranium in any concentration there are only 1.1 neutrons to use for any other purpose.

The reader should realize that the simple theories of reactors presented in the preceding sections are useful only for first estimates on reactor characteristics. More accurate (and usually more complicated) methods are applied before final designs are made. As an illustration, mention might be made of the "two group" approach, that may be applied to small reflected enriched reactors such as the "swimming pool" type. Neutrons are divided into two classes for mathematical convenience: (a) thermal, and (b) fast, where the properties of the second group are proper averages of the properties of all neutrons of energy above thermal. Both groups are pictured as diffusing through the medium, and interacting as follows: fast neutrons in slowing down serve as a source of thermals; the source for the fast group is made up of fission neutrons from the absorption of thermals in the fuel. For details of the methods of calculation, one should refer to books on reactor theory such as that of Glasstone and Edlund.

Problems

6.1 Compute the thermal utilization for a reactor composed of 2-in. diameter spheres of natural uranium, imbedded in beryllium blocks 1 ft on a side. Assume the ratio of moderator flux to uranium flux to be 1.5.

6.2 What is the value of η for uranium enriched to 2 per cent U^{235}? Repeat the calculation for 25 per cent U^{235} and discuss the trend with concentration.

6.3 Calculate the size-shape factor K^2 for a cylindrical tank 2 ft in diameter, 3 ft high.

6.4 Find the thermal diffusion length L for a solution of pure U^{235} in water for which the chemical U^{235} concentration is 2 per cent by weight of solution.

6.5 What is the fast leakage factor $\mathcal{L}_f$ for a 5-ft diameter spherical tank of D_2O?

6.6 Find the proper length of side of the reactor of Section 6.3, within 2 in., to make k_{eff} exactly unity.

6.7 From the definitions of diffusion length $L^2 = \frac{1}{3} \lambda_a \lambda_t$ (see Section 2.7) and the thermal utilization $f = \Sigma_a)_U / \Sigma_a$ show that the relation $L^2 = L_0^2(1 - f)$ is correct. What assumption must be made about λ_t? Explain.

6.8 A homogeneous water-boiler type reactor containing pure U^{235} has a volume of fifteen liters. What will be its average thermal neutron flux at a power level of 25 kw? Take the ratio of numbers of hydrogen and uranium atoms to be 500.

6.9 Find the ratio of average flux $\bar{\phi}$ in a spherical homogeneous reactor to the central flux ϕ_c. HINT: define $\bar{\phi}$ as $\int \phi \, dV / \int dV$ where dV is the shell volume element $4\pi r^2 \, dr$.

6.10 Find the lowest isotopic concentration of U^{235} that will yield $k_\infty = 1$ in a homogeneous graphite-uranium reactor. Take account of the variation with U^{235} content of all three variables η, f, and p. Explain what adjustments are needed in the resonance capture calculation.

6.11 The heterogeneous D_2O natural uranium reactor at Stockholm, Sweden, has a lattice arrangement as in Fig. 6.6b with a slug centerline separation of 14.5 cm. Find the radius of the equivalent cylindrical cell from the *triangle* area (not the hexagon). Explain why the use of a cylinder is somewhat more accurate for this arrangement than for a square lattice.

6.12 Calculate "Σ_M" used in the resonance escape probability formula, for beryllium metal.

6.13 What is the value of "Σ_U" for the slugs in the Oak Ridge reactor (Section 5.1)?

6.14 Compute the resonance escape probability p for the Oak Ridge reactor.

6.15 From the computed value of the thermal utilization for the BEPO reactor, find the *true* ratio of fluxes in moderator and uranium.

6.16 Calculate the fast fission factor ϵ from the cross-section data for the 0.9-in. GLEEP reactor slugs and compare with the quoted value of 1.029.

References

ISBIN, H. S., "Nuclear Reactor Catalog." *Nucleonics*, March (1952). p. 10. See also Supplement; *Nucleonics*, June (1953) p. 65.

HAFSTAD, L. R., "Reactors." *Scientific American*, April (1951), p. 43.

Selected Unclassified References on Nuclear Reactors, TID-3006. Oak Ridge, Tenn.: Technical Information Service Staff, Technical Information Service, October 16, 1951.

"BEPO British Experimental Pile," *Nucleonics*, June (1951) p. 36.

BORST, L. B., "The Brookhaven Nuclear Reactor," *Physics Today*, April (1951) p. 6.

"GLEEP, Design Construction and Use." *Nucleonics*, January (1951) p. 3.

"How to Load a Reactor," *Nucleonics*, February (1952) p. 24. Oak Ridge reactor.

"Major Activities in the Atomic Energy Programs." *Twelfth Semi-Annual Report of the Atomic Energy Commission to Congress, January–June, 1952*. Washington, D. C.: U. S. Government Printing Office, July, 1952.

GLASSTONE, S. and M. C. EDLUND, *The Elements of Nuclear Reactor Theory*. New York: D. Van Nostrand Co., 1952.

GOODMAN, CLARK, Ed., *The Science and Engineering of Nuclear Power*. Cambridge, Mass.: Addison-Wesley Press, 1949, Vols. I, II.

"Nuclear Data for Low Power Research Reactors." *Nucleonics*, January (1951) p. 8.

MURRAY, RAYMOND L. and A. C. MENIUS, JR., "Fast Fission Factor for Hollow Natural Uranium Cylinders." *Nucleonics*, April (1953) p. 21.

CHAPTER 7

THE WATER BOILER

The only nuclear reactor for which information is completely de-classified is the homogeneous, water moderated, enriched uranium system. It is usually called the "water boiler," presumably from the fact that it can be made to boil at a high-enough power level, although in normal operation it does not. The function of this low power machine is strictly experimental, but since almost every characteristic problem and principle of reactor behavior is demonstrated, a detailed examination of it is of considerable value. The homogeneous-enriched type reactor is one of the simpler, more inexpensive and safer types. Examples of water boilers are the Los Alamos homogeneous reactor and the Raleigh Research Reactor at North Carolina State College. For purposes of specific illustration we shall describe the latter. Dimensions and numerical characteristics will be quoted when an understanding of functions is thus facilitated.

7.1 The main reactor components

The basic parts of the unit are the core, reflector and shield, as shown in Fig. 7.1. The core is a 1/16-in. thick cylindrical stainless steel container of 14-liter capacity almost filled with a water (light) solution of a salt, uranyl sulfate, UO_2SO_4. The uranium is enriched in the U^{235} to a concentration of 93 per cent. The U^{235} weight is approximately 860 g. The mixture chosen is based on the fact that the small-est mass that is critical in water solution is obtained at an atom ratio $N_H/N_U \simeq 420$. This dilution corresponds to a chemical concentration of 6 per cent uranium by weight, and yields a solution density of 1.09 g/cm^3. The function of the core is to contain the fissionable material and to reduce the neutrons to thermal energy in a small volume. The small diameter of less than 1 ft is possible because of the short slowing down length of fast neutrons and diffusion length of thermal neutrons in water. The normal operating temperature is 80°C, maintained thus by water flowing through cooling coils in the interior of the container. The water continually removes the heat generated by fission. The standard power level is 10 kw, which is achieved with an average thermal neutron flux somewhat over $10^{11}/cm^2$-sec.

The *reflector*, composed of stacked graphite blocks with 4-in. by 4-in. cross section, closely fit around the core, serves to prevent many

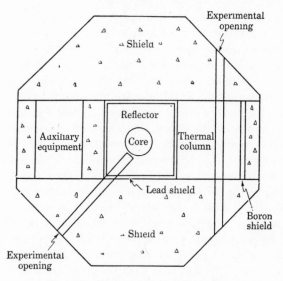

Fig. 7.1. Components of water boiler.

neutrons from escaping from the core. The chance of absorption in carbon is much less than that for scattering, so that a large fraction of the neutrons coming out of the active solution make collisions that "reflect" them back into it. Thus the effective multiplication constant is increased over that for a bare reactor, and the size of the core is smaller. Ideally, the reflector performs its function best if it is infinitely thick. A thickness of around 20 in. is found to reduce the critical mass to within 5 per cent of its minimum value. Since the overall size of the assembly is largely determined by the reflector, a practical choice is made, even at the expense of a slightly increased uranium inventory. The exact shape of the reflector is not at all important; it was convenient to make it in the form of a cube, 5 ft on a side. The *shield* surrounding the reflector is necessary to protect experimenters from fast neutrons, slow neutrons, and gamma rays emitted both in the fission process and by the radioactive fission products. Remote control of the reactor would be possible, without a shield, but the total space restricted to access would be prohibitive. In the interests of saving building size and to increase experimentation area, the shield is constructed of special dense concrete. Barytes, a barium ore, is used for the large particles; colemanite, a sand containing boron is the only fine aggregate. The barium, being a heavy element, is a good absorber of gamma rays. Water that remains in the concrete serves to render fast neutrons thermal, and the boron captures neutrons without emitting secondary gamma rays. A thickness of 5 ft of such concrete is more than ample to reduce the neutron and gamma flux to below maximum allowable values, around $20/cm^2$-sec for fast neutrons and close to 600 for thermals and gamma rays. One might expect that shielding would not be needed on the top of the reactor, but only on the sides, to protect the operator and experimenters. The scattering of neutrons by molecules of air, however, is sufficiently large to warrant installing a top shield.

In principle, the three basic components just described constitute the reactor, but without the many auxiliary systems and control devices, the unit would be inoperable. These may be classified by function—neutron-absorbing control rods and drive mechanism to set the desired power level; cooling water tubes and supply equipment to remove the fission heat from the core; vents in the core for the evolved fission gases; concentrators for the radioactive wastes; special ports for experimental tests and bombardment of samples; neutron counting instruments for indication of neutron flux or for tripping safety devices. In the series of schematic diagrams of the components to follow, each system will be shown separately, without regard to their installation into available space. In Fig. 7.1 several features beside the basic core, reflector, and shield, are seen. The thermal column is an extension of the reflector on one side, providing a beam of thermal neutrons for experiments. The lead shielding is designed to remove undesirable gamma rays. The $\frac{1}{2}$-in. boron layer at the end of the column is a substitute for the missing concrete shielding in that direction. Steel tubes threading the concrete serve as experimental openings or "ports." If not in use, they may be plugged with concrete cylinders. Some ports give access to the core surface, while others pass completely through the reflector or thermal column. For security of the fissionable material, combination locks on safe type doors terminate the steel tubes.

7.2 Cooling system

In the Raleigh reactor, the core cooling is achieved by a set of four coils, $\frac{1}{4}$-inch inside diameter, in parallel. Figure 7.2 shows the internal arrangement of cooling coils. These pipes, each 7 ft long, are made of stainless steel to resist the corrosion by the solution in which they

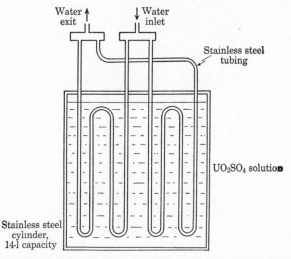

Fig. 7.2. Cooling coils for water boiler core (two of four shown).

are immersed. A flow of 1 gal of chilled water per minute in each tube is provided by pressure-flow regulation. After having traversed the high neutron flux in the reactor the water will be radioactive, because of the neutron absorption by impurities and by the isotope O^{18} which becomes the radioactive isotope O^{19}. As a typical example of the computations that are necessary in assessing the potential hazard of radioactivity in cooling water, we will estimate the yield of O^{19}/cm^3 of water. The following data will be needed:

Absorption cross section of O^{18}: $\sigma_a = 0.0002$ barns
Abundance of O^{18}: 0.204 per cent
Neutron flux: $\phi = 10^{12}/cm^2$-sec
Half-life of O^{19}: $t_H = 29$ sec.

The yield is proportional to the number of O^{18} nuclei per cubic centimeter, the cross section, the neutron flux and the time of exposure. The latter must be found from the flow rate V, and the tube area A and length L:

$$t \text{ (sec)} = L/v = \frac{L \text{ (in.)}}{V \text{ (in.}^3/\text{sec)}/A \text{ (in.}^2)}$$

We shall let the length be $L = 7$ ft or 84 in., a volume flow rate $V = 1$ gal/min $= 231/60$ in.^{3}/sec, and an area $A = (\pi/4)(\frac{1}{4})^2$ in.^{2}. The time of exposure comes out close to 1 sec. The number of water molecules/cm^3 is computed to be 0.0335×10^{24}/cm^3. Thus the number of O^{18} atoms N is $6.8 \times 10^{-5} \times 10^{24}$. The yield is

$$\mathfrak{N} = \phi N \sigma_a t = (10^{12})(6.8 \times 10^{-5})(2 \times 10^{-4})(1)$$
$$= 13{,}600 \text{ atoms/cm}^3$$

The activity of issuing water, using the decay constant $\lambda = 0.693/29 = 0.024$ sec^{-1}, is

$$\mathfrak{N}\lambda = (13{,}600)(0.024) = 326 \text{ d/sec-cm}^3$$

Health authorities have set the maximum allowable concentration for *drinking water* for typical beta and gamma emitting isotopes at around 10^{-5} microcuries per milliliter (μc/ml). Since one microcurie is 3.7×10^4 d/sec, the O^{18} activity is initially about 100 times this tolerance. Fortunately, the activity is reduced by a factor of two every 29 sec, so this discharge can be made completely safe with a few minutes' holding.

Similar problems exist with other reactor coolants. For example, sodium which in liquid form is useful as a heat exchange medium in power reactors, is converted into active Na^{24} by neutron absorption, which makes recirculation problems more difficult.

7.3 Recombining system

A problem that is peculiar to a water-moderated homogeneous reactor is the dissociation of water by the energetic fission fragments. Hydrogen and oxygen atoms are released, come to the top of the liquid, and collect in what could be explosive concentrations. It is thus necessary to provide some mechanism for treating the hydrogen-oxygen mixture to prevent inadvertent explosion that might break the core

walls or disrupt the piping. Several types of treatment are possible:
(a) to dilute the effluent with air of sufficient volume, with the disadvantage of having to store very large volumes of air containing
radioactivity; (b) to recombine in a controlled manner by a firing
chamber or gas engine; (c) to react the gas mixture of H_2 and O_2 in
a catalytic chamber. The best method appears to be the last. A

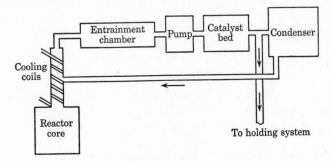

Fig. 7.3. Hydrogen-oxygen recombiner.

sketch of the apparatus used in the Raleigh reactor is shown in Fig.
7.3. The gases are pumped off through a tube that has a water cooled
jacket, which serves to condense out some of the water vapor and

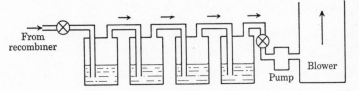

Fig. 7.4. Holding system for fission gases.

fission products in vapor form. A stainless-steel-wool filled entrain-
ment chamber then removes particulate matter. As the residual
hydrogen and oxygen gas passes through the catalysis bed, containing fine pellets of heated platinized alumina (Al_2O_3), the recombination takes place, leaving steam. This is condensed out and the water
returned to the reactor. Included in the circulating fluids will be
the radioactive fission gases xenon and krypton. These elements are
inert chemically, and thus their danger cannot be removed except
by holding until decay reduces them to stable particles. Just beyond

the catalyst chambers, where the total volume is smallest, a few cubic centimeters per minute of air containing these gases are withdrawn. These are allowed to flow to a series of holding tanks, shown in Fig. 7.4. After sufficient radioactive decay has taken place, the remaining air is diluted with a large volume of air and discharged to the atmosphere from a tall stack.

The radioactive isotope that gives the greatest difficulty in a water boiler is Xe^{133}, with 4.5 per cent yield in fission and a half-life of 5.3 days. It is formed in the chain

$$_{51}Sb^{133} \underset{< 10 \text{ min}}{\longrightarrow} {}_{52}Te^{133} \underset{60 \text{ min}}{\longrightarrow} {}_{53}I^{133} \underset{22 \text{ hr}}{\longrightarrow} {}_{54}Xe^{133} \underset{5.3 \text{ days}}{\longrightarrow} {}_{55}Cs^{133}$$

An estimate of the rate of accumulation of this gas will indicate what sort of storage and disposal problem exists. The simplest case to study is a reactor that starts operating at time zero, at fixed power level P and continues steadily and indefinitely. We assume that iodine is the effective initial product, since the decay of antimony and tellurium into it is very rapid. The growth formula of Section 1.5

$$A_1 = N_1\lambda_1 = g_1(1 - e^{-\lambda_1 t})$$

may be applied to find the iodine activity at a later time t. We attach the subscript 1 to all quantities related to iodine. With power P and yield y, the generation rate is

$$g_1 \left(\frac{\text{atoms}}{\text{sec}}\right) = P \text{ (watts) } c \left(\frac{\text{fissions}}{\text{watt-sec}}\right) y \left(\frac{\text{atoms}}{\text{fission}}\right)$$

where c is 3×10^{10} (see Problem 3.2). Let the water boiler power be 10 kw. Then

$$g_1 = (10{,}000)(3 \times 10^{10})(0.045)$$
$$= 1.35 \times 10^{13} \text{ atoms/sec}$$

The half-life of I^{133} is

$$t_H = (22 \text{ hr})(3600 \text{ sec/hr})$$
$$= 7.92 \times 10^4 \text{ sec}$$

its decay constant is

$$\lambda_1 = 0.693/t_H = 8.75 \times 10^{-6} \text{ sec}^{-1}$$

At the end of steady operation over a period of six hours (2.16×10^4

sec), an average operating day for an experimental machine, the activity is

$$A_1 = (1.35 \times 10^{13})[1 - e^{-(8.75 \times 10^{-6})(2.16 \times 10^4)}]$$

or $$A_1 = 2.32 \times 10^{12} \text{ d/sec (63 curies)}$$

This is about one-sixth of the equilibrium value, which is 1.35×10^{13} d/sec or 365 curies. The iodine atoms present serve as the source of xenon atoms, which in turn decay. We use the subscript 2 to designate xenon properties. The number of the latter, N_2, during the operation period is the solution of the equation

$$\frac{dN_2}{dt} + \lambda_2 N_2 = g_2$$

where the generation rate g_2 is the iodine activity $g_1(1 - e^{-\lambda_1 t})$. Integrating as indicated in Section 1.5 gives the result

$$A_2 = N_2 \lambda_2$$

$$= \frac{g_1}{\lambda_2 - \lambda_1} [\lambda_2 (1 - e^{-\lambda_1 t}) - \lambda_1 (1 - e^{-\lambda_2 t})]$$

Note from the form of the solution that for $t \to \infty$, $A_2 \to g_1$, meaning that after a long time has elapsed the rate of decay of xenon is the same as the original rate of formation of the mass 133 isotope. The half-life of Xe^{133} is

$$t_H = (5.3 \text{ days})(8.64 \times 10^4 \text{ sec/day})$$

$$= 4.58 \times 10^5 \text{ sec}$$

Also, $$\lambda_2 = 0.693/(4.58 \times 10^5) = 1.5 \times 10^{-6} \text{ sec}^{-1}$$

Substituting known numbers, the xenon activity at the end of six hours is

$$A_2 = 1.1 \text{ curies}$$

If the reactor is not operating for the remaining eighteen hours of the day, the xenon formed decays, but also the iodine continues to be converted into xenon. The repetition of this cycle over many days results in a build-up of iodine and xenon concentration to a final level. It may be shown that if the reactor is successively "on" a time τ and "off" a time $(c - 1)\tau$, the maximum iodine activity is a fraction $(1 - e^{-\lambda_I \tau})/(1 - e^{-c\lambda_I \tau})$ of that with continuous operation. Figure 7.5 shows the trend of the iodine activity with time at equilibrium. The xenon activity remains essentially constant. For

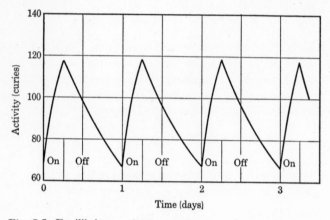

Fig. 7.5. Equilibrium activity of iodine in reactor, 10 kw power.

our problem this fraction is 0.324, implying an equilibrium iodine activity of 118 c. The xenon yield from this amount of material in a period of one day is computed to be close to 11 c.

7.4 Inherent safety in the water boiler

In the design of any reactor, serious thought must be given to the effects of temperature on the multiplication constant. If k_{eff} were to rise with temperature, any slight fluctuation that results in a small rise in neutron density, fission and thus temperature (T) would be magnified, and the reactor would "run away." The water boiler type has what is called a *negative temperature coefficient*, i.e., as T goes up, k_{eff} goes down. Mathematically, $k_{eff} = 1 + \alpha T$ where $dk_{eff}/dT = \alpha$ is a *negative* number. The derivative dk_{eff}/dT is inherently negative for various reasons, one of which is the expansion of the liquid. All nuclei are pushed farther apart if the fluid expands, leaving more gaps through which neutrons may escape without slowing down or causing fission. A partial compensation for this effect is provided by the larger physical volume, which tends to reduce leakage, but the net result is to reduce the effective multiplication constant. We may estimate the magnitude of the expansion contribution to changes in k by a simplified analysis. Assume first that the products $K^2\tau$ and K^2L^2 in the formula for leakage (see Section 6.3) are small, much less than unity. Under these conditions the effective multiplication constant may be written approximately

$$k_{\mathrm{eff}} = \frac{k_\infty}{1 + K^2M^2}$$

where $M^2 = L^2 + \tau$. For convenience, hereafter, we omit the subscript on k_{eff}, and let it be simply k. Take the derivative of k with respect to temperature.

$$\frac{dk}{dT} = \frac{-k_\infty}{(1 + K^2M^2)^2} \cdot \frac{d(K^2M^2)}{dT}$$

The dependence of K^2M^2 on temperature is as follows. The characteristic lengths L or $\sqrt{\tau}$ are inversely proportional to the number of particles per unit volume, and thus for a fixed mass of material are proportional to the volume. Thus $M^2 \sim V^2$. In a sphere of radius R, for example, $K^2 = (\pi/R)^2$ or K^2 is proportional to $V^{-2/3}$, and the product is $K^2M^2 \sim V^{4/3}$. Without needing to know the form of the proportionality constant, it may be seen that

$$\frac{(d/dT)K^2M^2}{K^2M^2} = \frac{(d/dT)V^{4/3}}{V^{4/3}} = \frac{4}{3V} \cdot \frac{dV}{dT}$$

Now substitute $K^2M^2 = (k_\infty/k) - 1$ to obtain the fractional change in k per degree of temperature

$$\frac{1}{k} \cdot \frac{dk}{dT} = -\frac{4}{3}\left(1 - \frac{k}{k_\infty}\right)\frac{1}{V} \cdot \frac{dV}{dT}$$

The temperature coefficient for the water boiler at room temperature, 20°C, may be estimated by the use of this formula. Assume that the presence of uranium does not change the expansion coefficient of water, as found in tables.* Now

$$V_T = V_0(1 + \alpha T + \beta T^2 + \gamma T^3)$$

where
$$\alpha = -0.06427 \times 10^{-3}$$
$$\beta = 8.5053 \times 10^{-6}$$
$$\gamma = -6.7900 \times 10^{-8}$$

* For example, *Handbook of Chemistry and Physics.*

The derivative of V_T with respect to temperature is

$$\frac{dV_T}{dT} = V_0(\alpha + 2\beta T + 3\gamma T^2)$$

and

$$\frac{1}{V} \cdot \frac{dV}{dT} = \frac{\alpha + 2\beta T + 3\gamma T^2}{1 + \alpha T + \beta T^2 + \gamma T^3}$$

Inserting the constants and the temperature, we find

$$\frac{1}{V} \cdot \frac{dV}{dT} = +1.95 \times 10^{-4}/°C$$

Letting $k_\infty = 1.68$ and $k = 1$, we have

$$\frac{dk}{dT} = -1.05 \times 10^{-4}/°C$$

At higher temperatures, the expansion coefficient is larger, thus also the negative temperature coefficient is larger. This agrees fairly well with the actual measured water-boiler coefficient of around $2 \times 10^{-4}/°C$. Bubbling, absorption changes and other factors must be included in the complete analysis of the problem, however.

By an application of a similar logic, but letting the sphere volume increase by adding more solution, one may show that the fractional change in reactivity with mass is given by the formula

$$\frac{1}{k} \cdot \frac{dk}{dm} = \frac{2}{3m}\left(1 - \frac{k}{k_\infty}\right)$$

7.5 Control and safety rods

The adjustment of neutron flux or power level in the reactor is achieved by movement of the *control rod*. It consists of a hollow cylinder partly filled with a strongly neutron-absorbing medium, boron. The rod has the property of reducing or increasing the effective multiplication constant, depending on whether it is inserted farther into or withdrawn from the body of the reactor. In the case of the water boiler, one rod of $\frac{5}{8}$-in. diameter, containing a 1-ft length of hot-pressed boron-carbide is mounted on a vertical axis as shown in Fig. 7.6. The rod may be lowered or raised in a sheath that guides it and protects it from the chemically active solution. A conventional motor and gear drive is employed for manual or automatic operation; in the event that a sudden insertion is required, the current to a holding magnet may be broken to allow the rod to fall.

In the Raleigh reactor, two identical systems are provided, one used for control, the other as a *safety rod*. If the neutron density were to increase above a pre-determined level, an electrical signal would cause this rod to be released, thereby suppressing the reaction.

The physical effects produced by a control rod can be visualized in the following way. If a thermal neutron, in the course of its diffusion through the core, enters the absorbing boron, its chance of getting through is almost nil. Mathematically, the chance of going a distance x into a (plane) surface is expressed by $e^{-\Sigma x}$ where Σ is the macroscopic absorption cross section. Since the boron cross section is $\Sigma = 104$ cm^{-1} (see Section 2.5), $e^{-\Sigma x}$ is small for a thickness x of a few millimeters. For all practical purposes, boron is "black," i.e., a perfect absorber, for thermal neutrons. This is the same situation as exists for the surface of a bare reactor, in that all neutrons that go through the surface are lost. Thus, the neutron flux and density effectively go to zero at the boundary of the absorber, as sketched in Fig. 7.7. With the rod "in," the average flux is reduced and the power level goes down accordingly. One might ask the question: Why does the power level not go to *zero*, if the effective

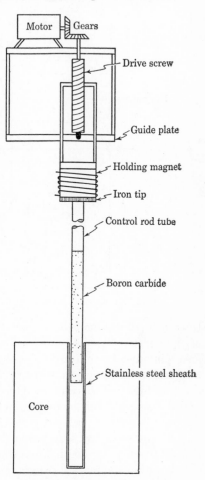

Fig. 7.6. Control rod mechanism.

multiplication constant were unity before the rod enters, and is then reduced below unity by the absorption due to the rod? The answer lies in the fact that temperature effects and control rod effects must be integrated. Assume that the reactor is operating at a power level of 10 kw, k is exactly 1.00, and the solution temperature is 80°C. The rod is inserted an inch or so. This tends to reduce k and the neutron density drops off exponentially with time. However, the heat generated is

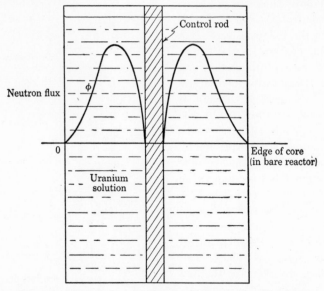

Fig. 7.7. Neutron flux distribution with control rod in place.

thus reduced also, and the temperature of the core drops. By virtue of the negative temperature coefficient of reactivity, k tends to increase in order to compensate for the rod effect. A new steady power level and a different core temperature are reached. Of course if the rod is dropped all the way in, the reduction in k below unity cannot be overcome by any temperature changes. The lower limit of temperature is that of the cooling water. The relation of the variables is shown in Fig. 7.8. The reason for the S-shaped rod-power characteristic is that the rod has less effect on the neutron flux when it is barely within the reactor (where the flux is low anyway) than when it is moving through the region of high flux, at the center of the core. Similarly, when it is nearly through its full motion in the region of low flux, the added absorption resulting from a given displacement downward is small.

The analysis of the value of a given control rod in suppressing neutron activity is best obtained by experimental measurement, particularly for cases in which the rod is located asymmetrically in the vessel. An understanding of the effects can be gained however, by examining an idealized geometry. Let us take a spherical, bare,

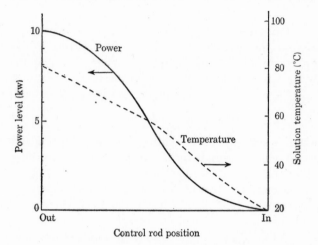

Fig. 7.8. Relation of power level, solution temperature, and control rod position for slow rod removal.

homogeneous water-moderated reactor of pure U^{235} in solution. We ask what effect the insertion of a *spherical* absorber has on critical mass. A rough estimate of critical size without the extra absorption can be obtained by application of the principles of Chapter 6, although it is known that the simple theory is least accurate for light water systems. For the case of a spherical bare reactor containing a water solution of pure U^{235} at an atomic ratio $N_H/N_{U^{235}} = 500$, the infinite multiplication constant is $k_\infty = 1.68$. The critical radius is computed to be close to 24 cm and the mass is 5 kg. (This radius is about 20 per cent higher than experimental values, but the result may be used for approximate calculations.) The thermal neutron flux distribution in a sphere is given by $\phi = \phi_c (\sin Kr)/Kr$ where ϕ_c is the flux at the center and $K = \pi/R$. Suppose that a cadmium or boron sphere of radius a were now inserted in the middle of the core. The flux would be absorbed out in the vicinity of the sphere, and k for the reactor would go below one. We may bring it back to the self-sustaining condition by adding more U^{235}, or by the more abstract method of expanding the core, keeping the same chemical concentration of fuel. In this new critical reactor, the flux will have a distribution

$$\phi \sim \frac{\sin K(r-a)}{Kr}$$

where the flux goes to zero at the surface of the absorbing sphere a distance from the center $r = a$. The flux must also go to zero at the new critical radius R_1, i.e., $K(R_1 - a)$ must be equal to π. The composition of the solution being unchanged, K is still π/R. Thus we obtain the relation between the old and new critical radii

$$R_1 = R + a$$

In words, this states that the addition of a shell of fuel of thickness a to a reactor will compensate for the presence of the absorbing sphere. (More rigorously, the correction should be $a' = a - 0.71\lambda_t$ where λ_t is the transport mean free path of the core material, since the flux effectively goes to zero slightly inside the geometric surface of the absorber.) The value of the control sphere in effective grams of uranium can be estimated. The ratio of the masses before and after is

$$\frac{m_1}{m} = \left(\frac{R_1}{R}\right)^3 = \left(1 + \frac{a'}{R}\right)^3 \simeq 1 + \frac{3a'}{R}$$

or

$$\frac{dm}{m} \simeq \frac{3a'}{R}$$

As stated in Section 7.4, the variation of k with mass is

$$\frac{dk}{k} = \frac{2}{3}\frac{dm}{m}\left(1 - \frac{k}{k_\infty}\right)$$

or

$$\frac{dk}{k} = \frac{2a'}{R}\left(1 - \frac{k}{k_\infty}\right)$$

As numerical illustration, let us find the effect of a cadmium sphere 1 in. in diameter. Taking a value of λ_t for water as 0.5 cm, we find $a' = 1.27 - 0.35 = 0.92$ cm. Thus

$$\frac{dk}{k} = \frac{(2)(0.92)}{(24)}\left(1 - \frac{1}{1.68}\right) = 0.031$$

Removal of the sphere at the critical point would result in a 3.1 per cent increase of multiplication constant. It must be reiterated that calculations such as the above are only of qualitative value in establishing control rod effects.

7.6 The swimming pool reactor

Another type of reactor in which the active material is essentially uniformly mixed with the moderator is the so-called "swimming pool" reactor. Ingenious use is made of water for a triple purpose, as moderator, coolant and shield. Its design is remarkably simple, consisting of a lattice of fuel elements immersed in a large pool of water, as sketched in Fig. 7.9. Convection in the tank water pro-

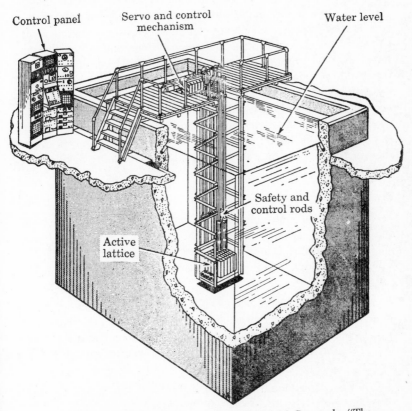

Control panel   Servo and control   Water level
                         mechanism

Safety and
control rods

Active
lattice

Fig. 7.9. Swimming pool reactor. [From W. M. Breazeale, "The 'Swimming Pool'—A Low Cost Research Reactor." *Nucleonics*, November (1952). Copyright, 1952, by McGraw-Hill Publishing Co.. Inc.]

vides the necessary cooling. Each active element contains between 30 and 40 g of enriched (90%) U^{235} in the form of thin uranium-aluminum alloy plates clad in aluminum, 3 in. wide, 24 in. long. Assuming a ratio of aluminum to water volume of 0.3, an alloy of 77.3% Al, 22.7% U by weight, and 37.5 g of U^{235} per plate, one deduces that the active layer is around 0.050 in. thick and the coating is 0.025 in. thick. Groups of five plates $\frac{1}{2}$ in. apart form bundles that engage in sockets at the bottom of the water tank. The total mass of U^{235} ranges from 2.4 to 3.5 kg, depending on whether or not a BeO reflector is used and on the nature of experimental openings. A thermal flux of $5.8 \times 10^{11}/cm^2$-sec and a power level of 100 kw may be obtained. One of the important advantages of the swimming pool type is that fission products are contained within the fuel elements. In the event of plate rupture and resultant contamination, the tank water may be drained and refilled. The power level of reactors of the swimming pool type would appear to be limited only by the rapidity with which heat can be removed by the cooling water. The convection cooling could presumably be replaced by forced circulation cooling. The coolant is in more intimate contact with the fuel and the distance the fission heat must be transferred is much smaller than in the case of the water boiler, which gives more flexibility for increasing the power.

Problems

7.1 From the following data on natural uranyl sulfate solution and molecular weights, determine the value of the atomic ratio N_H/N_U: weight of 1 liter, 1200 g, density of solution at 25°C = $0.9970 \times 0.01352K$ where K is the number of grams of U per 100 cm^3 of solution.

7.2 Estimate the activity of Cl^{38}, half-life 38.5 min, induced in a cubic centimeter of reactor cooling water, with a chlorine content of 5 parts per million (atoms per molecule of water). Use data of Section 7.2 as needed. σ_a for Cl^{37} is 0.6 barns, its abundance is 24.6 per cent.

7.3 How long should the water in Problem 7.2 be held to reduce the chlorine activity to 10^{-5} $\mu c/cm^3$ of water?

7.4 What size storage tank is needed to achieve the attenuation to 10^{-5} $\mu c/cm^3$ assuming continuous flow through it?

7.5 Find the activity due to the presence of the stable isotope Mg^{26}, with an Mg content of 10 ppm (t_H for Mg^{27} is 10 min.).

7.6 Find the activity of the fission gas Kr^{85}, half-life 4.5 hr, produced by a 6-hr operating period of a reactor at 10 kw. How long would this accumulation have to be held to reduce the activity to 0.01 c?

7.7 A homogeneous enriched-uranium graphite reactor is proposed having a value of k_∞ of 1.25. How does its temperature coefficient compare with that of the water boiler? The *linear* expansion coefficient of graphite is $7.86 \times 10^{-6}/°C$.

7.8 Estimate the absolute change in k of the reactor of Section 7.4 due to an increase in temperature from 20°C to 30°C. Hint: integration of the formula for dk/dT may be needed.

7.9 Verify the relation between mass and multiplication constant

$$\frac{dk}{k} = \frac{2}{3} \cdot \frac{dm}{m}\left(1 - \frac{k}{k_\infty}\right)$$

7.10 How much added U^{235} will increase the multiplication constant of a homogeneous water reactor by 0.76 per cent? Let $m = 20$ kg, $k_\infty = 1.6$.

7.11 Plans are made for installing a tall cylindrical storage container of 2-ft diameter for dilute U^{235} solutions in a chemical processing plant. What size cadmium lined tube would you propose to run down the axis of the tank in order to make the system safe for concentrations as high as 3 per cent U^{235} by weight of solution? Hint: see the expression for the flux distribution in a cylinder, Section 6.4.

7.12 An alternative container for storing the solutions in Problem 7.11 is a broad flat rectangular tank. What maximum height of the vessel would you recommend? Discuss possible applications of such a container in a homogeneous reactor system.

7.13 Compute the thicknesses of layers of B^{10}, B and Cd that will reduce an incident thermal flux to 0.01 of its surface value. From the nature of the cross-section curves in Fig. 2.3, can you suggest a reason that boron might be preferable to cadmium for use as a control rod?

7.14 The nuclear reactions induced in cadmium and boron by neutron absorption are

$$_{48}Cd^{113} + _{0}n^{1} \rightarrow _{48}Cd^{114} + \gamma$$
$$_{5}B^{10} + _{0}n^{1} \rightarrow _{3}Li^{7} + _{2}He^{4}$$

Explain why the boron shield (Section 7.1, and Fig. 7.1) is preferable, knowing that one could install a cadmium sheet of equivalent absorptive thickness.

7.15 Estimate the thermal utilization of the swimming pool core, using the following data:

Al/H_2O volume ratio = 0.3

U^{235} mass = 3 kg (90% enrichment)

Core dimensions = 12 in. $\times$ 12 in. $\times$ 24 in.

Number of plates = 5 per fuel element

Number of fuel elements = 16

What is the ratio N_H/N_{235}?

References

Los Alamos Scientific Laboratory Reports and Papers:

BAKER, C. P., H. K. DAGHLIAN, G. FRIEDLANDER, M. G. HOLLOWAY, D. W. KERST, and R. E. SCHREIBER, *Water Boiler*, AECD-3063. September 4, 1944. Description of LOPO.

BENTZEN, F. L., R. E. CARTER, J. HINTON, L. D. P. KING, J. G. NEVENZEL, R. E. SCHREIBER, J. W. STARNER, and P. H. WATKINS, *High Power Water Boiler*, AECD-3065. September 19, 1945.

"An Enriched Homogeneous Nuclear Reactor." *Rev. Sci. Inst.*, *22*, 489 (1951).

KING, L. D. P., *The Los Alamos Homogeneous Reactor, SUPO Model*, LA-1301. February 7, 1952.

HOFFMAN, F. DE, *Criticality of the Water Boiler and Effective Number of Delayed Neutrons*, AECD-3051. December 8, 1944.

HINTON, J., *Dependence of Reactivity of the Water Boiler on the Mass of 25 in the Sphere*, AECD-2956. December 27, 1945.

KING, L. D. P. and R. E. SCHREIBER, *Distribution and Power Measurements in the Water Boiler*, AECD-3054. October 19, 1944.

BUNKER, M. E., R. P. HAMMOND, L. D. P. KING, J. A. LEARY, and W. R. WYKOFF, *The Recombination System of the Los Alamos Homogeneous Reactor*, LA-1337. March 6, 1952.

North Carolina State College Reports and Papers:

BECK, C. K., A. C. MENIUS, G. N. WEBB, A. W. WALTNER, P. B.
   LEONARD, E. H. STINSON, and J. D. PAULSON, *Program Admin-
   istration and Installation Design of the Nuclear Reactor Project at
   North Carolina State College*, ORO-33. July 5, 1950.

BECK, C. K., "Nuclear Reactor Project at North Carolina State College." *Nucleonics*, December (1950) p. 5.

BECK, C. K., A. C. MENIUS, R. L. MURRAY, N. UNDERWOOD, A. W.
   WALTNER, and G. N. WEBB, *Further Design Features of the
   Nuclear Reactor at North Carolina State College*, AECU-1986.
   January, 1952.

MURRAY, R. L., "Storage of Radioactive Gases from Reactor Operation." *Nucleonics*, December (1952) p. 52.

Oak Ridge National Laboratory:

BREAZEALE, W. M., "The 'Swimming Pool,' a Low Cost Research
   Reactor." *Nucleonics*, November (1952) p. 56.

CHAPTER 8

REACTOR START-UP AND OPERATION

The method of reactor control by an absorbing "rod" was described in terms of slowly effected changes in the chapter just completed. At all times, the absorption and generation of neutrons were in balance. Were a control rod to be suddenly removed, however, the balance would be upset, the neutrons would multiply more rapidly and the power level would flash up. In the present chapter we shall look into the time dependent behavior of a reactor following a sudden change in k.

8.1 The transient reactor behavior

Care must be taken in the design of a reactor that the effective multiplication constant is very close to the critical* value of unity, with an excess sufficient only to take care of burn-up, temperature effects or poisoning. In any event the excess k must be less than that the control rods are expected to handle. The excess, $k - 1$, is labeled δk and called "excess reactivity." Assuming that the best estimates predict k to be equal to one, it is mandatory that the initial assembly and start-up of the reactor should proceed with great caution. This need can be appreciated by considering the transient behavior of a reactor. First take a case in which k is much larger than unity. If k is the number of neutrons left after one has completed its cycle, then $k - 1$, or δk is the number of extra neutrons per cycle *per starting neutron*. For n neutrons the gain each cycle is $n\delta k$. If we let the cycle time or neutron lifetime be l seconds, then the gain in neutrons each second is $n\delta k/l$. Let us put this result in the form of an equation for the rate of change of neutrons with time

$$\frac{dn}{dt} = \frac{n\delta k}{l}$$

If at time zero we had n_0 neutrons, at time t there will be

$$n = n_0 e^{(\delta k/l)t}$$

* The term "critical" will refer to an accumulation for which k is 1.0. If k is smaller, the system is "subcritical"; if k is larger, it is "supercritical."

The lifetime may be estimated from the thermal velocity v (the slowing down time may be neglected) and the average distance a neutron travels along its path before being absorbed in fissionable material, $\lambda_a = 1/\Sigma_a$ (see Section 2.7):

$$l = \frac{\lambda_a}{v} = \frac{1}{v\,\Sigma_a}$$

Take the absorption mean free path λ_a as 40 cm, v is 2200 m/sec so that $l \simeq 2 \times 10^{-4}$ sec. Now we may see how rapid the rise of neutron level is for an excess reactivity of as little as 0.01, or 1 per cent.

$$n/n_0 = e^{[0.01/(2\times 10^{-4})]t} = e^{50t}$$

At the end of 0.01 sec, n/n_0 has risen to $e^{0.5} = 1.65$; by 0.1 sec it is $e^5 = 148$, in 1 sec the multiplication has become e^{50}, which is an astronomical number, 5×10^{21}. In the case of a water boiler, temperature and bubbling effects set in to prevent the runaway condition, but in other reactor types, the possibility of near-bomb action is clearly suggested by the rapid exponential rise. An alternative expression that is convenient comes from the introduction of the reactor period $T = l/\delta k$.

$$n/n_0 = e^{t/T}$$

T is sometimes called the "e folding time," meaning that during every T seconds of operation, n/n_0 increases by a factor $e = 2.718$. For the example above, T is 0.02 sec.

The estimates just made did not take into account the effect of "delayed" neutrons. About 0.755 per cent of the 2.5 neutrons per

TABLE 8.1

DELAYED NEUTRON DATA

Emitter i	Half-life $(t_H)_i$ (sec)	Energy (mev)	Yield β_i	Mean life τ_i (sec)
1	0.05	...	0.00025	0.07
2	0.43	420	0.00085	0.62
3	1.52	620	0.00241	2.19
4	4.51	430	0.00213	6.52
5	22.0	560	0.00166	31.7
6	55.6	250	0.00025	80.3
			$\beta = 0.00755$	$\bar{\tau} = 12.2$ (weighted average)

fission are emitted by fission fragments as radioactive decay products, coming off statistically rather than instantaneously. The characteristic half-lives of the emitters are known, ranging from 0.05 to 55.6 sec, as shown in Table 8.1. For values of δk less than 0.755 per cent, the average half-life of the emitters (about 8.5 sec) is the determining factor in the cycle lifetime rather than the time between thermalization and absorption. For $\delta k < 0.00755$, the delayed neutrons have an opportunity to play their role in slowing down the cycle, and the neutron level rises much more slowly. The reactor is in the "delayed critical" condition. When $\delta k > 0.00755$, we revert back to the dangerous rise described before and the reactor is termed "prompt critical," for the reason that multiplication is based on neutrons emitted promptly, not delayed. The danger associated with this region depends on the value of the lifetime of the neutrons. An atomic bomb must be strongly prompt critical to be effective; in a graphite-uranium thermal reactor all efforts should be made to avoid such a condition; the water boiler fortunately has the "built-in" safety feature of a negative coefficient of reactivity that reduces the danger to a flash-up that is soon damped out.

The basic mathematical description of the effect of delayed neutrons is now presented. A reactor that has a slight excess multiplication $\delta k < \beta$ will rise in neutron density with time according to a sum of seven exponential terms

$$n = \sum_{m=1}^{7} a_m e^{-t/T_m}$$

where T_m are the several solutions for T in the algebraic equation for T called the "inhour formula"

$$\delta k = \frac{l}{T} + \sum_{i=1}^{i=6} \frac{\beta_i \tau_i}{T + \tau_i}$$

Here l is the lifetime of thermal neutrons, β_i is the fraction of the ith type of emitter (for example, in the case of the 55.6-sec emitter, β_i is 0.00025), and τ_i is its half-life divided by 0.693, which is called the "mean life." The mean life $1/\lambda_i$ for the emitter is the time it takes for the parent element to decay by a factor of e rather than of 2. The effective period may be obtained approximately by assuming a weighted average value of the various τ_i, labeled $\bar{\tau}$ and replacing the sum in the inhour formula by a single term

$$\delta k \simeq \frac{l}{T} + \frac{\beta \bar{\tau}}{T + \bar{\tau}}$$

The equation to be solved for T is now quadratic. The largest of the two roots, which is called the dominant period, is approximately

$$T = \frac{l + (\beta - \delta k)\bar{\tau}}{\delta k}$$

Now β, the sum of the fractions of the different emitters is 0.00755, and $\bar{\tau}$ is 12.2 sec. Consider again the reactor for which l is 2×10^{-4} sec, with $\delta k = 0.0025$. Then

$$T = \frac{2 \times 10^{-4} + (0.00755 - 0.0025)(12.2)}{0.0025}$$

$$T \simeq 25 \text{ sec}$$

This rise is very slow in comparison with the result for $\delta k = 0.01$ neglecting delayed neutrons. This demonstrates numerically that there is a very great difference between a reactor with $\delta k = 0.01$ and a reactor with $\delta k = 0.0025$. It is often convenient to interpret the sum $l + (\beta - \delta k)\bar{\tau}$ as an effective lifetime l_e, so that the period may be again written simply

$$T = l_e/\delta k$$

The formula for l_e is applicable for both rising (supercritical) and falling (subcritical) periods within the range

$$-0.00755 < \delta k < +0.00755$$

It is necessary only to note that the sign of δk should be reversed for calculations of the falling period.

It should be noted that if δk is much greater than 0.00755, one may neglect delayed neutron effects, and the inhour formula reduces to $\delta k = l/T$ which is just what we first used to compute the period T. The existence of delayed neutrons is one of the fortunate small factors found in nature, reminiscent of the density variation of water near 4°C that prevents lakes from freezing permanently solid. Isbin and Gorman have devised useful graphs of the coefficients a_m and the

reciprocal periods $1/T_m$ (A_j and S_j in their notation) for a variety
of δk values in the range 0 to 0.004. The variation of computed
neutron flux density with time for a graphite-uranium reactor for
which the neutron lifetime is 10^{-3} seconds, is plotted in Fig. 8.1 for

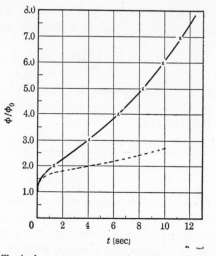

Fig. 8.1. Typical reactor response including delayed neutrons.
$\delta k = 0.003$. Solid line shows the analytical solution; dashed line, the
two term method; crosses, the kinetic simulator. [After H. S. Isbin
and J. W. Gorman, "Applications of the Pile Kinetic Equations."
Nucleonics, November (1952). Copyright, 1952, by McGraw-Hill
Publishing Co., Inc.]

illustration of the typical response to a step change in reactivity
of 0.003.

8.2 Start-up procedures

Certain precautions are employed in the initial start-up of all reactors
to make sure the system does not get out of hand. In this section
we shall describe the principles behind these precautionary tests.
It will be assumed that all testing of the system prior to the accumulation of active material has been completed. For example, the
cooling system will have been checked for leaks; the instruments will
have been tested and calibrated by bringing artificial sources near
the detecting elements; the control rods will have been operated.

It will be convenient to use the experimental water boiler as a specific reactor to illustrate a start-up procedure.

Before admitting any active material, the presence of an artificial neutron *source* must be guaranteed, and a decision on its proper location made. A typical source consists of pulverized and compressed mixtures of radium and beryllium, or polonium and beryllium, that emit neutrons by nuclear reaction. Alpha particles emitted by the heavy element are absorbed in $_4Be^9$ to produce neutrons and $_6C^{12}$.* At first glance this would appear to be "carrying coals to Newcastle," since a reactor is such a copious neutron source itself. It is dangerous, however, to assemble fissionable material without considerably larger neutron background than that provided by stray cosmic rays or spontaneous fission. The critical mass may be reached and exceeded without appreciable indication on the instruments. One neutron, with a k of 1.1, will give 1000 neutrons in around 70 cycles. This may be registered on the detector, however, as a negligibly small counting rate.

It is preferable to locate the source within the core rather than at its side, in order to obtain the most sensitive indication of multiplication. A comparison of the two geometrical arrangements, "good" and "poor," shown in Fig. 8.2 will help to demonstrate this point. If

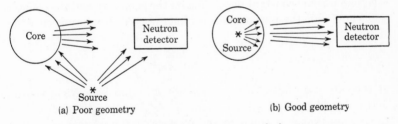

(a) Poor geometry   (b) Good geometry

Fig. 8.2. Source arrangements in reactor during start-up.

there is a large constant neutron supply to the detector, as in case (a), the effect on neutron level of adding material is proportionately smaller. The difference is quite pronounced for a bare reactor.

* Source "strengths" are measured in curies of the radioactive element. The neutron yield from a Ra-Be source is about 1.6×10^7 n/sec per curie; that from a Po-Be source is 3×10^6 n/sec per curie. The photo-neutron source Sb^{124}-Be yields around 3×10^5 n/sec per curie. At least 10^6 n/sec are desirable for reactor start-up.

The effect of the source neutrons on counting rate may be evaluated in a semi-quantitative manner. One of the neutrons emitted by it will proceed through the reactor, slow down, be absorbed, and on the average give k neutrons. (The reactor does not distinguish between fission neutrons and those from the source.) Each of these in turn will produce k more, and so on. The total number of neutrons produced, including the initial one, is the sum

$$1 + k + k^2 + k^3 + \ldots$$

For k less than unity, as will be the case during the assembly of material, this sum can be written as $1/(1 - k)$.* With the source emitting S neutrons per second, the total number produced each second is $S/(1 - k)$. Of course, a finite time is needed to produce all these neutrons, but if a steady state has been reached, with a continuous supply of source neutrons, this also will be the *rate* of production. Now the number of neutrons that escape from the reactor and strike the counter will be proportional to the total number produced. We need not know what the factor is, but may write the counting rate simply as

$$C = \frac{AS}{1 - k}$$

where A is some constant depending on the geometry and the counter efficiency. For the purpose this formula is used, we may even write it as

$$C = \frac{1}{1 - k}$$

If the core were filled with plain water, k would be zero, of course, and C would be 1 (in arbitrary units). As a first approximation, let us assume that k is equal to the fraction of the critical mass that has been added, and tabulate the counting rate as a function of k.

k	C	$1/C$	k	C	$1/C$
0	1	1	0.9	10	0.1
0.10	1.11	0.9	0.99	100	0.01
0.25	1.33	0.75	0.9999	10,000	0.0001
0.50	2	0.5	1	∞	0
0.75	4	0.25			

* To check this, expand $(1 - k)^{-1}$ by the binomial theorem, or better, refer to the sum of the *geometric series* as given in algebra books.

The following table lists experimental data taken at the start-up of the Raleigh research reactor.

Step	Time	Mass of U^{235} (g)	Δm (approx)	Volume (cm³)	Solution level (cm)	$C = $ counts/ 5 min	$\dfrac{1000}{C}$
1.	11:57 am	zero		6,652	12.9	924	1.082
			(400)				
2.	2:50 pm	398.30		6,652	13.8	1993	0.502
			(100)				
3.	4:25 pm	498.30		8,323	15.8	2598	0.385
			(100)				
4.	5:43 pm	598.44		9,801	18.5	3536	0.283
			(100)				
5.	7:45 pm	698.64		11,022	20.8	7584	0.132
			(50)				
6.	9:12 pm	748.91		11,700	22.0	16656	0.0600
			(25)				
7.	10:50 pm	773.73		12,255	23.0	48128	0.0208
			(10)				
8.	11:30 pm	783.87		12,477	23.3	...	...
			(4)				
9.	12:18 am	787.95		12,566	23.5	...	...

Estimated critical mass, 787.0 g.

At each stage of the addition of material the counting rate is observed and recorded. A graph of the *reciprocal* of the counting rate $1/C$ is plotted, as a function of the mass of uranium added, as in Fig. 8.3. Note that as the critical mass is approached, the reciprocal counting rate goes to zero. Successive extrapolations of the curve through the available set of points to the horizontal axis provide ever improving predictions of the critical size or mass. As the critical point is approached, the amount of material that is added between taking counting rates is cut down.

8.3 Tests near the critical point

An auxiliary method of observation is adopted as the reactor gets very close to the critical point. Having established the critical mass rather accurately by reciprocal count graphs, material is added even more slowly than before. The neutron flux, as represented continuously on a moving paper tape, will have a steady value at any given mass of material. As uranium is added, the indicator responds, showing that the flux is rising. If the system is still subcritical, the quick removal of the neutron source from its original position will be followed by a decline of the neutron flux with time. This can be

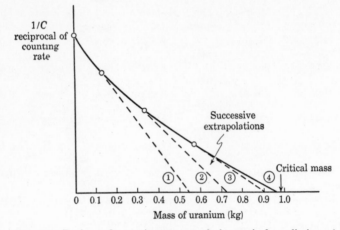

Fig. 8.3. Reciprocal counting-rate graph for typical prediction of critical mass.

attributed to the reduction in effective S in the counting rate formula. Removal of the source when the assembly is exactly critical yields a steady neutron level, since the system is operating without "assistance." If the mass is slightly above the critical value, the trend upward that has started on the last admission of material will continue, even with the source completely out. These trends have been described in terms of the addition of uranium; movements of the control rod made in conjunction with the additions in solution will give similar responses. A typical sequence of steps and the corresponding indications on the recorder are shown in Fig. 8.4. The graph variations may be explained by the solutions of the general differential equation for the neutron density in the reactor:

$$\frac{dn}{dt} = \frac{\delta k}{l} n + S$$

The new term S accounts for the neutron contribution of the artificial source. Since δk is defined as $k - 1$, its value will be negative if the reactor is subcritical, zero if critical and positive if supercritical.

We may describe a variety of situations by adaptations of this single equation.

Case A. A source is dropped from a shielded position to a point

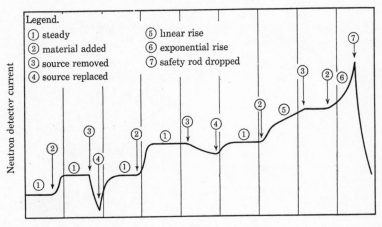

Fig. 8.4. The approach to critical.

within a subcritical reactor at time zero, when n is zero. Now $\delta k = k - 1 = -|\delta k|$, where the quantity $|\delta k|$ is inherently *positive*. The equation becomes

$$\frac{dn}{dt} + \frac{|\delta k|}{l} n = S$$

for which the solution is the familiar growth equation

$$n = \frac{Sl}{|\delta k|} (1 - e^{-|\delta k|t/l})$$

The number of neutrons in the system rises from zero to a maximum value, for large t, of

$$n_\infty = \frac{Sl}{1 - k}$$

This saturation response has been observed in several effects previously. See Fig. 8.5a. The form of this result, proportional to $1/(1 - k)$, agrees with the analysis of the source effect in Section 8.2.

Case B. The source is removed quickly from the subcritical reactor at a time $t = 0$ when the neutron level is constant, n_0. Since the term S is now zero, the equation reduces to

$$\frac{dn}{dt} = \frac{-|\delta k|}{l} n$$

the solution of which is a simple exponential decay formula

$$n = n_0 e^{-|\delta k|t/l}$$

If k is close to zero, $|\delta k| = 1 - k$ is larger than if k is close to unity.

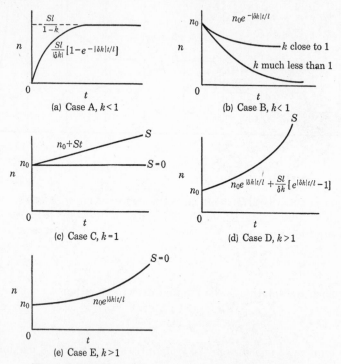

Fig. 8.5. Solutions of the neutron multiplication equation.

The rate of decline of n with time thus becomes smaller as the critical point is reached. See Fig. 8.5b.

Case C. Enough material is added to make the reactor exactly critical, but the source is left in the system. The equation is now

$$dn/dt = S$$

which predicts a linear rise in level

$$n = n_0 + St$$

as shown in Fig. 8.5c. A special case arises if the source is removed from a critical reactor. Then $dn/dt = 0$, meaning that n remains constant at level n_0.

Case D. The reactor is slightly supercritical, with $\delta k = k - 1$ a positive number. The equation with the source in place becomes

$$\frac{dn}{dt} - \frac{|\delta k|}{l} n = S$$

Since the level at $t = 0$ is n_0, the answer is

$$n = n_0 e^{|\delta k|t/l} + \frac{S}{|\delta k|}\left(e^{|\delta k|t/l} - 1\right)$$

The first term describes the multiplication of the original n_0 neutrons; the second term gives the growth of those supplied by the source. The rise is exponential, as shown in Fig. 8.5d.

Case E. If the source is removed ($S = 0$) at $t = 0$, $n = n_0$, with the reactor supercritical, the rise is still exponential, Fig. 8.5e, but only the first term in Case D is present.

$$n = n_0 e^{|\delta k|t/l}$$

It must be pointed out that the analysis given above is intended to give only a qualitative understanding of the trends since the complex effects of delayed neutrons are neglected. The formulas can be applied with reasonable accuracy even when delayed neutrons are considered by replacing l by l_e, the effective lifetime, described in Section 8.1.

Having reached the critical point, further adjustments are made by use of the control rod as described in Chapter 7. The power level is brought up slowly to the operating value by the removal of the control rod; the excess reactivity is zero except for the time it takes for temperature effects to compensate for changes in rod position.

8.4 Safety practices

When the word "reactor" is heard, one is likely to think first of some large machine like those at Hanford. There the construction and instrumentation of the reactor is completed before the system is loaded with fissionable material and all operations are performed remotely, behind thick concrete protective shields. With careful planning, such a machine may be operated more safely than many non-nuclear manufacturing processes. For every safe reactor that is constructed, however, there are dozens of experimental assemblies of fissionable material, each of which can be called a reactor in the general sense. Because of the transitory nature of these tests, the desire for quick answers, and the laboratory conditions under which they are performed, the chances of a radiation accident are tremendously increased. The number of serious accidents in the atomic energy project fortunately has been very small. In an expanding reactor program, however, the potential danger is increased, particularly as the novelty of such machines wears off. Certain basic administrative and operation policies that have been developed to provide some measure of protection in reactor experiments are reviewed below.

(1) Whenever practicable, the apparatus is to be arranged so that the active assembly is controlled remotely. Observations are to be made from a separate control area by the display of electrical signals or through shielded viewing windows.

(2) The plans for the experiment are carefully laid out in advance, and understood by all participants. The expected behavior of the system is reviewed, but possible alternative responses are discussed. The proper action to be taken in case of run-away is anticipated.

(3) Each experimenter is assigned some definite function such as adding fuel, adjusting controls, reading instruments, recording data, or directing the operations. It is imperative in this connection that each person knows where others are stationed and what they are doing at all times. One person who is not actively engaged in manipulations should serve as coordinator of the experiment. Even though each member of the team is expected to weigh the consequences of his actions in terms of safety, the coordinator is least distracted by the physical equipment.

(4) No adjustments to the assembly are to be made without having a positively-acting safety device such as a spring- or gravity-actuated absorbing rod, separation mechanism or a "dump valve" that will render the system safe under any conditions. For example, it is forbidden to lower a safety rod and subsequently relocate the fuel to gain additional reactivity.

(5) All manipulations are to be made deliberately, in sequence, and reversibly. Two examples of non-reversible operations in the building of a stack of fuel elements and moderator are: (a) one in which the addition of one slug or block causes a rise in temperature of the assembly and consequent reduction in neutron losses that will not be compensated by removal of the added unit; and (b) addition of a fuel element to a configuration that may shift to a more compact form, reducing neutron leakage and increasing the multiplication constant sharply. Assuming that the manipulations are actually reversible, the operator must still be able to remove one unit as quickly as it was introduced in the event that an excess of reactivity is met.

The policies listed above may appear so stringent that ingenuity is stifled and some important observations on the experiment may be missed. They are necessary, however, because of the human tendency to become careless when familiarity with surroundings is developed. It is very easy to forget about neutrons and gamma rays when they cannot be seen or felt.*

Problems

8.1 What is the thermal lifetime for a graphite-U^{235} reactor with an atom ratio $N_C/N_U = 2000$?

8.2 Calculate the reactor period from the answer in Problem 8.1 for an excess reactivity of 0.015.

8.3 Find the second root of the equation

$$\delta k = \frac{l}{T} + \frac{\beta \bar{\tau}}{T + \bar{\tau}}$$

assuming that $\delta k \ll \beta$. How does this period compare in size with the dominant period?

---

* Those who knew and admired Dr. Louis Slotin, who died as a result of a radiation accident at Los Alamos in 1946, can wholeheartedly subscribe to the practices we have discussed.

An assembly related to the atomic weapon accidentally became prompt critical. Without hesitation, and knowing that he would receive a fatal radiation dose, Dr. Slotin dispersed the accumulation to protect the others in the team, just as he had earlier instructed his pupils to do. He continued to advise in the plans for the reactor experiments, and assisted in the medical investigation of effects of his irradiation until his death several days later.

8.4 Find the principal reactor period for a system in which l is 10^{-3}, $\delta k = 0.001$.

8.5 The recording instruments for a reactor have a provision for changing the reading on the scales by a factor of 10. If it takes 5 sec to stabilize the instrument after such a change, what limits should be put on the allowed rise in δk for a reactor for which $l = 5 \times 10^{-4}$?

8.6 A reactor with neutron lifetime 2×10^{-4} sec is operating steadily at 10 kw, with the heat that is generated being removed by cooling water. The reactivity is suddenly increased by 0.005. Estimate the time that would be required for the temperature effect (see Section 7.4) to nullify this δk. Let the temperature coefficient be $2 \times 10^{-4}/°C$. Discuss any assumptions or approximations that must be made in solving this problem.

8.7 The following data were taken in the start-up of the Raleigh Research Reactor:

Time (sec)	0	180
Recorder current (arbitrary units)	27	9

Assuming that 1 g of U^{235} corresponds to $\delta k = 0.0002$, estimate how many grams must be added to bring the reactor to the critical point.

8.8 Calculate the period and excess mass of the same reactor in Problem 8.7, from the data below:

Time (sec)	0	180
Recorder current (arbitrary units)	27	40

References

FERMI, ENRICO, "Experimental Production of a Divergent Chain Reaction." *Amer. Journ. Phys.*, December (1952). Construction of and measurements on the Chicago reactor CP-1, 1942.

ALLARDICE, CORBIN, and EDWARD R. TRAPNELL, *The First Pile*, TID-392. Oak Ridge, Tenn.: Technical Information Service, AEC, November 17, 1949. Narrative account of first chain reaction based on recollections of scientists present.

ANDERSON, HERBERT L., *Neutrons from Alpha Emitters*, Report No. 3. Washington, D. C.: National Research Council Nuclear Science Series, December, 1948.

WATTENBERG, A., *Photo-Neutron Sources*, Report No. 6. Washington, D. C.: National Research Council Nuclear Science Series, July, 1949.

SOODAK, HARRY and E. C. CAMPBELL, *Elementary Pile Theory*. New York: John Wiley & Sons, 1950, Secs. 16, 17.

GLASSTONE, SAMUEL and MILTON C. EDLUND, *The Elements of Nuclear Reactor Theory*. New York: D. Van Nostrand Co., 1952, Chap. X.

ISBIN, H. S. and J. W. GORMAN, "Applications of Pile Kinetic Equations." *Nucleonics*, November (1952).

HUGHES, D. J., J. DABBS, A. CAHN, and D. HALL, "Delayed Neutrons from Fission of U^{235}," *Phys. Rev.*, *73*, 111 (1948).

CHAPTER 9

MATERIALS OF REACTOR
CONSTRUCTION

The choice of appropriate materials for various components of a reactor—fuel, moderator, coolant, piping, reflector, and control rods—is based on the required function of the part, as in any machine. The properties that are unusual are those having to do with neutrons, i.e., the nuclear absorption and radioactive properties of the substances. In many cases the standard mechanical features are still important, but modified for nuclear reasons. In this chapter we shall list the different components and discuss some of their special requirements. No attempt is made to achieve completeness.*

9.1 Fuel

The obvious requirement that the fuel be fissionable must be qualified to include the number of fission neutrons per absorption, η. If one is designing a reactor for power production only, then it is necessary to obtain only one neutron (plus) to replace each one formed on the previous fission. The η of natural uranium, 1.32, may be sufficient. If, however, it is desirable to have extra neutrons for absorption in an inert material such as thorium for the generation of U^{233}, this number of neutrons per absorption may be too small, and enriched uranium with η approaching 2.1 would have to be used. Except for the serious health hazard, plutonium would appear to be good reactor fuel, since 3 neutrons per fission are released. It should be noted, however, that plutonium is a reactor product in itself and thus its availability must be guaranteed before a design is contemplated. U^{233} is in the same category, of course.

The second consideration is the chemical form in which the fuel is to be put. Uranyl sulfate (UO_2SO_4) and uranyl nitrate $UO_2(NO_3)_2$

---

* Reference should be made to the special report, "Materials and Equipment for Reactors." *Nucleonics*, June (1953) for many more tables and a more thorough discussion than is attempted here. Good bibliographies on different aspects are also provided in the above report.

were used at various times in the Los Alamos water boiler. There seems to be no reason why various other compounds such as the hydride, carbide or fluoride might not be useful, in particular for homogeneous reactors. Although the first pile at Chicago contained some uranium oxide (UO_2), most of the reactors in existence are constructed of uranium metal.

Table 9.1 gives some of the useful physical properties of the metal.

TABLE 9.1

PHYSICAL CONSTANTS OF URANIUM METAL

Atomic weight: 238.07

Density: 18.685 at 13°C (18.7 assumed for most calculations)

Melting point: 1100–1150°C (2012–2102°F)

Lattice arrangement: alpha (ortho-rhombic) to 665°C (1229°F)
    beta (58-atom cell) 665–775°C (1229–1427°F)
    gamma (body centered cubic) above 775°C (1427°F)

Thermal expansion coefficient (anisotropic):
    28×10^{-6} per °C; -1.4×10^{-6} per °C;
    22.0×10^{-6} per °C along axes a_1, a_2, a_3

Heat capacity: 0.0275 cal/g-°C at 0°C

Heat conductivity: 19 Btu/hr-°F-ft

Electrical resistivity: 60×10^{-6} ohm-cm at 20°C

The phase changes at 1229°F and 1427°F must be considered in the design of a high temperature reactor. In the alpha phase the tensile strength is high, normally 40,000 lb/in.², but with work hardening it is 200,000 lb/in.². The beta phase is brittle, while the gamma phase is very soft and weak. At room temperatures, the metal is stable chemically, but oxidizes violently at temperatures as low as 100°C. In finely divided form, uranium is dangerously pyrophoric so that turnings from metal parts must be bathed with and stored under liquid. It may be corroded readily by water. Low melting-point alloys are formed with a variety of elements: Na, Hg, Pb, Bi, Sb, and Ti. High melting-point alloys are formed with Be, Mg, Al, Cu, Fe, W, Hg, Zn, V, and Th.

9.2 Moderator

The function of the moderator is to reduce neutrons of fission energy to thermal energy within the smallest space and with the least loss. The descriptive term attached to a moderator, "slowing down power" can be given quantitative meaning in the following way. The effectiveness of a moderator in slowing neutrons first depends on the number of collisions per second per unit volume, thus the product of the number of nuclei per unit volume N and the scattering cross section σ_s. Its moderating value also depends on the amount of neutron energy loss achieved in each collision. Analysis of the neutron-nucleus collision mechanism shows that the quantity ξ, defined in Section 2.6 as the average change in $\log_e E$ per collision is independent of the energy at which the collision occurs. It is thus characteristic of the moderator only. Compounding the above factors, one defines the slowing down power (SDP) as

$$(SDP) = N\sigma_s\xi = \Sigma_s\xi$$

A good moderator has a large (SDP). It may be seen from the approximate relation $\xi \simeq 2/(M+1)$ that ξ is larger for the light elements in the order appearing in the periodic chart. Table 9.2

TABLE 9.2

LOGARITHMIC ENERGY LOSS AND SLOWING DOWN POWERS OF LIGHT ELEMENTS

Element	ξ	(SDP)	Element	ξ	(SDP)
H*	1.000	1.32	B	0.176	0.09
D*	0.726	0.16	C	0.159	0.064
He	0.428	...	N†	0.137	0.032
Li	0.264	0.017	O*	0.121	0.016
Be	0.208	0.11			

* Number of atoms as in water.

† Number of atoms as in liquid ammonia, density 0.618 g/cm².

gives accurately computed values of ξ and (SDP). A simple connection exists between the fast diffusion length L_f or age τ and the average slowing down power,

$$\tau = \frac{18.2\lambda_t}{(SDP)}$$

λ_t is the average transport mean free path and 18.2 is the difference between the natural logarithms of the fission energy (2×10^6 ev) and the thermal energy (1/40 ev). Thus the larger (SDP) is, the shorter is the distance required to thermalize neutrons.

The second property of the moderator that must be considered with the slowing down power is the absorption cross section $\Sigma_a = N\sigma_a$, which determines the amount of competition with useful absorption in the fissionable fuel. We may rule out lithium and boron immediately from the list of elements above as having much too high absorption cross sections—70 barns and 750 barns respectively. The cross sections of hydrogen, 0.33 barns and nitrogen, 1.78 barns, are relatively low. In the large quantities of moderator needed, even these elements contribute enough absorption to make them of borderline value for some uses. Although helium has a negligible cross section, its density is too low at ordinary temperatures and pressures to be of any value as a moderator. Only D, Be, and C are left of the lighter elements or isotopes. One finds that most of the present reactors use H_2O, D_2O, and C as moderators.

Of those listed above beryllium is the most unfamiliar to the average person. Two of the principal uses of beryllium in industry have been in light, hard tools of beryllium-copper alloy, and as an ingredient in fluorescent lights. The occurrence of the ore is widespread throughout the world, but in small deposits, which accounts for the high cost, about four cents a gram. A second contributing factor to the high cost is the physiological danger in handling of the element. Only within the last few years the "beryllium poisoning" lung disease has become widely known. The melting point is high (1350°C), but sublimation occurs at a rate of about 0.020 in. per month at 900°C. For reactor use, the oxide, with melting point 2530°C may be preferable.

Two economical rather than nuclear factors that affect the consideration of beryllium are the *availability* and *cost* of materials. They are related in one sense because almost any substance can be mined or fabricated, given enough money. A striking example serves to illustrate the importance of including these factors in any reactor study. Our first inclination might be to choose deuterium as it appears in heavy water as a moderator. The lowest commercial price, that of Norwegian D_2O, is of the order of 25 cents a gram, however. The cost of D_2O in a cubical reactor as small as 15 ft on a side (9.6×10^7 cm^3) would be around 25 million dollars.

9.3 Coolant

Two modes of cooling a reactor are employed in general.

(1) A fluid is passed through annular ducts surrounding metal

slugs. For example, in the Oak Ridge and Brookhaven reactors, high velocity air is used.

(2) Tubes threading a homogeneous uranium-moderator mixture carry the coolant, as in the water boiler.

It is conceivable that the homogeneous mixture itself might be circulated through the reactor and to some external heat exchanger, although the associated radioactivity problems attendant probably would be serious. A type of cooling that is unique in the reactor field is the convective cooling of the swimming pool reactor described in Section 7.6.

The absorption requirement on the medium that removes fission heat from the reactor is similar to but not as stringent as that for the moderator because of the relatively low total volume of coolant that is needed. The coolant must obviously be fluid at the operating temperature of the machine. Its specific heat and thermal conductivity should be high, in order to achieve the maximum heat transfer from the uranium to the body of the fluid. Further, if the coolant is a compound, stability from the standpoint of dissociation by heat or neutron bombardment must be guaranteed. Finally, the type of radioactivity induced by neutron bombardment will determine the ease of handling the cycling fluid. Table 9.3 shows possible coolants

TABLE 9.3

PROPERTIES OF REACTOR COOLANTS*

	Conductivity (k, Btu/hr-°F-ft)	Specific heat (c, Btu/lb-°F)	Melting point (°F)	Boiling point (°F)
Gaseous				
H_2	0.089	3.4		
He	0.075	1.25		
Air	0.014	0.25		
Steam	0.012	0.45		
Liquid				
H_2O	0.35	1.0	32	212
Li	22	1.0	354	2403
Na	50	0.33	208	1621
NaK	15	0.27	66	1518
Bi	9.0	0.034	520	2691
Hg	4.8–7.3	0.033	−38	675
Pb	9.4	0.039	621	3159

* Sources: *Handbook of Chemistry and Physics.* Cleveland: Chemical Rubber Publishing Co., 1952; R. N. Lyon, Ed., *Liquid Metals Handbook,* 1952.

with a partial listing of their properties. Various factors that are not revealed by tables must come into the design. For instance, hydrogen or deuterium gas might be suitable coolants except for the ease with which they leak from any closed system. If a coolant is to be passed once through a reactor, and exhausted to the atmosphere, its replacement cost must be considered. Air would be a practical choice while helium gas clearly would not, because of its scarcity. On the other hand, if a closed cycle is desired, helium might be preferable because of its high conductivity relative to air. Water and heavy water are useful for reactors operating at temperatures lower than their boiling points. In going to the steam phase, the ability to remove heat is greatly reduced. The fact that thermodynamic efficiency in a cycle goes up with the exit operating temperature serves as a further limitation on the use of water. Of the group of liquid metals, lithium and mercury are not desirable for reactors depending on fission by thermal neutrons because of high cross sections. Only by minimizing the amount of coolant could one hope to achieve an operable reactor. Liquid sodium, by virtue of its very high conductivity, would seem to be a natural choice. Examination of lists of neutron reactions shows that Na^{23} becomes Na^{24}, of relatively long half-life (14.9 hr). This effect complicates coolant handling. In Chapter 10 we shall have occasion to study the nature of heat transfer with liquid sodium.

9.4 Necessary properties of structural materials

A few of the components of a reactor for which some structural strength is needed are listed below.

(1) Coatings for uranium slugs and ducts for coolant in a heterogeneous reactor.

(2) Containers and auxiliary piping for the active fluid in homogeneous reactors.

(3) Supports for any equipment located near a reactor, but not an intimate part of it. Cases for neutron detectors might also be in this category.

The experience at the Hanford Plutonium Works reported by Smyth serves as a good illustration of the slug canning and water-cooling duct problems. The requirement on the duct was that it should not absorb too many neutrons to reduce the multiplication constant below unity; it should not disintegrate with irradiation;

and it should be relatively resistant to corrosion. The can containing the slugs, serving to prevent fission products from entering the coolant, had to meet the above requirements plus giving a low heat-resistance path from the slug to the coolant. Seven elements were considered: lead, bismuth, beryllium, aluminum, magnesium, zinc, tin; at least one criterion for this initial selection of these materials was the thermal neutron absorption cross sections, as listed in Table 9.4. Thermal conductivities of these metals and others are

TABLE 9.4

CROSS SECTIONS OF SLUG COATINGS AND DUCT MATERIALS

Metal	σ_a (barns)	Metal	σ_a (barns)
Pb	0.17	Mg	0.059
Bi	0.032	Zn	1.06
Be	0.010	Sn	0.65
Al	0.215		

listed in Table 9.5. The next basis for decision was the ability to

TABLE 9.5

THERMAL CONDUCTIVITY OF METALS*

Metal	Thermal conductivity	Metal	Thermal conductivity
Pb	20	Cu	221
Bi	4.5	Brass (70–30)	57
Be	90	Ni	36
Al	116	Mild steel	26
Mg	91	Stainless steel (304)	8.4
Zn	64	Graphite	85
Sn	38		

* At room temperature, Btu/hr-°F-ft.

fabricate tubes that had the necessary strength and corrosion resistance. The final choice was aluminum, which proved to be very satisfactory. This material, which was found to be appropriate for a system using water cooling, would be completely unsuitable for containing liquid metal coolants that alloy with aluminum. Knowledge has relatively recently been accumulated on the resistance of different substances to corrosion by liquid metals. The *Liquid Metals Handbook* tabulates data based on experiments with many combinations of the two reacting components—coolant and container. No general rules can be formulated, apparently; explanations of the effects taking place remain on a qualitative basis. As a typical example of the type of data available, part of one chart is reproduced in Table 9.6. The containment of uranium in a homogeneous fluid

TABLE 9.6

RESISTANCE OF MATERIALS TO ATTACK BY NA AND NAK*

Temperature (°C)

▨▨▨ Good: consider for long time use	⬚⬚⬚ Poor: no structural possibilities	
▥▥▥ Limited: for short time use only	☐ Unknown: no data for these temperatures	

* Adapted from *Liquid Metals Handbook*, Chart II, page 152.

reactor, of which the water boiler is a simple example, is subject to more difficulties than in the case of the heterogeneous reactor, because of the properties of the solution. First, the uranium is present as a salt solution such as the uranyl sulfate UO_2SO_4 or the nitrate $UO_2(NO_3)_2$. The solution must be kept acidic to prevent precipitation, but the amount of corrosion goes up with the acidity. Aluminum under acid conditions erodes rather rapidly. If the temperature is kept low, from room temperature to around 80°C, a vessel constructed of stainless steel is quite adequate, as evidenced by the successful use in the Los Alamos water boiler. Were the solution temperature allowed to rise, in order to abstract useful power, corrosion reactions would undoubtedly be accelerated, and new effects might appear.

9.5 Stainless steels

The use and demand for stainless steel in reactor construction and all phases of the related work is so universal that every engineer should have some acquaintance with its properties. These iron base alloys are characterized by their ability to resist corrosion—defined generally as the deterioration of the metal by chemical reaction with its environment. There are various mechanisms and manifestations of corrosion:

(1) *Galvanic corrosion:* pitting due to direct chemical action.

(2) *Stress corrosion:* in which reaction is induced and accelerated by unrelieved stresses in the metal.

(3) *Erosion corrosion:* due to the scouring action of a stream of particles on the surface.

(4) *Scaling:* formation of surface layers of corrosion product at high temperatures.

(5) *Intergranular corrosion:* subsurface corrosion, between crystals or grains.

The various elements that are alloyed with iron to form stainless steel are listed below with the contribution of each to its properties.

Chromium. A minimum of 12 per cent of this element is needed for prolonged chemical service. Its oxide, formed when the surface is bathed in dilute nitric acid solution, is inert and resists further chemical action.

Nickel. The mechanical and welding properties of the alloy are improved by adding as much as 7 per cent of Ni. The resistance to corrosion fatigue, the combined effect of corrosion and structural weakening at a damaged point, is increased by the addition of Ni.

Carbon. The hardness is increased by the presence of carbon. The corrosion rate however goes up with its content, but the ability to form the protective oxide coat is also improved.

Columbium and Titanium. These elements are of extreme importance in stainless steel that is expected to withstand high temperature conditions, such as in a power reactor. Their addition tends to reduce the precipitation of carbides such as that of chromium at grain boundaries in the transition from 900 to 1650°F. Such precipitation leads to serious intergranular corrosion, in which vessels or piping may leak, or in extreme cases crumble apart. "Columbium-stabilized" stainless steel such as Type 347 does not require heat treatment after welding, since the columbium carbide that competes with chromium carbide is always formed. "Titanium-stabilized" stainless steel requires a careful heat treatment after welding. An important conclusion to be noted is that installations where joints are made by gaskets or by direct pressure contact have no need for the stabilized stainless steels. Availability of materials plays such a critical role in the accomplishment of a development or production goal that differences that seem minor are well worth knowing. An inspection of the physical constants of two stainless steels, Types 304 and 347, reveals that at low temperatures in almost every respect their properties of elasticity, expansion, creep, strength, and tensile strength are the same. The addition of columbium to form Type 347 makes it preferable for high temperatures.

Other stainless steels have the following Type numbers: 301, 302, 303, 303B, 308, 309, 310, 316, 321.

Thermal neutron cross sections are tabulated for most of the elements, but not usually for compounds or alloys. Since stainless steel is an important reactor material, a computation of its effective cross section is given in Table 9.7 as an illustration of the method applicable

TABLE 9.7

MACROSCOPIC CROSS SECTIONS OF STAINLESS STEELS

Element	Per cent by weight	Density (g/cm³)	Number of atoms per cm³ × 10²⁴	σ_a (barns)	Σ_a (cm⁻¹)
Type 304 stainless steel:					
Cr	18.0	1.3040	0.01510	2.9	0.0488
Ni	8.0	0.5795	0.00595	4.5	0.0268
C	0.08	0.0058	0.00029	0.0045	negligible
Mn	2.0	0.1490	0.00158	12.6	0.0200
Si	1.0	0.0725	0.00155	13.0	0.0202
Mo	0.6	0.0434	0.00027	2.4	0.0065
Se	0.07	0.0051	0.00004	11.8	0.0005
S	0.03	0.0022	0.00004	0.49	negligible
P	0.04	0.0029	0.00056	0.19	negligible
				Subtotal of "impurities":	0.1228
Fe	69.98	5.0604	0.0546	2.43	0.1330
				Total:	0.2558

Element	Per cent by weight	Density (g/cm³)	Number of atoms per cm³ × 10²⁴	σ_a (barns)	Σ_a (cm⁻¹)

Type 347 (Cb) stainless steel:
(Contains same impurities as Type 304 except for stabilizing agent)

			Subtotal of "impurities":		0.1228
Cb	0.80	0.0579	0.00038	1.10	0.0004
Fe	69.08	4.930	0.0532	2.43	0.1295
				Total:	0.2527

Type 347 (Ti) stainless steel:
(Contains same impurities as Type 304 except for stabilizing agent)

			Subtotal of "impurities":		0.1228
Ti	0.48	0.0348	0.00044	5.6	0.0025
Fe	69.40	5.020	0.54200	2.43	0.1315
				Total:	0.2568

to all alloys. It should be noted that a number of decimal places were retained for consistency. Also, since this example refers to a specific sample of stainless steel, the results may not be used with any guarantee of the accuracy implied.

9.6 Special metals

Three metals that have high melting points, good structural strength and high corrosion resistance have been investigated for reactor use. We shall mention below some of their pertinent properties and list in Table 9.8 certain useful constants.

TABLE 9.8

PROPERTIES OF SPECIAL METALS

Metal	Atomic weight	Specific gravity	Linear expansion coefficient	Thermal conductivity*	Specific heat†	Electrical resistivity (ohm-cm)
Zirconium	91.22	6.49	5.4 × 10⁻⁶/°C at 20–200°C; 8.9 × 10⁻⁶/°C at 200–700°C	0.05	0.069	39 × 10⁻⁶
Molybdenum	95.95	10.2	5.4 × 10⁻⁶/°C	0.346	0.065	5.7 × 10⁻⁶
Titanium	47.90	4.5	5 × 10⁻⁶/°C	0.130	0.1125	3.2 × 10⁻⁶

* cal/sec-°C-cm.   † cal/g-°C.

Zirconium. The element is found in the rather abundant mineral zircon, but until recently was not produced in appreciable quantities.

Its thermal neutron cross section of 0.18 barns is less than one-tenth that of iron. For reactors without sufficient k_∞, Zr coolant tubes would be ideal. Its melting point is 1860°C (3380°F), which should be high enough for almost any conceivable reactor. Zirconium has excellent corrosion resistance to acids, except for hydrofluoric acid, aqua regia, or hot concentrated sulfuric or phosphoric acids. That these are the only exceptions is certainly a good recommendation. Its cost, $20 a pound, is rather high in comparison with materials like nickel and stainless steel (60 cents a pound). This may stem from the fact that the large scale processes that separate it have been developed only in the last few years.

Molybdenum. This metal has an exceptionally high melting point of 2627°C (4760°F), and a relatively low thermal cross section, 2.4 barns. It has the unfortunate property of forming a volatile oxide MoO_3 at 1500°F in an atmosphere with only a few per cent oxygen. At 1800°F the surface of the metal recedes at a rate of 0.05 in. per hour, which clearly makes use of the unprotected metal impractical. A vaporized silicon coating can be used to extend the life of the metal at these elevated temperatures.

Titanium. The value of titanium lies in its abundance in the earth's crust and the many iron and copper base alloys that may be formed from it. The strength-weight ratio of some of the alloys are the highest known. Its cross section is higher than that for iron, 5.6 barns; its corrosion resistance is comparable to that for stainless steels. The melting point of the pure metal, which is very ductile, is 1800°C. It is interesting to note that the cost of the metal is five dollars a pound, while that for the ore is two and a half cents.

9.7 Induced radioactivity

The activation by neutron absorption is an important factor in the choice of structural parts of and near the reactor that must be replaced on occasion, or which constitute the detection instruments. Of the common metals or alloys, we would first think of steel, copper, and aluminum. Copper, along with brass and bronze, may be immediately ruled out for some purposes because of the formation of the radioactive isotope Cu^{64}, half-life 12.8 hr, from the stable constituent Cu^{63}. Although the main isotope of iron, Fe^{56} (92 per cent) goes into another stable form Fe^{57} on absorbing neutrons, activation of iron results from absorption in Fe^{54} and Fe^{58} yielding Fe^{55} and Fe^{59}

respectively. The impurities of and additives to iron to form steel, such as manganese, may contribute more to the total induced activity than does the iron itself. Pure aluminum is activated but with a product of very short half-life. An analysis of the activation of a structural material is now given for illustrative purposes. Let us assume that it has been decided to construct a housing for reactor equipment from aluminum, which has a low cross section. A selection from three available commercial types, 2S (pure), 3S (common, Mn alloy), and 61S (strong, Mg alloy), is yet to be made. The first information to be collected is the impurity content. The specifications of the types above are listed in Table 9.9. In addition to the

TABLE 9.9

ALUMINUM IMPURITIES (PER CENT)

Impurity	2S*	3S	61S	Impurity	2S*	3S	61S
Fe	1.0	0.7	0.7	Cr			0.35
Si		0.6	0.8	Ti			0.15
Cu	0.2	0.2	0.4	Mg			1.2
Mn	0.05	1.2	0.15	Others	0.15	0.15	0.15
Zn	0.1	0.1	0.2				

* Minimum aluminum 99.0%.
From *Aluminum Data Book*. Louisville, Ky.: Reynolds Metal Co.

amount of each impurity, four factors determine the activation by thermal neutrons:

(1) the isotopic abundance,
(2) the isotopic cross section,
(3) the half-life of the product,
(4) the nature of the radiations from the product.

Table 9.10 gives numerical values of each of the four factors as applied to the elements.

We may now study Tables 9.9 and 9.10 together. Our first inclination would be to rule out Type 61S because it contains additional impurities, namely Cr, Ti, and Mg. However, Cr^{51} does not emit beta or gamma rays; the half-lives of Ti^{51} and Mg^{27} are very short so that the activity is soon gone. Thus the decision must be made from all three types, on the basis of the other elements. Only the maximum amount of Fe plus Si is specified for Type 2S. It is reasonable however, to assume that 0.5 per cent of each is present.

TABLE 9.10

ACTIVATION ANALYSIS OF IMPURITIES IN ALUMINUM

Element	Target Isotope	Abundance (%)	σ_a (barns)	Product Isotope	Half-life	Principal Radiations (type, mev)
$_{13}$Al	27	100	0.215	28	2.3 min	β^-3.01, γ1.80
$_{26}$Fe	54	5.1	2.2	55	2.9 yr	K
	56	91.6			stable	
	57	2.20			stable	
	58	0.33	0.7	59	47 days	β^-0.4, γ1.2
$_{14}$Si	28	92.22			stable	
	29	4.70			stable	
	30	3.08	0.12	31	2.7 hr	β^-1.5
$_{29}$Cu	63	69.0	4.3	64	12.9 hr	β^+0.66, β^-0.57
	65	31.0	2.1	66	4.3 min	β^-2.6, γ1.3
$_{25}$Mn	55	100	12.6	56	2.6 hr	β^-2.8, γ0.84
$_{30}$Zn	64	48.9	0.5	65	250 days	γ1.1
	66	27.8			stable	
	67	4.1			stable	
	68	18.6	0.1	69	14 hr	β^-0.86, γ0.44
			1.0		52 min	
	70	0.63	0.085	71	2.2 min	β^-2.1
$_{24}$Cr	50	4.4	16.3	51	26.5 days	K
	52	83.7			stable	
	53	9.5			stable	
	54	2.4	<0.3	55	1.3 hr	...
$_{22}$Ti	46–59	94.7			stable	
	50	5.3	0.14	51	6 min	β^-1.6
$_{12}$Mg	24	78.6			stable	
	25	10.1			stable	
	26	11.3	0.050	27	9.6 min	β^-1.8, γ0.8

On this basis it is clear that 2S is activated the least of the three. The Mn^{56} activity induced in 3S will be very high because of the 100 per cent abundance and 12.6 barn cross section of Mn^{55}. If it is necessary to make repairs on the equipment within a period of a few hours of the time the neutron irradiation stops, the 61S type will be preferable. If, however the apparatus may "cool" for a period as long as several months before it is necessary to work on it, the long lived Zn^{65} will be the principal remaining emitter. The activity per unit volume of 3S will be only half that of 61S in this case.

The equilibrium activity of each isotope on essentially infinite steady bombardment can be calculated from the condition that the

rate of decay is equal to the rate of formation in steady state. The
latter is the generation rate

$$g = \phi N A \sigma_a$$

where ϕ is the incident flux, N the atom density of the substance,
as an impurity, A the isotopic abundance, and σ_a the isotopic absorption cross section. To illustrate the more detailed analysis let
us compare the equilibrium activity due to the Mn present in 3S
with that from Al itself. Since one isotope constitutes the whole
element in each case, we may write for aluminum, per unit flux,
$g = N\sigma_a = (0.060 \times 10^{24})(0.215 \times 10^{-24}) = 0.013$; for Mn, the number of grams per cubic centimeter is 1.2 per cent of the number of grams
of aluminum or $(0.012)(2.7) = 0.0324$. This means that the number
of Mn atoms per cubic centimeter is $(0.0324)(6.023 \times 10^{23})/55$ or
0.000356×10^{24}. Thus g is $(0.000356 \times 10^{24})(12.8 \times 10^{-24}) = 0.00455$.
The yield of Mn^{56} is thus about one-third that of Al^{28}. The activity
of aluminum however, drops off very rapidly after the material is
removed from the flux ($t_H = 23$ min), while the Mn activity persists
($t_H = 2.6$ hr).

9.8 Thermal stress and thermal creep

Fuel elements or ducts separating the fuel from the coolant are
subject to distortions due to thermal stress. The degree of such
force and the amount of response to it, either immediately or over
a long time is dependent on the metal. This new factor must be
considered along with absorption, activation and corrosion resistance.

Elastic properties. In order to understand these thermal effects,
let us first review the elementary principles of elasticity.* If a
rectangular solid is subjected to a stress (or force per unit area) in
the x direction of amount σ_x, it will be extended an amount ϵ_x, the
strain (or elongation per unit length). So long as the substance
remains within its elastic limits, Hooke's law may be applied:

$$\epsilon_x = \frac{\sigma_x}{E}$$

where E is the modulus of elasticity. A shrinkage in the other two
directions y and z will occur in amount

$$\epsilon_y = \epsilon_z = -\nu \frac{\sigma_x}{E}$$

* The notation adopted is that found in S. Timoshenko and J. N. Goodier,
Theory of Elasticity, New York: McGraw-Hill Book Co., 1951.

where the negative sign denotes contraction and ν is Poisson's ratio. For many materials, ν is around 0.3. A plastic material would have $\nu \simeq 0.5$; a brittle substance that breaks before contraction occurs has $\nu \simeq 0$. The strain in the x direction in a solid to which is applied a stress having x, y and z components may be written as

$$\epsilon_x = \frac{1}{E}\left[\sigma_x - \nu(\sigma_y + \sigma_z)\right]$$

with similar expressions for ϵ_y and ϵ_z. Now consider independently the effect of heating. We recall that a metal bar of unit length with a coefficient of linear expansion α will expand a distance $\epsilon_x = \alpha T$ when heated by an amount T in excess of its original value. The more general form of Hooke's law includes the possibility of both mechanical and thermal effects

$$\epsilon_x = \frac{1}{E}\left[\sigma_x - \nu(\sigma_y + \sigma_z)\right] + \alpha T$$

$$\epsilon_y = \frac{1}{E}\left[\sigma_y - \nu(\sigma_z + \sigma_x)\right] + \alpha T$$

$$\epsilon_z = \frac{1}{E}\left[\sigma_z - \nu(\sigma_x + \sigma_y)\right] + \alpha T$$

Let us estimate the amount of thermal stress in a fuel element composed of an aluminum-uranium alloy in the form of a cube that is held rigidly on all sides. We assume that the original size is preserved by the forces of constraint, $\epsilon_x = \epsilon_y = \epsilon_z = 0$. With this ideal symmetric shape, the stresses will all be the same $\sigma_x = \sigma_y = \sigma_z = \sigma$. Adding the three equations above, we find

$$0 = \frac{1}{E}\left[3\sigma - \nu(6\sigma)\right] + 3\alpha T$$

or

$$\sigma = \frac{-E\alpha T}{1 - 2\nu}$$

Assume the temperature rise in the element is 100°F. The modulus of elasticity of high purity aluminum is 10.3×10^6 lb/in.², the coefficient of thermal expansion is around $15 \times 10^{-6}/$°F, and ν is 0.33. The stress would be estimated to be

$$\sigma \simeq \frac{(10.3 \times 10^6 \text{ lb/in.}^2)(15 \times 10^{-6}/°\text{F})(100°\text{F})}{1 - 0.66}$$

$$\simeq 46{,}000 \text{ lb/in.}^2$$

This is considerably above the ultimate strength of aluminum, which is around 13,000 lb/in.², at its maximum value, at room temperature. It is clear that the conditions to which the fuel element was subjected in our example are excessively stringent. The example demonstrates however, that thermal stresses can be important in reactor design. As a more practical illustration, let us find the axial stress in a long solid uranium slug of radius r_0 with a radial temperature distribution $T(r)$. The ends of the cylinder are fixed, thus the axial strain ϵ_z is zero. The appropriate formula for the axial stress for this case is

$$\sigma_z = \frac{\alpha E(\overline{T} - T)}{1 - \nu}$$

where $\overline{T}$ is the average radial temperature (here the arithmetic average). The maximum stress for a uranium cylinder in which the temperature at radius zero is 1000°F, the temperature at the surface $r = r_0$ is 500°F, $\alpha = 15 \times 10^{-6}/°F$, $\nu = 0.3$ and $E = 10^7$ lb/in.² (assumed) is

$$(\sigma_z)_{max} = \frac{(15 \times 10^{-6})(10^7)(750 - 500)}{1 - 0.3}$$

$$= 54,000 \text{ lb/in.}^2$$

With work hardening, the tensile strength of uranium is quoted as 200,000 lb/in.², presumably at room temperature. At this high operating temperature, one would expect creep distortions if the ends of the metal cylinder were fixed.

Stress analysis of a special type is needed in the study of internal heating of containers for liquid fuel or reflectors by gamma ray absorption. Suppose that a flux of gammas from a reactor core is incident on the inside surface of a large steel container. The amount of thermal stress can be estimated by a sequence of three calculations: (a) the heat source distribution, from the gamma energy attenuation; (b) the temperature drop between inner and outer surfaces that will remove the internal heat; (c) the stress resulting from this temperature gradient. As an illustration, assume that the flux of 2-mev gammas is $10^{14}/cm^2$-sec, on a steel vessel with thickness $t = 1$ in. If the radius of the container is large, the gamma attenuation may be written

$$I = I_0 e^{-\mu x}$$

or

$$dI = -\mu I_0 e^{-\mu x}\, dx$$

where I refers either to flux or energy and x is the radial coordinate. The fraction of incident energy that is absorbed is

$$\int_{x=0}^{x=t} \frac{dI}{I_0} = -\mu \int_0^t e^{-\mu x} dx = 1 - e^{-\mu t}$$

Taking $\mu = 0.02$ cm^2/g or 0.16 cm^{-1} for iron (neglecting Compton scattering) and $t = 2.54$ cm, μt is 0.4 and the absorbed fraction is 0.33. The incident power is $(2\text{ mev})(1.6 \times 10^{-13}\text{ watt-sec/mev})$ $(10^{14}/\text{cm}^2\text{-sec}) = 32$ watts/cm^2. To simplify the further calculations assume that the heat source within the shell is uniform, of amount $\bar{q} = (32\text{ watts/cm}^2)(0.33)/2.54\text{ cm} = 4.2$ watts/cm$^3 = 1.0$ cal/sec-cm^3. The temperature drop in the metal is found by applying the rule that all heat generated between the outside (assumed to be insulated), and any surface x must cross that surface (see Section 10.1). Thus,

$$k \frac{dT}{dx} = \int_x^t \bar{q}\,dx = \bar{q}(t - x)$$

The temperature drop is

$$T = \frac{\bar{q}}{k} \int_0^t (t - x)\,dx = \frac{\bar{q}t^2}{2k}$$

Taking the conductivity of steel as $k = 0.1$ cal/sec-°C-cm, we find

$$T = \frac{(1.0\text{ cal/sec-cm}^3)(2.54\text{ cm})^2}{(2)(0.1\text{ cal/sec-°C-cm})} = 12.7\text{°C}$$

Applying the approximate stress formula $\sigma = -\alpha E T/(1 - \nu)$, and with $E = 3.0 \times 10^7$, $\alpha = 11.7 \times 10^{-6}$/°C, $\nu = 0.33$, the stress is approximately

$$\sigma = \frac{(3.0 \times 10^7)(11.7 \times 10^{-6})(12.7)}{1 - 0.33} = 6660\text{ lb/in.}^2$$

This is a surprisingly large value, considering the relatively low temperature drop. One might find it desirable to protect the vessel by a layer of heat absorbing material in which stresses would not matter. It will be noted that the calculation may be refined by taking account of the actual non-uniform heat source and applying rigorous stress formulas.

Creep. The consequences of thermal stress in a reactor may be immediate distortion and rupture of the fuel element or structural part. A more insidious phenomenon is *creep*, which makes itself felt over a long period of time. Under conditions of constant stress, a material progressively elongates with time at a rate depending on many factors: the load, the temperature, the dimensions and, of course, the material. Until around 1920, the importance of creep was not realized; since then studies have been used by gasoline engine and steam turbine designers; the development of the high temperature reactor has prompted new investigations, many of which are in progress. The effect apparently is due to both elastic and plastic deformation. A graph of the creep for a typical material consists of four parts: initial extension, a region of decreasing rate, a linear rate, and finally a rising rate toward rupture. The time required for strains to become appreciable may be very long. As a typical example for a laboratory test, the time for mild steel to change by 3 per cent in length may be 5000 hr. The term *creep limit* or *creep strength* is a rather loosely defined term, being the stress for which rupture does not occur for a "very long time." A stress can always be found however, for which the rate of change of strain is of the order of 10^{-5}/day. For a steel with ultimate tensile strength of 44 tons/in.^{2}, the creep limit at 300°C was found to be around 18 tons/in.^{2}. Over a portion of the curve, the creep rate, at constant temperatures, may be represented by an exponential curve

$$u = Ce^{\gamma\sigma}$$

where C and γ are constants and σ is the stress. Certain trends are found: (a) the increase in creep rate with loading, as expected. In some cases, however, the initial strain work hardens the sample, rendering it less subject to creep; (b) Increase in creep rate with temperature. Above a certain temperature, any stress seems to give continued creep. Although many data have been collected on basic alloys, an understanding of the processes is far from complete, as is the case with many phenomena involving the solid state of matter. Several ways of improving creep strength have been found. The heat treatment that results in high initial strength is not necessarily the best over long periods. A new criterion for heat treatment is needed— one that yields the stable metallurgical condition. Creep resistant alloys usually are composed of two or more of the elements, Ni, Cr, Fe, and Co. As expected from this general rule, the stainless steels are less subject to creep than is ordinary steel. For example, the stresses needed to cause rupture in 1000 hr at 600°C were found to be

	Stress (tons/in.²)
0.15 per cent carbon steel	2
carbon-molybdenum steel	5.5
molybdenum-vanadium steel	10
18-8 stainless steel	14

There is also a correlation between the melting point of an alloy and the temperature range in which creep is small. Thus high melting-point elements such as titanium, vanadium, zirconium, columbium, molybdenum, tantalum and tungsten appear to be useful for alloying purposes.

9.9 Radiation damage

No discussion of reactor materials would be complete without including the effect of nuclear radiation on their structural character and physical properties. Relatively little information has yet been made available on the magnitude of effects of radiation on reactor components, although many laboratory scale tests have been described. Review articles by Slater and by Dienes (see References) contain references to such work. In this section, we shall describe briefly the mechanism of radiation damage. A number of years ago, Lind studied the effects of alpha particles and accelerated electrons on a large variety of chemicals, finding that dissociation of compounds and changes in color and other attributes of materials could be produced. It was not until reactors were developed that the effects were of more than academic interest.

The high energy particles that cause damage to materials are (a) neutrons, which give an impetus to the nucleus with which they collide, sending it forward as a fast positive ion, and (b) gamma rays, which tear from the atom some of the electrons and give them enough energy to do further ionization, (c) fission fragments, which initially are fast positive ions also. We may easily estimate the average energy given to various nuclei by neutron or fission product collision. As shown in Chapter 2, the average change in the logarithm of E of a neutron on an elastic collision is ξ; the corresponding change in energy ΔE is $(1 - e^{\xi})E$ which for most elements of atomic weight above ten can be written approximately ξE. The amounts of energy imparted to nuclei of three common substances used in reactors on being struck by a 1-mev neutron are listed in Table 9.11. The result-

TABLE 9.11

ENERGY GIVEN TO NUCLEI BY 1-MEV NEUTRON

Nucleus	Mass Number	ξ	E (ev)
U	238	0.0084	8,400
Al	27	0.073	73,000
C	12	0.159	159,000

ing energies of nuclei are far above the binding energy of atoms in molecules or metal lattices, which lie in the range of a few electron volts. In order to understand the effects of energetic particles, it is necessary to review the classification of the chemical or physical bonds that hold atoms together into molecules.

The atoms of *covalent* compounds, such as the gases, liquids and organic materials, are held by strong forces of the exchange type, the latter term stemming from the fact that two or more atoms share the same electron. The resultant molecules do not attract each other to any degree. Radiation of sufficient energy to overcome the binding forces causes these molecules to break up permanently into free atoms or radicals. The chemical composition is evidently changed for these materials by the radiation. *Ionic* compounds, such as oxides and high melting salts, e.g. KCl, consist of a lattice of ions held together by the attraction of the positive and negative charges. Radiation causes only temporary ionizations of the lattice particles, which soon become neutral. Discoloration may occur, but this is due to free electrons being trapped at imperfections in the lattice, and does not affect the general material properties. *Metals* are composed of positive ions with a large number of free electrons. If radiation impinges on a metal, the electrons are given more kinetic energy or are temporarily excited into a higher energy state, but shortly return to the normal level. In either case there is no permanent damage. The ionic and metallic compounds are subject to the *Wigner effect*, however, a term given to the displacement of atoms from their normal positions by heavy particle bombardment. Few details of the manifestation of the effect are found in the unclassified literature, but it appears to be important in metals.

Figure 9.1 shows the effect of neutrons on a reactor fuel element. Quoting from *Nucleonics*, "Initially the sample was a smooth cylinder. After irradiation it increased in size, and after still more exposure it actually crumbled. The post-irradiation photographs were taken

Fig. 9.1. Effect of neutrons on a reactor fuel element. Top—before metallurgical treatment: (1) before insertion, (2) after exposure, (3) after double exposure. Bottom—after metallurgical treatment: (1) before insertion, (2) after exposure, (3) after double exposure. [From *Nucleonics*, September (1952). Copyright, 1952, by McGraw-Hill Publishing Co., Inc.]

in a hot laboratory and through a thick glass window and do not give very good detail. . . . In the bottom row there is a similar fuel piece which has had the benefit of metallurgical treatment of a particular kind (prior to irradiation), and although radiation damage is still present, it is very considerably ameliorated."

In the case of the covalent compounds, this process is not as significant as is the disruption of molecules since heavy particles lose most of their energy by ionization rather than by elastic collision.

The effects of radiation on gases have been studied more extensively than the effects of other materials. It is unfortunate that the reverse is not true, since our main interest lies in solids for structural strength or electrical insulation, or in liquids for reactor coolants or in the suspension of nuclear fuel in homogeneous reactors.

As an example of known mechanisms of radiation effects in liquids, we shall discuss the effect in water, for example by fission product bombardment. The reaction takes place in two steps with hydrogen peroxide as an intermediate product.

$$2H_2O \rightarrow H_2O_2 + H_2$$

$$H_2O_2 \rightarrow H_2O + \tfrac{1}{2}O_2$$

The hydrogen peroxide, which arrives at a final equilibrium concentration on continued irradiation, may unbalance the chemical stability of a salt such as one of uranium dissolved in water. The rate of formation of these dissociation products in a water boiler operating at 10 kw is quoted to be 25–33 cm^3/sec. This has already been discussed in connection with the gas disposal problem in the water boiler, Chapter 8.

An exhaustive study of the effects on many commercial plastics of a reactor neutron-gamma flux has been made by Sisman and Bopp. From their data and a knowledge of the exposure to be expected in a given location, one can make an appropriate choice of plastics for containers, insulators, gaskets, and shields. The flux under which the experiments were carried out was a mixture of thermal neutrons, epithermal neutrons (60 per cent of the thermal flux) and gamma rays (50 per cent of the thermal flux). For reference, their damage data are quoted in terms of integrated thermal flux ϕt (or nvt). As can be seen from Table 9.12, most plastics are unaffected by a

TABLE 9.12

RADIATION RESISTANCE OF PLASTICS*

Plastics	Exposure 10^{18} nvt	Change in Properties
1. Mineral filled furan and mineral filled phenolics: Duralon, Haveg 41, asbestos fiber Bakelite, asbestos fabric Bakelite, and Karbate	10	Little change except for darkening in color.

TABLE 9.12 (continued)

Plastics	Exposure 10^{18} nvt	Change in Properties
2. Styrene polymers: Amphenol and Styron 411C	10	Little change except for darkening in color.
3. Modified styrene polymer: Styron 475	10	Impact strength and elongation decrease until the same as unmodified styrene polymers.
4. Aniline formaldehyde (Cibanite) and polyvinyl carbazole (Polectron)	10	Tensile strength decreases a little.
5. Polyethylene and Nylon	10	Impact strength decreases but tensile strength increases. These plastics become so brittle that the corners of the specimens chip off.
6. Mineral filled polyester: Plaskon Alkyd	10	Tensile strength and impact strength are decreased about 50 per cent.
7. Unfilled polyesters: Selectron 5038 and CR-39	5	Develop small cracks. Tensile strength and impact strength decrease.
8. Phenolics with cellulosic fillers: paper base Bakelite, linen fabric Bakelite, and Micarta	3	Become brittle, swell, and decrease in tensile and impact strength.
9. Melamine and urea: Melmac, Beetle, Plaskon urea, and Plaskon Melamine	2	Tensile strength and impact strength are decreased about 50 per cent.
10. Unfilled phenolic: Catalin	1	Tensile strength and impact strength are decreased about 50 per cent.
11. Vinylidene chloride (Saran B-115) and vinyl chloride acetate (Vinylite)	0.5	Soften, blacken, evolve HCl, and decrease in tensile strength.
12. Casein (Ameroid), methyl methacrylate (Lucite), Teflon, Fluorothene, and the cellulosics: Cellulose nitrate (Pyralin), cellulose acetate butyrate (Tenite II), cellulose propionate (Forticel), and ethyl cellulose (Ethocel R-2)	0.1	Tensile strength and impact strength are decreased about 50 per cent.

* SISMAN, O., and C. D. BOPP, *Physical Properties of Irradiated Plastics,* ORNL-928. Technical Information Service; Oak Ridge National Laboratory. June 29, 1951.

value of *nvt* of 10^{17}. Thus, the insulation of a particle detector would be safe in a flux (of this type) of 10^9 for a period of

$$\frac{10^{17} \left(\dfrac{\text{neutrons}}{\text{cm}^2} \right)}{10^9 \left(\dfrac{\text{neutrons}}{\text{cm}^2\text{-sec}} \right) 3 \times 10^7 \left(\dfrac{\text{sec}}{\text{yr}} \right)} \simeq 3 \text{ yr}$$

In summary of the findings on plastics, one can say that materials such as polyethylene, Nylon, and asbestos-filled phenolics are good; and Teflon, Lucite and cellulose base plastics are poor.

Problems

9.1 Compare the effective or average slowing down powers of liquid ammonia and light water by use of the recipe $(\overline{SDP})$ $= \xi_1 \Sigma_1 + \xi_2 \Sigma_2 + \ldots$ where the subscripts refer to element 1, element 2, etc.

9.2 Make a rough cost analysis of two reactors:

(1) beryllium moderated, pure U^{235},
(2) D_2O moderated, natural uranium.

Assume that natural U costs \$35/lb and U^{235} costs \$20/g (see W. H. ZINN, *Nucleonics*, September (1952) p. 8), and further that the volume ratios of fuel to moderator are the same.

9.3 Find the macroscopic thermal neutron cross section of brass (67% Cu, 33% Zn, specific gravity 8.4). Repeat for Monel (60% Ni, 33% Cu, 6.5% Fe, specific gravity 8.9).

9.4 What wall thickness of one-in. diameter zirconium tube could be used to replace a 0.020 in. stainless steel tube without increasing the thermal neutron absorption?

9.5 Determine which is the most and least serious impurity in a metal from the activation standpoint: Mg, Mn or Si, if the weight per cent of each is the same. Consider (a) equilibrium activity and (b) activity after "cooling" for 1 hr.

9.6 A choice between a lead and a Teflon gasket for a seal at a location where the neutron flux is 10^{11} is to be made. What would your decision be?

9.7 If the thermal flux at the surface of a 2-ft diameter reactor core is 10^{12} neutrons/cm²-sec, how far out in a thermal column should a detecting instrument, using Micarta insulation, be placed for safe operation over 1 year's time? The neutron flux in the graphite surrounding a reactor falls off roughly as $e^{-0.02r}/r$ where r is in centimeters.

9.8 Compare the thermal stress in the steel vessel described in Section 9.8 by taking account of the actual exponential heat source in the metal with the result from making an assumption of uniform generation.

9.9 It is necessary to achieve a multiplication constant k_∞ of 1.4 in a U^{235}-water-metal reactor with metal to water ratio 0.3. Compare inventories of materials needed for two choices of metal—stainless steel and zirconium, and estimate relative costs including fuel. HINT: use cost data of Section 9.6 and Problem 9.2.

References

LYON, RICHARD N., Ed., *Liquid Metals Handbook*. Washington, D. C.: U. S. Government Printing Office, June, 1952.

TROCKI, THOMAS, "Liquid Metals Are Good Heat-Transfer Agents." *General Electric Review*, May (1952) p. 22.

SMYTH, H. D., *Atomic Energy for Military Purposes*. Princeton: Princeton University Press, 1945. See especially Chaps. VI, VII, VIII.

THE AEC CROSS SECTIONS ADVISORY GROUP, *Neutron Cross sections*, AECU-2040. Washington, D. C.: Office of Technical Services, U. S. Department of Commerce, 1952.

Stainless Steels. Cleveland: Republic Steel Corp., 1951.

UDY, M. C., H. L. SHAW and F. W. BOULGER, "Properties of Beryllium." *Nucleonics*, May (1953) p. 52.

McCORKLE, W. H., "Heavy Water in Nuclear Reactors." *Nucleonics*, May (1953) p. 21.

WAY, K., et al., Eds., *Nuclear Data*, NBS Circular 499. Washington, D. C.: U. S. Government Printing Office, September 1, 1950. Also see supplements 1, April 25, 1951; 2, November 26, 1951; 3, June 9, 1952.

GELLER, R. F., "A Survey of Ceramics for Nuclear Reactors." *Nucleonics*, October (1950).

"Ceramic Materials for Reactors." *Nucleonics*, July (1953) p. 20.

The Role of Engineering in Nuclear Energy Development, TID-5031. Technical Information Service; Oak Ridge National Laboratory,

December, 1951. See sections by J. A. LANE, p. 58; G. E. EVANS, p. 272.

SHELTON, S. M., "Zirconium." *Scientific American, 184* Nos. 6. 18 (1951).

MILLER, E. C., "Zirconium: A Structural Material for Nuclear Reactors." *Nucleonics,* July (1953) p. 27.

BILLINGTON, D. S. and S. SIEGEL, *Effect of Nuclear Reactor Radiation on Metals,* AECD-2810. Oak Ridge National Laboratory, declassified March 22, 1950.

ALLEN, A. O., *Effects of Radiation on Materials,* MDDC-962. Clinton Laboratories, declassified May 20, 1947.

SISMAN, O. and C. D. BOPP, *Physical Properties of Irradiated Plastics,* ORNL-928. Technical Information Service; Oak Ridge National Laboratory, June 29, 1951.

"Radiation Damage in a Reactor." *Nucleonics,* September (1952) p. 11.

TIMOSHENKO, S. and J. N. GOODIER, *Theory of Elasticity.* New York: McGraw-Hill Book Co., 1951.

SULLY, A. H., *Metallic Creep and Creep Resistant Alloys.* London: Butterworth's Scientific Publications, 1949.

SAMANS, CARL H., *Engineering Metals and Their Alloys.* New York: The Macmillan Co., 1949.

SLATER, J. C., "The Effects of Radiation on Materials." *Journ. Appl. Phys., 22,* 237 (1951).

Annual Review of Nuclear Science. Stanford, Cal.: Annual Reviews, Inc., 1953, Vol. 2. Article by G. D. DIENES, "Radiation Effects in Solids."

"Materials and Equipment for Reactors." *Nucleonics,* June (1953) p. 17. *Nucleonics'* special report.

MARIN, JOSEPH, *Engineering Materials.* New York: Prentice-Hall, Inc., 1952.

KEYSER, C. A., *Basic Engineering Metallurgy.* New York: Prentice-Hall, Inc., 1952.

CHAPTER 10

PRINCIPLES OF HEAT TRANSFER
AND FLUID FLOW

An understanding of the principles of heat transfer and how to apply them is as important as a knowledge of the nuclear aspects of a reactor, because the two problems must be closely integrated throughout the design. A reactor built only on the basis of the critical condition may yield very low power; one built only to power specifications may not operate at all. This situation points up the need for the nuclear engineer to have at least an appreciation for several branches of engineering as well as a knowledge of nuclear physics.

In this chapter we shall discuss heat transfer and fluid flow calculations from a fundamental viewpoint, and lead up to convenient design formulas. The description and emphasis will be pointed at reactor heat transfer analysis and design, using actual numerical values of various properties of the cooling medium and the fissionable material.

10.1 Basic equations of heat transfer as applied to reactor cooling

Let us assume that we wish to find out under what conditions a given amount of heat can be removed from a heterogeneous reactor by

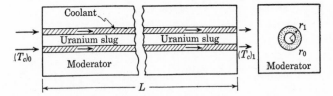

Fig. 10.1. Cooling of heterogeneous reactor cell.

passing a coolant through annuli about cylindrical uranium slugs imbedded in a solid moderator. Let the pattern sketched in Fig. 10.1 be repeated over and over throughout the reactor. Heat is generated by fission within the slugs, and is given up to the flowing fluid. For the sake of simplifying the problem, we assume that the neutron flux is constant across the slug diameter and is also perfectly uniform throughout the reactor. This is an idealized condition that is never strictly true, even if there is a good reflector making the flux more uniform. The more realistic situation will be treated in Chapter 12 when the principles are applied more rigorously to a specific power reactor.

The first principle of heat transfer is simply this: *The heat generated goes to raising the temperature of the coolant.* Other losses of heat by conduction through the moderator or by radiation are safely neglected. If we let the inlet and outlet coolant temperatures be $(T_c)_0$ and $(T_c)_1$, the total rate of development of heat be Q, the mass flow rate of coolant be M, and c the specific heat of the coolant, the above principle may be expressed as

$$Q = cM \left[(T_c)_1 - (T_c)_0\right] \tag{10.1}$$

$$\frac{\text{Btu}}{\text{hr}} = \left(\frac{\text{Btu}}{\text{lb-°F}}\right)\left(\frac{\text{lb}}{\text{hr}}\right)(°\text{F})$$

The appropriate units in the British system and a dimension check accompany the equation above. For convenient reference, conversion factors are listed in Table 10.1. The mass flow rate is the product

TABLE 10.1

HEAT CONVERSION FACTORS BRITISH TO METRIC SYSTEM

1 Btu = 1054.8 watt-sec = 0.293 watt-hr = 252.0 cal
1 cal = 4.186 joules

$$1 \frac{\text{Btu}}{\text{hr-°F-ft}} = 4.13 \times 10^{-3} \frac{\text{cal}}{\text{sec-°C-cm}}$$

$$1 \frac{\text{Btu}}{\text{lb-°F}} = 1 \frac{\text{cal}}{\text{g-°C}}$$

$$1 \frac{\text{Btu}}{\text{hr-°F-ft}^2} = 1.35 \times 10^{-4} \frac{\text{cal}}{\text{sec-°C-cm}^2}$$

$$M = \rho v A$$

$$\left(\frac{\text{lb}}{\text{hr}}\right) = \left(\frac{\text{lb}}{\text{ft}^3}\right)\left(\frac{\text{ft}}{\text{hr}}\right)(\text{ft}^2)$$

where ρ is the coolant density, v its velocity, and A the cross-sectional area through which it flows. Let us compute the total heat that can be removed from a line of 1-in. diameter slugs 15 ft long, with a $\frac{1}{4}$-in. annulus through which liquid sodium passes at a rate of 10 ft per sec (36,000 ft/hr). The inlet sodium temperature will be taken as 250°F, somewhat above its melting point of 208°F; the exit temperature is assumed to be 550°F. At the mean temperature of 400°F, the specific gravity of Na is 0.85 (density $\rho = 53$ lb/ft^3); its specific heat is $c = 0.30$ Btu/lb per °F. The cross-sectional area of the coolant duct is $A = \pi(r_1^2 - r_0^2) = \pi[(\frac{3}{4})^2 - (\frac{1}{2})^2] = 0.98$ in.^{2} or 0.0068 ft^2. Thus the mass flow rate is $M = (53)(3.6 \times 10^4)(6.8 \times 10^{-3}) = 13,000$ lb/hr. According to Eq. 10.1, the heat removed with a temperature rise of 300°F is $Q = (0.30)(13,000)(300) = 1.17 \times 10^6$ Btu/hr. The above calculation was based on two assumptions that are not necessarily valid: (a) that the flowing sodium is actually able to remove the heat as fast as it is generated; (b) that the temperature of the slug remains within reasonable bounds. If the coolant used had a very low conductivity, for instance, the temperature to which the metal would have to rise to give the necessary temperature drop across the boundary between metal and coolant might be thousands of degrees. We are led to the second principle of heat transfer: *The heat generated must flow from the source to the coolant.* The larger the surface area S of the boundary and the larger the temperature difference between the slug and coolant, $(T_s - T_c)$, the greater will be the heat flow. In addition, the flow will depend on the properties of the coolant (specific heat, conductivity, its flow rate), and the nature of the contact. All of the coolant features are characterized by the heat transfer coefficient h. The equation describing the second principle is thus:

$$q_1 = hS(T_s - T_c) \tag{10.2}$$

$$\left(\frac{\text{Btu}}{\text{hr-ft}}\right) = \left(\frac{\text{Btu}}{\text{hr-°F-ft}^2}\right)\left(\frac{\text{ft}^2}{\text{ft}}\right)(\text{°F})$$

The symbol q_1 which refers to the heat removed from a unit length (taken as a 1-ft section of the slugs, over which the coolant temperature is approximately constant) is to be distinguished from Q. We may deduce from this equation the maximum temperature to which the metal surface must rise, to get the heat out. We know that the coolant temperature is a maximum at the exit end of the tube. Further, the heat supply q_1 is constant along the length of the line of slugs which we shall take to be 15 ft. Thus the temperature difference $T_s - T_c$ is constant, and the maximum value of T_s occurs where

$T_c = (T_c)_1$. Assume that the total heat generated is that found earlier, $Q = 1.17 \times 10^6$ Btu/hr. The amount produced in a length of 1 ft is $q_1 = Q/15 = 7.8 \times 10^4$ Btu/hr. Now the heat transfer coefficient for 10 ft/sec sodium is found to be around 9000 (see Sections 10.5 and 12.8), and the area of surface per foot of slug is $S = 2\pi r_0(1) = (2\pi)(1/24)(1) = 0.26$ ft^2. Thus the temperature difference is $T_s - T_c = (7.8 \times 10^4)/(6400)(0.26) = 47°F$. The maximum metal surface temperature $(T_s)_{max}$, would be $550 + 47 = 597°F$. The center of the slug will be somewhat hotter than this. Suppose now that the total power that the line of slugs actually developed by fission heat amounted to three times the calculated Q, i.e., 3.5×10^6 Btu/hr. Assuming that ρ, c, and h remain substantially the same, the outlet coolant temperature must go up from 550 to 1150°F. Further, the temperature difference $T_s - T_c$ will go up to 141°F, implying a maximum surface temperature of 1291°F.

If we desire to restrict the surface temperature of the metal to a value such as 1200°F, it is clear that the initial design must be modified. Various approaches can be considered—increase of the surface area of the slug, keeping the annulus flow area fixed; increase of the annulus area to keep down the temperature rise of the coolant, increase of the flow speed, thus improving h. The two principles can be combined to predict compatible data. Let the outlet coolant temperature be unknown, to be determined by a limitation on the maximum slug surface temperature, labeled $(T_s)_{max}$. Eliminate $(T_c)_1$ from the two equations below

$$Q = cM \left[(T_c)_1 - (T_c)_0 \right]$$

$$\frac{Q}{L} = hS \left[(T_s)_{max} - (T_c)_1 \right]$$

to obtain
$$Q = \frac{(T_s)_{max} - (T_c)_0}{(1/hSL) + (1/cM)} \tag{10.3}$$

The problem may now be solved again to find the maximum power generation, with $(T_s)_{max}$ set at 1200°F, as suggested above. Thus

$$Q = \frac{1200 - 250}{\dfrac{1}{(9000)(0.26)(15)} + \dfrac{1}{(0.30)(13,000)}}$$

$$= 3.3 \times 10^6 \text{ Btu/hr}$$

The exit coolant temperature will now be $(T_c)_1 = (T_c)_0 + Q/cM = 250 + (3.3 \times 10^6)/(0.30)(13{,}000) = 250 + 850 = 1100°F$. The next refinement to the problem has to do with the temperature drop in the slug. The third basic principle that must be applied is: *The heat generated within the source must flow out across its boundary.* Consider a section of a cylindrical slug of radius r_0 of unit length, as shown in Fig. 10.2. The heat that flows each second across any surface defined by a radius r must be equal to the amount that is produced each second *within that surface.* The rate of heat transfer is given by the familiar formula for the conduction of heat

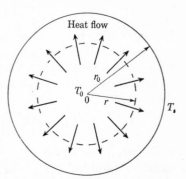

Fig. 10.2. Heat flow in cylindrical uranium slug.

$$H = -kS \frac{dT}{dr} \tag{10.4}$$

$$\left(\frac{\text{Btu}}{\text{hr-ft}}\right) = \left(\frac{\text{Btu-ft}}{\text{hr-ft}^2\text{-°F}}\right)\left(\frac{\text{ft}^2}{\text{ft}}\right)\left(\frac{\text{°F}}{\text{ft}}\right)$$

where k is the metal conductivity, S is again the surface area per foot of length at radius r and dT/dr is the temperature gradient. The negative sign implies that the heat flow is in the direction the temperature is *decreasing.* Now assume that the rate of generation of heat in the metal is q per unit volume, taken to be a constant, $q_1/\pi r_0^2$, since the neutron flux in the slug is taken as uniform. Within an area bounded by any radius r, Eq. 10.4 may be written

$$(q)(\pi r^2) = -k(2\pi r)\frac{dT}{dr}$$

Substituting and rearranging,

$$\frac{dT}{dr} = \frac{-q_1 r}{2\pi r_0^2 k}$$

Integrate between the limits $r = 0$ at the center where $T = T_0$ and $r = r_0$ at the edge, where $T = T_s$

$$T\Big]_{T_0}^{T_s} = \frac{-q_1 r^2}{4\pi r_0^2 k}\Big]_0^{r_0}$$

$$T_0 - T_s = \frac{q_1}{4\pi k} = \frac{Q}{4\pi kL}$$

It is interesting to note that the temperature drop is independent of slug size for this cylindrical geometry and uniform heat distribution. We may now compute the temperature drop in the slugs of the previous problem, assuming k for uranium to be 19 Btu-ft/hr-°F-ft²; thus

$$T_0 - T_s = \frac{3.3 \times 10^6}{(4\pi)(19)(15)} = 920°F$$

If the maximum surface temperature $(T_s)_{max}$ is 1200°F, the *central* metal temperature $(T_0)_{max}$ will be $1200 + 920 = 2120°F$. This is far above the temperature at which phase changes take place in uranium, as discussed in Section 9.1. Again the principles must be combined to yield a formula that automatically limits the temperature *at the center of the slug* to some value $(T_0)_{max}$. The heat removal from the system can now be computed on the basis of the maximum central slug temperature instead of the surface temperature. Insert the condition $(T_0)_{max} - (T_s)_{max} = Q/4\pi kL$ in Eq. 10.3, and solve the result for Q.

$$Q = \frac{(T_0)_{max} - (T_c)_0}{(1/hSL) + (1/cM) + (1/4\pi kL)} \qquad (10.5)$$

This is the final formula for the maximum safe power level in a line of slugs with uniform flux. The total power per line of slugs under the following conditions is readily computed.

$$
\begin{aligned}
(T_0)_{max} &= 1000°F \text{ (200°F below phase changes)}\\
(T_c)_0 &= 250°F\\
h &= 9000 \text{ Btu/hr-°F-ft}^2\\
S &= 0.26 \text{ ft}^2/\text{ft}\\
k &= 19 \text{ Btu/hr-ft-°F}\\
M &= 13{,}000 \text{ lb/hr}\\
c &= 0.30 \text{ Btu/lb-°F}\\
L &= 15 \text{ ft}
\end{aligned}
$$

We find $Q = 1.33 \times 10^6$ Btu/hr $= 3.9 \times 10^5$ watts $= 390$ kw. If there were 500 lines in the whole reactor, the total power would be 195 mw.

10.2 Types of fluid flow

Reactor cooling systems, as in other applications, may employ either high-velocity or low-velocity moving fluid. Since the nature of the pressure drops in a pipe depend strongly on the range of operation, we shall review the distinction between laminar* flow and turbulent flow, and make a few simple applications to reactor systems. Laminar flow exists if particles move only in the direction of flow, while turbulent flow occurs if there are eddies in the core of the stream. The regions are distinguished by the dimensionless Reynolds number $N_R = D\rho v/\mu$ where D is the pipe diameter, ρ the density, v the velocity, and μ the coefficient of viscosity (absolute viscosity). When N_R is less than 2000, the flow is streamline; if N_R is greater than 4000, it is turbulent. It will be well to digress to review the meaning, and particularly the units of the viscosity. If one layer of fluid flows past another at rest, a shearing force tends to reduce the velocity of the moving layer. The mechanism for the effect is the relative transfer of particle momentum from the high speed stream to the low, which corresponds to a force. The amount of force on a unit area is proportional to the velocity gradient in a pipe dv/dr and dependent on the nature of the fluid. Thus $F/A = \mu\, dv/dr$ where μ is the viscosity. The units of μ may immediately be determined. With F in dynes, A in cm², v in cm/sec and r in cm, the units of μ are dyne-sec/cm³ or g/cm-sec. This unit is a *poise*. The *centipoise*, 0.01 poise, is the more commonly used unit in practice. In the British system, the units are lb-mass/ft-sec. The conversion factor

μ (in British viscosity units, Bvu) $= 6.72 \times 10^{-4}\ \mu$ (in centipoises)

is useful.

The pressure drop required to achieve a flow of fluid of density ρ (lb/ft³) in a circular pipe of diameter D (ft), length L (ft), with a flow velocity v (ft/sec) may be written in the general form

$$\Delta p \ (\text{lb/ft}^2) = \rho f(L/D)(v^2/2g) \tag{10.6}$$

where f is a "friction factor" and g is the acceleration of gravity, 32.2 ft/sec². The difference between laminar and turbulent flow appears in the factor f.†

* Or streamline or viscous flow.

† Some confusion may arise with reference to various f's found in the literature. Before graphical data are used, it is well to check the definition of symbols.

Laminar flow. The flow velocity is characterized by a parabolic distribution as in Fig. 10.3, with zero velocity at the wall and a maximum at the center that is twice the average speed. The roughness of the inside layer of the pipe does not affect the flow particularly,

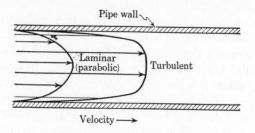

Fig. 10.3. Types of fluid flow.

since the speed is essentially zero at the wall. Both the theory of Poiseuille and careful experiments verify the fact that the friction factor for laminar flow is

$$f_L = 64/N_R$$

so that the pressure drop is

$$\Delta p = \rho \left(\frac{64}{N_R}\right)\left(\frac{L}{D}\right)\left(\frac{v^2}{2g}\right) = \frac{32\mu Lv}{gD^2} \qquad (10.7)$$

Since the volume rate of flow F is $v\pi D^2/4$, this may be written

$$\Delta p = \frac{128\mu LF}{\pi D^4 g}$$

Turbulent flow. The velocity distribution across a pipe in turbulent flow is flatter than in the laminar case because of the averaging effects of the agitation (see Fig. 10.3). The roughness of the walls affects the flow rate. As expected, it increases the friction factor f. Figure 10.4 shows f as a function of N_R for smooth pipes. A good fit to the curve for the turbulent region is $f_T/4 = 0.046 \, (N_R)^{-0.2}$. A typical situation that can be handled by these formulas is the following. A cooling coil for a homogeneous enriched reactor consists of a 10-ft length of $\frac{1}{4}$-in. (inside diameter) tubing, through which a turbulent flow of 3 gal/min of water at room temperature is desired. We wish to find out whether the available line pressure of 30 lb/in.² is adequate or whether an auxiliary pump is needed. The flow rate is

$$\frac{3/60 \text{ (gal/sec)}}{7.48 \text{ (gal/ft}^3)} = 6.68 \times 10^{-3} \text{ ft}^3/\text{sec} = vA$$

With the pipe diameter $D = 0.0208$ ft, the cross-sectional area of the pipe is

$$A = \frac{\pi D^2}{4} = \frac{\pi}{4} (0.0208)^2 = 3.40 \times 10^{-4} \text{ ft}^2$$

and the flow velocity is

$$v = (vA)/A = (6.68 \times 10^{-3})/(3.40 \times 10^{-4}) = 19.6 \text{ ft/sec}$$

Taking the viscosity of water at room temperature as 1.0 centipoises or 6.72×10^{-4} lb/ft-sec and its density as 62.4 lb/ft^3, the Reynolds number is

$$N_R = Dv\rho/\mu = (0.0208)(19.6)(62.4)/(6.72 \times 10^{-4})$$
$$= 3.79 \times 10^4$$

which puts the flow well in the turbulent region. From the graph of f_T as a function of N_R, we find $f_T = 0.022$ and from Eq. 10.6

$$\Delta p = \rho f_T(L/D)(v^2/2g)$$
$$= (62.4)(0.022)(10/0.0208)(384/64.4)$$
$$= 3935 \text{ lb/ft}^2$$

or
$$\Delta p = 27.3 \text{ lb/in.}^2$$

This result indicates that no auxiliary pump is needed.

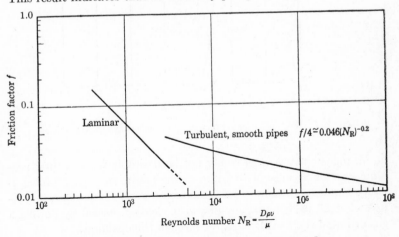

Fig. 10.4. Friction factor in laminar and turbulent flow.

10.3 Flow of fluids through particle beds

When the size of tubing needed to achieve adequate heat transfer surface in a reactor becomes prohibitively small, one may turn to an inherently or artificially porous mixture of moderator and fuel. Such

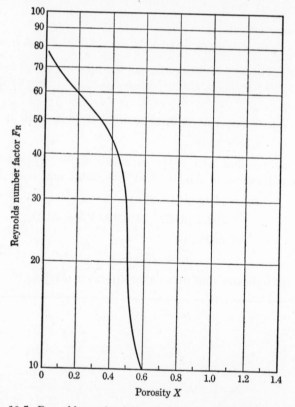

Fig. 10.5. Reynolds number factor F_R for beds of spherical particles.

an arrangement would probably not be desirable for a natural uranium reactor because of the drop in the resonance escape probability p. One can visualize a U^{235} reactor however, composed of a mixture of small pellets of uranium and moderator, cooled by flowing a gas or liquid such as air or water through the openings.

The rules for computing flow rates consist of empirical modifications of the laws of fluid flow in simple tubes. Several factors determine the available flow through the tortuous passages:

(1) the porosity X, the ratio of void volume to the total volume.

(2) the sphericity ψ, of the particles, which is the ratio of the sur-

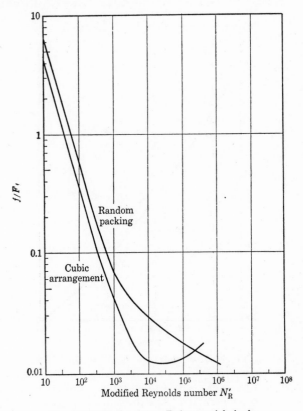

Fig. 10.6. Ratio of f to F_f for particle beds.

face area that the particles would have if they had a spherical shape, to their actual surface area. ψ is unity or less.

(3) the particle *diameter* D_p.

(4) the *orientation* or packing arrangement.

(5) the *roughness* of the particles.

First, a new Reynolds number N'_R is defined by

$$N'_R = F_R \left(\frac{D_p v \rho}{\mu} \right)$$

where the particle diameter appears in place of the tube diameter, v is the "velocity" of the fluid (i.e. the actual flow rate divided by the

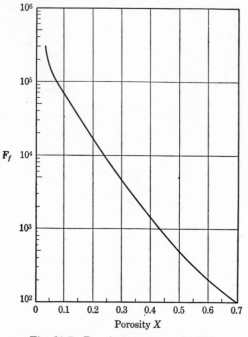

Fig. 10.7. F_f as it depends on porosity.

cross-sectional area) and F_R as a function of porosity X for spherical particles is shown in Fig. 10.5. The pressure drop Δp may be written to compare with the formula in Section 10.2.

$$\Delta p = \rho f \left(\frac{L}{D_p} \right) \left(\frac{v^2}{2g} \right)$$

The ratio of f to a new factor F_f can be obtained as a function of the new Reynolds number N'_R. The results for a large variety of shapes of particles in random packing and for spheres in cubic array is given in Fig. 10.6. Values of F_f are plotted in Fig. 10.7 for spherical particles. Calculations on an actual system, even though idealized, will serve to orient the student in this type of analysis.

Let us assume that a cylindrical reactor of 3-ft diameter and 3-ft length is composed of $\frac{1}{8}$-in. spherical fuel-moderator particles. We wish to find the air flow that can be achieved with a 1-atm pressure drop (14.7 lb/in.^{2} = 2117 lb/ft^2) through this arrangement. The average air temperature will be high if the flow serves to cool a reactor of reasonable power level, but for our illustrative purposes, it will be sufficient to take it as room temperature. If the spheres were stacked in the reactor in a perfect cubic array, the void volume per particle would be simply the space between a sphere and an enclosing cube, $d^3 - (4/3)\pi(d/2)^3$, and the porosity would be $X = 1 - \pi/6 = 0.476$. Other packings yield porosities as low as 0.26. From Fig. 10.5 and Fig. 10.7, F_R is 31, F_f is 620. We know the specific gravity to be 1.29×10^{-3} or $\rho = 0.0807$ lb/ft^3, and the viscosity $\mu = 0.0182$ centipoise or 1.22×10^{-5} British units; the reactor length is 3 ft, the particle diameter D_p is 0.0104 ft. Only the velocity v is not known in the Reynolds number and in the pressure drop formula. Divide through the latter by F_f and rearrange to obtain

$$\frac{f}{F_f} = \frac{2g\Delta p D_p}{\rho F_f L v^2}$$

$$= \frac{2(32.2 \text{ ft/sec}^2)(2117 \text{ lb/ft}^2)(0.0104 \text{ ft})}{(0.0807 \text{ lb/ft}^3)(620)(3 \text{ ft})v^2}$$

$$= \frac{9.4}{v^2}\left(\frac{\text{ft}}{\text{sec}}\right)^2$$

The Reynolds number is

$$N_R = \frac{D_p F_R v \rho}{\mu} = \frac{(0.0104)(31)(0.0807)v}{1.22 \times 10^{-5}}$$

$$= 2130v$$

The value of v is found by trial and error, using the formulas and Fig. 10.6, to be around 27 ft/sec. The mass flow through the area of $\pi(3)^2/4 = 7.07$ ft^2 is

$$M = \left(27 \frac{\text{ft}}{\text{sec}}\right)\left(3600 \frac{\text{sec}}{\text{hr}}\right)(0.0807 \text{ lb/ft}^3)(7.07 \text{ ft}^2)$$

$$= 55,500 \text{ lb/hr}$$

10.4 Dimensionless groups

The method of *dimensional analysis* is widely used in fluid flow and heat transfer calculations. The derivation of Poiseuille's formula (Eq. 10.7) serves as a good example of its application. Assume that the pressure gradient $\Delta p/\Delta x$ depends in some way on the factors μ, D and v. In particular, let

$$\Delta p/\Delta x = KD^a v^b \mu^c$$

where K, a, b, and c are constants to be determined. Express each quantity in the equation except K in terms of the basic dimensions, length L, mass M, and time T.

Factor	D	v	μ	$\Delta p/\Delta x$
Dimensions	L	L/T	M/LT	M/L^2T^2

* Force per unit area divided by length.

Substituting dimensions,

$$\frac{M}{L^2 T^2} = KL^a \left(\frac{L}{T}\right)^b \left(\frac{M}{LT}\right)^c$$

Equate exponents of each dimension on the two sides of the equation,

$$c = 1, \quad a + b - c = -2, \quad -b - c = -2$$

or $\qquad b = 1 \quad$ and $\quad a = -2$

Thus $\Delta p/\Delta x = Kv\mu/D^2$ which agrees with Poiseuille's formula. The quantity $K = (D^2/v\mu)(\Delta p/\Delta x)$ has no dimensions, and is called a dimensionless group. Such groups play an important role in the study of fluid flow and heat transfer. One assumes the factors that go into the experimental quantity for which an empirical formula is sought, for example a heat transfer coefficient. The dimensional analysis then suggests how the experimental data should be plotted to discover the proper exponents. The method thus consists of a judicious combination of theory and experimentation. The names that have been given to various useful dimensionless groups are as follows:

N_R: Reynolds number $Dv\rho/\mu$

N_{Pr}: Prandtl number $c\mu/k$

N_N: Nusselt number hD/k

N_{Pe}: Peclet number $Dv\rho c/k = (N_R)(N_{Pr})$

N_G: Graetz number $(\pi D/4L)N_R N_{Pr}$

where all symbols have been defined previously.

10.5 Calculation of heat transfer coefficients

The amount of heat that can be removed from a heated surface by a flowing fluid was shown in Section 10.1 to be expressible in terms of a heat transfer coefficient h, appearing in Eq. 10.2

$$q_1 = hS(T_s - T_c)$$

The value of h depends on the type of flow, laminar or turbulent, and on the medium. Further, coolants can be divided into two classes according to their conductivities. Ordinary fluids such as air and water are governed by different empirical formulas than are the liquid metals, which have exceptionally high values of k. The heat transfer coefficient is a factor in the Nusselt number $N_N = hD/k$, so that if N_N can be found, h is immediately available.

Ordinary fluids. The standard working formulas for many coolants with forced convection transfer in circular pipes, are

Laminar flow, $N_R < 2000$: $N_N = 2.0 \ (N_G)^{1/3}$
Turbulent flow, $N_R > 2000$: $N_N = 0.023 \ (N_R)^{0.8} \ (N_{Pr})^{0.4}$

Liquid metals. The standard working formulas are

Circular tubes: $N_N = 7 + 0.025 \ (N_{Pe})^{0.8}$
Thin annuli: $N_N = 5.8 + 0.02 \ (N_{Pe})^{0.8}$

where D is given by twice the width of the annulus. As an illustration of the method, let us find h for a 1-in. diameter tube containing sodium potassium alloy, NaK. Two mixtures have been studied (a) 44.8% K, 55.2% Na, and (b) 78.3% K, 21.7% Na, the composition for the eutectic. We shall compute h for the first mixture using these data:

$T = 400°C = 752°F$
$v = 20 \ \text{ft/sec} = 7.2 \times 10^4 \ \text{ft/hr}$
$D = 1.0 \ \text{in.} = 0.083 \ \text{ft}$
$\rho = 0.775 \ \text{g/cm}^3 = 48 \ \text{lb/ft}^3$
$\mu = 0.205 \ \text{centipoises} = 1.38 \times 10^{-4} \ \text{Bvu}$
$k = 0.0662 \ \text{cal/sec-cm-°C} = 16 \ \text{Btu/hr-ft-°F}$
$c = 0.252 \ \text{cal/g-°C} = 0.252 \ \text{Btu/lb-°F}$

The Peclet number is formed from its components

$$N_{\text{Pe}} = N_R N_{\text{Pr}} = \frac{Dv\rho c}{k}$$

$$= \frac{(0.083)(7.2 \times 10^4)(48)(0.252)}{16} = 4520$$

From the formula above for circular tubes, $N_N = 7 + (0.025)(840) = 28$. Finally,

$$h = kN_N/D = (16)(28)/0.083 = 5400$$

This compares well with data from the *Liquid Metals Handbook*.

Free-Convection Cooling. The heat transfer formulas in the preceding paragraph referred to situations in which the fluid was *forced* past heated surfaces. When the coolant is a body of fluid in which natural convection motion removes the heat, different heat transfer coefficient relations are applied. Dimensionless quantities are still used, but in a new empirical way. A system in which such computations would be needed is a heterogeneous heavy-water reactor. A primary coolant next to the slugs serves to remove most of the reactor heat, but some will be lost through the outside duct to the D_2O. If the loss is appreciable, it may be necessary to circulate the D_2O through a separate heat exchanger. Its flow velocity will probably be small (even though the mass flow rate is large) and for practical purposes it may be considered stationary. The heat transfer coefficient h as before appears in the Nusselt number $N_N = hD/k$, but a new dimensionless quantity, the Grashof number, is defined:

$$N_{\text{Gr}} = \frac{D^3 \rho^2 \beta g \Delta T}{\mu^2}$$

where β is the coefficient of volume expansion, g is the acceleration of gravity, T is the temperature difference between the heated surface and the fluid, and other symbols have been defined before. The Nusselt number is given in terms of N_{Gr} and the Prandtl number $N_{\text{Pr}} = c\mu/k$ by

$$N_N = 0.52(N_{\text{Gr}}N_{\text{Pr}})^{0.25}$$

These relations may be applied to a simple reactor example. Assume that the outside diameter of the duct surrounding the slugs is 3.0 cm, and that the surface has a uniform temperature of 100°C, just under the boiling point of D_2O. Let the heavy water temperature be 40°C so that ΔT is 60°C. Other numerical values can be listed:

Density ρ = 1.1 g/cm^3
Coefficient of expansion β = 2.8 $\times$ 10^{-4}/°C
Acceleration of gravity g = 980 cm/sec^2
Heat capacity c = 1.0 cal/g-°C
Conductivity k = 1.4 $\times$ 10^{-3} cal/cm-°C-sec
Viscosity μ = 6.5 $\times$ 10^{-3} poises

Now

$$N_{Gr} = \frac{(3.0)^3(1.1)^2(2.8 \times 10^{-4})(980)(60)}{(6.5 \times 10^{-3})^2}$$

$$= 1.27 \times 10^7$$

$$N_{Pr} = \frac{(6.5 \times 10^{-3})(1.0)}{1.4 \times 10^{-3}} = 4.64$$

$$N_N = (0.52)\,[(1.27 \times 10^7)(4.64)]^{0.25} = 47.8$$

$$h = \frac{(47.8)(1.4 \times 10^{-3})}{3.0} = 0.0223 \text{ cal/sec-°C-cm}^2$$

The heat removed per square centimeter of slug surface area is thus

$$Q = h\Delta T = (0.0223)(60) = 1.34 \text{ cal/sec-cm}^2$$

10.6 Heat exchangers

Having completed our analysis of the general principles of heat transfer and the relation of reactor design to heating of a fluid, we may turn to the next logical problem, that of utilization of the heat for practical purposes. The most desirable arrangement would consist of a turbine or turbo-generator driven by the fluid that has just passed through the reactor. Difficulties can be seen immediately. The coolant will probably be highly radioactive, because of neutron absorption, so that repair of the mechanical system beyond the reactor becomes practically impossible. Second, little information is known on the use of liquid metals in turbines with the exception of mercury. This latter element, with its thermal cross section of 380 barns, could be used in fast or epithermal reactors, but only with a serious waste of neutrons in an enriched thermal reactor. The present mode of approach is to employ a heat exchanger to transfer the reactor heat to a more conventional driving fluid such as steam. Trocki, in reviewing some of the problems in the use of liquid metal to water exchangers, points out that ability of the fluid to leak through every small crack or hole requires that the complete system be welded vacuum tight.

Precautions taken to prevent the two fluids from coming in contact includes double concentric channels with space between, with a leak detecting system to note the appearance of either fluid. The space is filled with a fluid that does not react with water, but which allows heat conduction between the primary and secondary cycles. The resistance concept of heat transfer best describes the factors determining the dimensions of the heat exchanger tubes. Let sodium be the inner fluid, contained by a metal tube, surrounded by boiling water as the outer fluid. By analogy with Ohm's law for electricity

$$I \text{ (current flow)} = \frac{E \text{ (potential difference)}}{R \text{ (electrical resistance)}}$$

one writes

$$q \text{ (heat flow)} = \frac{T \text{ (temperature difference)}}{R \text{ (thermal resistance)}}$$

The "resistance" to heat transfer across an interface between the coolant and slug, for instance, from Eq. 10.2 would be $R = 1/hS$. For the transfer through a metal from Eq. 10.4, the resistance is $R = \Delta r/kS$. The units in both cases are °F-hr/Btu. The total resistance through the heat exchanger tube sketched in Fig. 10.8 would be

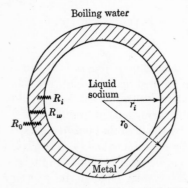

Fig. 10.8. Cross section of heat exchange tube.

$$R_t = R_i + R_w + R_0$$
$$= \frac{1}{h_i S_i} + \frac{r_0 - r_i}{k S_w} + \frac{1}{h_0 S_0} .$$

where the R's are resistances of the sodium-metal interface, the metal wall, and the metal-water interface, h_i and h_0 are corresponding heat transfer coefficients, S_i and S_0 are the two surface areas, and S_w is the effective surface area of the metal wall. The overall transfer coefficient U is expressed by

$$R_t = 1/US_0$$

Trocki gives the distribution of resistances for an example in which $r_0 = 1$ in., $r_0 - r_i = 0.1$ in. (carbon steel) for the transfer from sodium to boiling water and for comparison, two other primary media. Table 10.2 shows these computed data.

TABLE 10.2

RESISTANCES IN HEAT EXCHANGER TUBES

	Sodium	Heat transfer salt	Gas
R_i (per cent)	22.4	59.0	99.0
R_w (per cent)	33.0	17.4	0.6
R_0 (per cent)	44.6	23.6	0.4
R (°F-hr/Btu)	11.2×10^{-4}	21.2×10^{-4}	386×10^{-4}
U (Btu/hr-°F-ft²)	890	470	18

The important differences to note are (a) the very large overall coefficient, (b) the contribution of the tube to the resistance. The need for minimum wall thicknesses of high conductivity metal is apparent in liquid metal exchangers. As an indication of sizes of exchangers needed, let us estimate the heat transfer area needed to handle the output of the Experimental Breeder reactor (see Chapter 20) with the replacement of NaK as coolant by Na. Assume that the heat transferred is 250 kw (850,000 Btu/hr), the sodium temperature is 660°F, and the boiling water temperature is 212°F.

$$S_0 = \frac{Q}{U\Delta T}$$

$$= \frac{850,000 \ (\text{Btu/hr})}{890 \ (\text{Btu/hr-°F-ft}^2)(448°F)} = 2.15 \ \text{ft}^2$$

A total length of heat exchanger tubing of 1-in. diameter would be a little over 8 ft, which is surprisingly small.

10.7 Electromagnetic pumps for liquid metals

Conventional mechanical pumps have several disadvantages if used to propel liquid metals of the alkali type—Li, Na, and K, or alloys of these elements. The non-metallic packing materials react chemically with the liquid metal; the bearing materials are corroded, or resistant materials cannot withstand metal-to-metal contact. Inadvertent leaks that normally would not be serious leave open the possibility for violent chemical reaction. The electromagnetic or Faraday pump, based on the principle of the electric motor, has none of these difficulties, since there are no moving parts, and the liquid metal is completely contained in a metal tube. Such pumps were investigated as early as 1907 by E A. Northrup; Szilard first proposed their use in chain reactors. Since 1946, A. H. Barnes and others of Argonne National Laboratories have developed the system now in use in the Experimental Breeder reactor. Two types operate successfully: the a-c pump having a varying magnetic field and the d-c pump with a constant field. The physical arrangement of the d-c type is shown

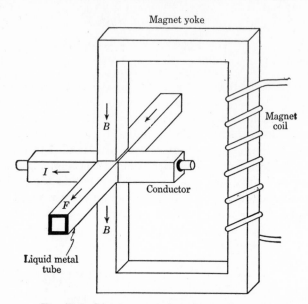

Fig. 10.9. Direct-current electromagnetic pump.

in Fig. 10.9. The tube through which the liquid metal flows is flattened in a short section and placed between poles of a d-c electromagnet; an electric current is passed through the coolant by means of copper bars welded to the tube. As in the electric motor, the conductor (here a fluid) experiences a force perpendicular to the magnetic field and the current. The familiar formula for the force F on a conductor of length L in a flux density B due to a current I is

$$F = BIL$$

Here L is the diameter of the square section of pipe. The static pressure is $P = F/A = BIL/A = BI/W$, where W is the width of the pipe in the field direction. In useful units,

$$P \ (\text{lb/in.}^2) = \frac{0.57 \ B \ (\text{kilogauss}) \ I \ (\text{kiloampere})}{W \ (\text{in.})}$$

We shall make a few simple calculations on a typical liquid sodium unit to find out the size, currents and the electrical power needed to provide a given static pressure. Assume that the square pipe has a 1-in. inside diameter, and the necessary pressure is 20 lb/in.²; let the conductor and pole piece each have a 1-in.² cross section. The product BI must thus be $(20)(1)/0.57 = 35$.

In order to avoid insulation failure at high operating temperatures, it will be necessary to design the magnet for low voltage drop, and high current. We shall assume that the current I is 20,000 amp. Thus the magnetic flux density must be

$$B = \frac{35 \ (\text{kiloampere-kilogauss})}{20 \ (\text{kiloamperes})} = 1.75 \ \text{kilogauss}$$

The total flux in a 1-in. area is $\phi = BA = (1750 \ \text{gauss})(6.45 \ \text{cm}^2)$ $= 11,300$ lines, where the permeability of sodium is taken as unity. An arbitrary choice of a 2-ft (61 cm) effective path length in the magnet will be made. We shall choose a magnet yoke material of high permeability such as Hipernik, for which $\mu \simeq 6000$. The fundamental equation of the magnetic circuit may be applied.

Magnetomotive force $= (\text{flux})(\text{reluctance})$

$$0.4\pi NI = \phi \left(\frac{l_1}{\mu_1 A_1} + \frac{l_2}{\mu_2 A_2} + \ \dots \right)$$

We neglect the contribution of the copper tubing and leakage in air and assume that the magnet yoke area is 1 in.². The area factors cancel and the formula reduces to

$$NI = \frac{1}{0.4\pi} 1750 \left(\frac{61}{6000} + \frac{2.54}{1} \right)$$
$$= 3550 \ \text{ampere turns}$$

A reasonable choice of magnet current is 20 amp, which implies 178 turns. Number 12 wire (0.08 in. in diameter) would have adequate capacity. The magnet power can now be computed. With account taken of wire insulation, the length of wire per turn is about 5 in., and the total length is 890 in. or 74 ft. With a resistance of number 12 wire per 1000 ft at 1.93 ohms at 167°F, the resistance of the magnet coil is $(0.074)(1.93) = 0.143$ ohms. The voltage needed is thus $(20\text{ amp})(0.143\text{ ohms}) = 2.86$ v; the magnet power is $(2.86\text{ v})(20\text{ amp}) = 57.2$ watts. Thus the magnetic circuit is found not to require appreciable power. We next turn to the current supply. The analogy between the electromagnetic pump and the motor gives the relation

$$E = IR + KBlv$$

where IR is the voltage drop across the conductor and $KBlv$ is the counter emf with $K = 10^{-8}$. The resistivity of sodium is 13.2×10^{-6} ohm-cm at 200°C; the resistance of a 1-in. cube is thus 5.2×10^{-6} ohms. The voltage drop is $(20{,}000\text{ amp})(5.2 \times 10^{-6}\text{ ohm}) = 0.104$ v. With a fluid velocity of 100 ft/sec = 3050 cm/sec, the back emf is $10^{-8} (1750)(2.54)(3050) = 0.136$ v, making the total emf needed $0.104 + 0.136 = 0.240$ v. The electrical power is

$$EI = (0.240)(2 \times 10^4) = 4800\text{ watts}$$

In order to accommodate the flow through a large power reactor with some 500 tubes, each of 1-in.² area, average velocity 4.3 ft/sec, it would be necessary to provide some twenty such pumps. An alternative is to increase the pole face area and tube size. The total power in any event is a small fraction of the reactor power.

The electromagnetic principle can also be adapted to the measurement of flow rate. The two poles of a permanent Alnico magnet are placed on opposite sides of the pipe through which the liquid metal flow is to be measured. The potential developed across the diameter of the fluid in the pipe is proportional to the number of flux lines cut by the fluid conductor, and hence the flow rate.

10.8 Heat transfer in enriched reactors

The description of reactor cooling in the preceding sections has been related only to a heterogeneous natural uranium system, largely for security reasons. In the general remarks that follow on the arrangement of coolant and fuel in enriched reactors, no reference is made to specific machines. In a reactor using nearly pure U^{235}, the volume of fuel is very small in comparison with the coolant and duct volume. For example, in a reactor that is 3 ft on a side (27 ft³) the typical fuel weight of 5 kg of U^{235} would occupy only about 16 cubic *inches*. It is desirable to avoid the necessity of fabricating thin tubes or plating thin layers of uranium on tubes of other metal.

One system that has been studied extensively by metallurgists consists of a mixture of a uranium compound and a metal. E. J. Boyle[*] of the Oak Ridge National Laboratory has quoted uranium sulfide and cerium as (improbable) examples. The materials are powdered and hot-pressed into sheets of the required shape. The heat generated within the highly diluted fuel is transferred through the metal "binder." Many combinations of compounds and metals have been studied from the standpoint of strength, stability, and particularly for corrosion of the non-fissionable metal, a layer of which usually separates the coolant from the fuel-bearing component. It is clear that such a layer is needed to isolate fission products from the coolant. The fuel and metal must be chemically compatible. For example the materials should be chosen to prevent high temperature alloying that would carry uranium through the metal into the coolant. For low temperature reactors, a stable alloy of uranium and aluminum appears to be satisfactory for fuel elements. Much consideration has been given to fluidized reactors, in which the fuel is suspended or dissolved in another element or compound. Exclusive of water, there appear to be few materials containing light elements that are suitable. Most hydroxides, which would be good moderators, being rich in hydrogen and oxygen, attack metals severely at the operating temperatures. For instance with barium hydroxide, the type of corrosion labeled "mass transfer" occurs. The metal of the ducts dissolves in the heated fluid at one point and deposits elsewhere in the form of crystalline dendrites.

Problems

10.1 Find the temperature drop in a slug in which the flux and thus the heat generation is approximately *parabolic* across its diameter. How does this result compare with $q_1/4\pi k$?

10.2 Calculate the total power that may be developed in a 9-ft long line of slugs using the data of Section 10.1, assuming that the maximum metal temperature is 750°F.

10.3 From a study of Eq. 10.5, and the heat transfer formulas of Section 10.5, state what would be expected to happen to the total heat if:

(1) the slug radius is increased, keeping the annulus thickness fixed.

[*] In a talk at North Carolina State College, March 31, 1953.

(2) the annulus thickness is increased, at fixed slug radius.

(3) the inlet temperature of the coolant is reduced.

10.4 Find the temperature drop in a slug that is cooled only by a fluid passing through a tube down its axis. Discuss the nuclear and heat transfer advantages and/or disadvantages of such cooling in comparison with annular cooling.

10.5 Show that one British viscosity unit is equal to 6.72×10^{-4} centipoise.

10.6 Find the pressure drop in a 1-in. circular tube through which 100 gal/hr of water flows. Is the flow laminar or turbulent?

10.7 If the cooling air for the porous reactor (Section 10.3) were heated from 68°F to 250°F, what reactor power would it handle?

10.8 Show that the various "groups" of Section 10.4 are actually dimensionless.

10.9 Calculate the heat transfer coefficient h for 600°C liquid bismuth flowing in a $\frac{1}{8}$-in. diameter circular pipe, using the following data: speed = 20 ft/sec; density = 9.66 g/cm³; heat capacity = 0.0397 cal/g-°C; viscosity = 0.996 centipoise; thermal conductivity = 0.037 cal/sec-cm-°C.

10.10 Estimate whether or not the *radiative* heat loss from a slug at 1000°F to a graphite moderator at 200°F is an important factor to consider.

10.11 It is proposed to cool an intermediate neutron reactor consisting of thin circular tubes of enriched uranium by a flow of mercury down the central axis. Assume that the power developed in the cubical core 1 ft on a side is 1 mw. Assuming that liquid mercury at average temperature 300°C is to be used as coolant, estimate the size, spacing and number of cooling tubes to remove the heat. Miscellaneous data on Hg at 300°C: density = 12.88 g/cm³; heat capacity = 0.0323 cal/g-°C; viscosity = 0.90 centipoise; thermal conductivity = 0.033 cal/sec-cm-°C.

References

Bonilla, C. F., *An Up-to-Date Review of the Principles of Heat Transfer, with Particular Application to Nuclear Power*, M-4476. Gibbs and Cox, Inc., 1949.

Hyman, S. C. and C. F. Bonilla, *Heat Transfer by Natural Convection from Horizontal Cylinders to Liquid Metals.* (Three progress reports): NYO-77, September 30, 1949; NYO-558, December 31, 1949; NYO-559, March 31, 1950. New York: Columbia University.

BUCHBERG, H., R. BROMBERG, et al., *Final Report on Studies in Boiling Heat Transfer*, COO-24. University of California, March, 1951.

JAKOB, M., *Heat Transfer*. New York: John Wiley & Sons, 1951, Vol. I.

MCADAMS, W. H., *Heat Transmission*. New York: McGraw-Hill Book Co., 1947.

COWEN, DON, Ed., *Heat Transfer Lectures*. Vol. I, December, 1948, AECU-116; Vol. II, June, 1949, NEPA-979. Fairchild Engine and Airplane Corp.

SCHWARTZ, H., *Natural Convection Cooling of Liquid Homogeneous Reactors*, AECU-706. Downey, Cal.: North American Aviation, Inc., December, 1949.

LYON, RICHARD N., Ed., *Liquid Metals Handbook*, 2d Ed. Washington, D. C.: U. S. Government Printing Office, June, 1952. A recommended purchase.

BROWN, GEORGE GRANGER, Ed., *Unit Operations*. New York: John Wiley & Sons, 1950. Very useful reference on fluid flow.

HALL, N. A., *Thermodynamics of Fluid Flow*. New York: Prentice-Hall, Inc., 1951.

TROCKI, THOMAS, "Engineering Aspects of Liquid Metals for Heat Transfer." *Nucleonics*, January (1952) p. 28.

BARNES, A. H., "Direct Current Electromagnetic Pumps." *Nucleonics*, January (1953) p. 16.

CARTER, J. C., *Temperature and Stress Distribution in Spheres, Rods, Tubes and Plates in which the Heat Source is within the Boundaries of the Solids*, ANL-4690. Argonne National Laboratory, September 7, 1951.

BINDER, R. C., *Fluid Mechanics*. New York: Prentice-Hall, Inc., 1949.

CHAPTER 11

DESIGN OF GAS-COOLED ENRICHED URANIUM REACTOR

The concepts, facts about materials, and formulas described in previous chapters are sufficient to allow us to make a first approximation calculation of a complete reactor. No reference to actual machines aside from those that are unclassified needs to be made; any resemblance to real reactors will be due to the fact that the same basic theory is used for the most common of them. We shall attempt to estimate the critical size, devise a reasonable cooling system, and indicate the materials of which the unit is constructed with the simple mathematics and engineering data at our disposal. It is expected that the results of the computations will be nearly, but not exactly the same as those done by more refined methods, or those found by experiments.

11.1 Choice of purpose and general features

The first consideration is "For what is the reactor to be used?" As discussed in Chapter 6, the possible choices are power, propulsion, breeding, and experimental work. A reactor for an airplane or submarine would have many special requirements on size, shape, weight and shielding. We shall reserve investigations of such a machine until a later chapter. The water boiler has served as an introduction to the experimental unit. Thus we shall investigate a simple stationary power breeder reactor. In this hypothetical example, we take the following:

(1) The reactor should provide practical amounts of electrical power, corresponding to a steam or hydro-electric plant. A typical power rating might be 100 megawatts. If the efficiency of conversion of reactor heat into useful electricity is of the order of 20 per cent, then the reactor core must be designed for 500 mw.

(2) The system should replace some of the fissionable material that is used up to give the power. We shall examine the possibility of exact regeneration or breeding.

(3) The reactor should be small. This will give us a low cost of moderator, flexibility of location, and a minimum of space for housing the machine.

Some of the requirements listed above fix the choice of type; others are left to our discretion. The restriction to small size, for instance, strongly suggests an enriched uranium reactor. For the coolant, however, either a gas or a liquid might be used. We adopt helium because of its negligible neutron absorption and good heat conductivity. The reactor that is most familiar, easiest to control and safest is the one depending on thermal neutrons for fission; thus, the choice of a thermal type is logical. The cheapest low cross-section moderator (other than water) is graphite. The U^{235} will be homogeneously dispersed through the graphite. This mixture might be achieved by introducing finely divided uranium or uranium carbide in the graphite during its manufacture. A summary of the choices taken is made:

Type: Thermal, homogeneous
Function: Power and breeding
Fissionable material: Pure U^{235}
Moderator: Graphite
Coolant: Helium
Shape: Cubical

There are two possible arrangements of the material in which breeding is achieved. One might insert layers of U^{238} or natural uranium within the core to absorb neutrons and be converted into plutonium. We shall instead line the outside of the unit with natural uranium to capture the neutrons that would otherwise escape. Thus the disadvantage of high leakage in a small reactor is turned into an advantage. How thick the shell or "blanket" should be to be satisfactory and what will be the degree of conversion to Pu^{239} must be analyzed. We know that the power level at which the reactor operates is set only by the amount the control rods are removed, assuming that the coolant is adequate to maintain a safe core temperature (well below the point graphite vaporizes). The important consideration at this stage is the *neutron economy*. The amount of absorbing moderator must be such that there are enough neutrons left over to give plutonium. As discussed on several occasions, for each fission in U^{235}, 2.5 neutrons are released but only 2.1 neutrons are available per absorption in U^{235}. One neutron is required to keep the chain going, leaving 1.1 as the maximum number in excess. If the 1.0 neutron is reserved for absorption in U^{238} for plutonium production, there will only be 0.1 to take care of all absorption in moderator, poisons, and structural parts. This is a very close margin, and it might turn out in practice that only 80 or 90 per cent of the U^{235} burned could be replaced by plutonium. On the basis of the argument above, however, we shall aim for exact replacement.

11.2 Reactor calculations

Let us assume that the absorption in the carbon moderator is only 0.1 of that in U^{235}, i.e., $\Sigma_C = 0.1 \Sigma_U$. The proper carbon-to-U^{235} atom ratio follows from this condition: $N_C \sigma_C = 0.1 N_U \sigma_U$ or

$$N_C/N_U = (0.1)(650)/0.0045 = 1.44 \times 10^4$$

Since the U^{235} is uniformly distributed through the graphite, the thermal utilization f is easily calculated to be

$$f = \frac{\Sigma_U}{\Sigma_U + \Sigma_C} = \frac{1}{1 + \Sigma_C/\Sigma_U} = \frac{1}{1 + 0.1} = 0.909$$

and the multiplication constant is $k_\infty = \eta f = (2.1)(0.909) = 1.91$. The critical size can be found by applying the leakage factors. Now $k_{eff} = k_\infty \mathcal{L}_f \mathcal{L}_t$ must be unity, or

$$1 = \frac{k_\infty e^{-K^2 \tau}}{1 + K^2 L^2}$$

We take the value of the age τ for pure graphite as 300 cm², while L is 50 cm. We assume no correction to the age for the uranium, but adjust the thermal diffusion length by the relation

$$L^2 = L_0^2 (1 - f)$$

Thus
$$L^2 = (2500)(0.091) = 227 \text{ cm}^2$$

By trial and error we may find a value of K^2 that satisfies the equation

$$k_{eff} = \frac{1.91 e^{-300K^2}}{1 + 227K^2}$$

where k_{eff} is a function of K^2 that must be made equal to 1.

Trial	1	2	3	4	5
K^2	0.005	0.002	0.001	0.0013	0.00129
k_{eff}	0.200	0.721	1.153	0.999	1.003

The effective multiplication constant for the last trial is close enough to unity for our purpose. The size-shape factor for this cubical reactor is $K^2 = 3(\pi/s)^2 = 0.00129$ so that the side is $s = \pi\sqrt{3/0.00129} = 152$ cm or 5.0 ft. The mass of graphite, if its density is 1.65 g/cm³, is thus $M_C = (152)^3(1.65) = 5.79 \times 10^6$ g $= 5790$ kg $= 6.4$ tons. The U²³⁵ mass may be found from the relative atomic weights and the ratio of numbers of atoms:

$$\frac{M_U}{M_C} = \frac{235 N_U}{12 N_C} = \frac{19.6}{N_C/N_U}$$

or $M_U = (5790)(19.6/1.44 \times 10^4) = 7.88$ kg. This completes our first rough approximation to the reactor size and weights of material. The U²³⁵ weight is not excessive, being only 10 times that for the water boiler.

No account has yet been taken of space needed for coolant tubes. Here we resort to arbitrary assumptions and perform trial and error estimates. One could presumably set up the whole nuclear and heat transfer problem in one formula, but the approach adopted here is

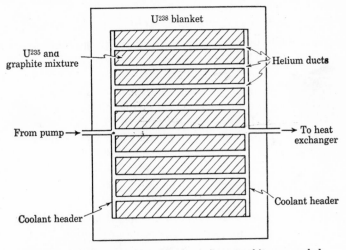

Fig. 11.1. Homogeneous enriched uranium-graphite gas-cooled reactor.

the more natural for exploratory purposes. Let the reactor be pierced with horizontal tubes of such a number and size that they occupy one-third of the total volume of the reactor, whatever final size it has. See Fig. 11.1. It is clear that more uranium and graphite must be added to compensate for this space. The next task is to estimate this amount. With one-third voids, the fast and thermal diffusion lengths will be increased, i.e., neutrons will make fewer collisions in moving about, and thus go farther before becoming thermal or being absorbed. Our first guess as to the effect the voids have is that their volume is distributed uniformly through the cube, reducing the density to two-thirds of its original value. Thus L is increased by a factor of $3/2$, L^2 by $9/4$, as is τ. Returning to the critical reactor formula we note that the equation is still satisfied if K^2 is $4/9$ as big as it was. This implies that the side s is $3/2$ times as large as before. The volume, however, is now increased by $(3/2)^3 = 3.375$. Carbon and uranium only occupy two-thirds of this total space, so they are each increased by a factor $(2/3)(3.375) = 2.25$. The appropriate factors are applied, to yield the specifications of the modified reactor.

Mass of graphite: $M_C = 13,000$ kg
Mass of U^{235}: $M_U = 17.7$ kg
Reactor side: $s = 228$ cm $= 7.5$ ft

11.3 Determination of cooling system

We are now ready to check what the helium flow and pumping power requirements are to handle the 500-mw core power. Several simplifying assumptions are made. (a) The flux through the reactor is uniform. This is certainly not the case, even with a reflector, but will eliminate the slight complication of sine functions. (b) The heat conductivity through the core is very good, so that the temperature of the graphite-uranium mixture and the tube wall are the same throughout the reactor. We take this temperature T_r to be 1000°C. (c) The inlet helium temperature is $T_0 = 150$°C; the outlet temperature $T_1 = 750$°C. For purposes of calculating heat transfer from the core to the gas, the average value $\overline{T} = 450$°C will be used. (d) The helium will be at 10 atm inlet pressure. In Chapter 10, the British thermal system of units were used in heat transfer calculations. Here, the cgs system will be substituted for variety and to serve as illustration of its equal validity and convenience. We apply the first principle of heat transfer, Section 10.1, described by

$$Q = cM(T_1 - T_0)$$

All quantities are known except the helium mass flow rate M. Now

$$Q = 500 \, \text{mw}$$
$$= 5 \times 10^8 \, (\text{watts})/4.186(\text{watt-sec/cal})$$
$$= 1.19 \times 10^8 \, \text{cal/sec}$$
$$c = 1.25 \, \text{cal/g-°C}, \quad \text{and} \quad T_1 - T_0 = 600°C$$

The mass flow rate is therefore

$$M = \frac{1.19 \times 10^8 \, (\text{cal/sec})}{1.25 \, (\text{cal/g-°C}) \, 600 \, (°C)} = 1.59 \times 10^5 \, \text{g/sec}$$

The flow velocity v may now be found from the definition $M = \rho v A$. The total area of all pipes through which helium flows was set by the one-third volume condition. The area of a face of reactor is $(228)^2 = 5.20 \times 10^4 \, \text{cm}^2$, and the total tube area is one-third of this or $1.73 \times 10^4 \, \text{cm}^2 = A$. For helium at an average temperature of $450°$ and 10-atm pressure, the density ρ is $(10)(273/723) = 3.78$ times its value of $1.785 \times 10^{-4} \, \text{g/cm}^3$ at standard temperature and pressure ($0°C$, 1 atm). Thus $\rho = 6.75 \times 10^{-4} \, \text{g/cm}^3$. Thus the flow velocity is

$$v = \frac{M}{\rho A}$$
$$= \frac{1.59 \times 10^5 \, (\text{g/sec})}{(6.75 \times 10^{-4} \, \text{g/cm}^3)(1.73 \times 10^4 \, \text{cm}^2)}$$
$$= 13,600 \, \text{cm/sec}$$

The only quantity left to be found is the diameter D of each individual pipe, which must come from the heat transfer calculations. Apply the second heat transfer principle

$$q = h S_1 (T_r - T)$$

where T_r is the reactor temperature, T is the coolant temperature, and S_1 is the surface area per unit length of the helium duct. If the reactor is assumed to be uniformly at $1000°C$, the average coolant temperature is $450°$, and the heat generation is uniform in the reactor, the use of the formula above may be extended to apply to the whole reactor.

$$Q = h S (T_r - \overline{T})$$

where S is now the total cooling surface area. S may be computed in terms of the (unknown) pipe diameter. For one pipe, the surface is $\pi D s$, where s is the tube length, the same as the reactor side. The number of pipes is simply the total tube area in the reactor face divided by the cross section per pipe, i.e. $\left(\dfrac{s^2/3}{\pi D^2/4}\right)$, making the total surface $S = 4s^3/3D = 1.58 \times 10^7/D$. Now solve for h in terms of known constants

$$h = \frac{Q}{S(T_r - \overline{T})} = \frac{1.19 \times 10^8 D}{(1.58 \times 10^7)(1000 - 450)}$$
$$= 0.0137D$$

The heat transfer coefficient also contains D explicitly from the semi-empirical relation applicable to gases (see Section 10.5)

$$N_N = 0.023(N_R)^{0.8}(N_{Pr})^{0.4}$$

where
$$N_N = \frac{hD}{k}, \quad N_R = \frac{D\rho v}{\mu}, \quad N_{Pr} = \frac{c\mu}{k}$$

The necessary new constants are listed:

$$\mu = 3.60 \times 10^{-4} \text{ g/cm-sec (poises)}$$
$$k = 3.39 \times 10^{-4} \text{ cal/sec-°C-cm}$$

Thus

$$N_{Pr} = \frac{(1.25 \text{ cal/g/°C})(3.60 \times 10^{-4} \text{ g/cm-sec})}{(3.39 \times 10^{-4} \text{ cal/sec-°C-cm})}$$
$$= 1.33$$
$$N_R = \frac{(D \text{ cm})(6.75 \times 10^{-4} \text{ g/cm}^3)(13,600 \text{ cm/sec})}{(3.60 \times 10^{-4} \text{ g/cm-sec})}$$
$$= 2.55 \times 10^4 D$$
$$(N_{Pr})^{0.4} = 1.12, \quad (N_R)^{0.8} = 3.35 \times 10^3 D^{0.8}$$

Thus

$$h = \frac{N_N k}{D}$$
$$= \frac{(0.023)(3.35 \times 10^3 D^{0.8})(1.12)(3.39 \times 10^{-4})}{D}$$

The two relations for h in terms of D are now

$$h = 0.0293/D^{0.2}, \qquad h = 0.0137D$$

Eliminating h, we obtain, $D = 1.88$ cm, or 0.74 in. The total number of tubes is 6250. The Reynolds number turns out to be

$(2.55 \times 10^4)(1.88) = 47{,}900$, far above the value of 2000 at which turbulent flow sets in. Several more calculations may now be made: (a) the pressure drop through the coolant ducts and the pumping power; (b) the average neutron flux; (c) the necessary thickness of natural uranium to capture the leakage neutrons; (d) the conversion factor (plutonium produced/U^{235} burned).

11.4 Auxiliaries

Pressure drop and pumping power. According to Fanning's equation (see Section 10.2) the total pressure drop in the reactor is

$$\Delta p = \frac{fv^2\rho s}{2D}\left(\frac{\text{dynes}}{\text{cm}^2}\right)$$

where the friction factor is given by

$$f/4 = 0.046(N_R)^{-0.2} = 0.046(0.479 \times 10^5)^{-0.2}$$
$$= 0.00533$$
$$\Delta p = \frac{(2)(0.00533)(13{,}600 \text{ cm/sec})^2(6.75 \times 10^{-4} \text{ g/cm}^3)(228 \text{ cm})}{(1.88 \text{ cm})}$$
$$\Delta p = 1.61 \times 10^5 \text{ dynes/cm}^2$$

Using the conversion factor 1 atm $= 1.013 \times 10^6$ dynes/cm^2 this amounts to 0.159 atm. The pumping power is the product of pressure drop and volume flow rate:

$$P_p = (\Delta p)(vA)$$
$$= (1.61 \times 10^5 \text{ dynes/cm}^2)(13{,}600 \text{ cm/sec})(1.73 \times 10^4 \text{ cm}^2)$$
$$P_p = 3.8 \times 10^{13} \text{ ergs/sec} = 3.8 \times 10^6 \text{ joules/sec}$$
$$= 3800 \text{ kw}$$

The pumping requirement is thus less than 4 per cent of the total useful power output.

Average neutron flux. The macroscopic fission cross section is

$$\Sigma_f = N_U\,(\sigma_f)_U = \frac{N_C(\sigma_f)_U}{N_C/N_U}$$
$$= \frac{(0.0827 \times 10^{24})(549 \times 10^{-24})}{(1.44 \times 10^4)}$$

or $$\Sigma_f = 3.15 \times 10^{-3}$$

Thus the average flux is (see Section 6.4)

$$\bar{\phi} = \frac{cP}{\Sigma_f V} = \frac{(3 \times 10^{10})(500 \times 10^6)}{(3.15 \times 10^{-3})(7.90 \times 10^6)}$$
$$= 6.0 \times 10^{14}/\text{cm}^2\text{-sec}$$

Note that V is the volume of uranium-graphite mixture, not that of the reactor as a whole, since only the flux in the medium yields power.

Blanket thickness. The layer of natural uranium must be of such thickness that the neutron flux is reduced essentially to zero at its outer edge. A first estimate may be obtained by applying the exponential relation $\phi/\phi_0 = e^{-\Sigma_a x}$ and assuming an attenuation of a factor of 1000 as being sufficient. For thermal neutrons in natural uranium, $\Sigma_a = 0.351$. Thus $e^{-0.351x} = 10^{-3}$, and $x = 20$ cm or a little over 6 in.

Conversion factor, plutonium production, and U^{235} burn-up. The number of plutonium atoms produced per U^{235} atom burned is presumably close to unity by the criterion on which the design was made. Several factors may complicate the calculation, however. First, the escaping neutrons are of all energies. The relative amounts of resonance capture and thermal capture in the blanket are not known. The former gives rise to plutonium; there is competition in the latter between U^{238} and U^{235}. Some fission would thus be expected in the blanket, giving neutrons without burning any of the core U^{235}. This gain would help to offset the net loss by capture of core neutrons in U^{235} to form U^{236}. Let us assume that all the neutrons escaping from the core produce plutonium as if the blanket were pure U^{238}. These amount to $k_\infty - 1 = 0.91$. The number absorbed in U^{235} is simply $f = 0.91$, so the conversion factor is

$$(\text{CF}) = \left(\frac{\text{number of Pu atoms formed}}{\text{number of U}^{235}\text{ atoms burned}}\right)$$
$$= 1.0 \text{ (as desired)}$$

Thus the plutonium production and U^{235} consumption rates are equal. The number of fissions per second is $(3 \times 10^{10})(500 \times 10^6) = 1.5 \times 10^{19}$. There are $\sigma_a/\sigma_f = 650/549 = 1.18$ times as many absorptions as fissions, or 1.77×10^{19}/sec. The U^{235} usage is

$$(1.77 \times 10^{19})(235/6.023 \times 10^{23}) = 6.9 \times 10^{-3} \text{ g/sec}$$

or 218 kg/yr. It is seen that the burn-up is many times the initial loading. Thus a means to remove used material and add new would have to be devised. A lattice arrangement of fuel and moderator blocks might be considered. If the value of electrical energy were taken to be approximately 5 mills per kwhr, the electricity generated in one year would be worth $(10^5 \text{ kw})(8.76 \times 10^3 \text{ hr/yr})(\$0.005/\text{kwhr})$ = 4.4 million dollars. This is all the more remarkable in that the net fissionable material used is exactly zero.

Problems

11.1 Devise a numerical formula relating the mass of U^{235} in a light-water moderated reactor to the atom ratio $N_H/N_{U^{235}}$.

11.2 Find the critical size of the graphite-uranium reactor if its length is twice each of the two sides.

11.3 Find out how much change in thermal utilization would result from using air at 5 atm pressure, 500°C temperature, as the coolant for the uranium-graphite reactor.

11.4 Estimate the total amount of heat produced by the thermal flux in the 6-in. breeding blanket because of fission in U^{235}. Consider an appropriate system for cooling the blanket.

11.5 If the conversion factor from U^{235} to Pu were only 0.75, how long would it take to accumulate a mass of fuel equal to that initially loaded in the reactor?

11.6 Investigate the possibility of deliberately adding to the fuel-moderator mixture uniformly, a strong neutron absorber such as cadmium or boron, the burn-up of which in time would compensate for the loss of U^{235} so far as f is concerned. What happens to the neutron economy for Pu production if a poison is added?

11.7 Prove that for an enriched reactor surrounded by pure U^{238} $(CF) = (k_\infty - 1)/f$.

References

SOODAK, HARRY and E. C. CAMPBELL, *Elementary Pile Theory*. New York: John Wiley & Sons, 1950.

MCADAMS, W. H., *Heat Transmission*. New York: McGraw-Hill Book Co., 1947.

GOODMAN, C., Ed., *The Science and Engineering of Nuclear Power*. Cambridge, Mass.: Addison-Wesley Press, 1949, Vols. I, II.

CHAPTER 12

DESIGN OF LIQUID-METAL COOLED NATURAL-URANIUM REACTOR

A detailed description of the method of calculating the properties of a heterogeneous reactor is presented in this chapter in a form that is believed to be most useful to the reader who does not have an extensive background of advanced mathematics.*

12.1 Choice of reactor

The process of resonance capture of neutrons in U^{238} makes it impossible to sustain a chain reaction in a *homogeneous* mixture of natural uranium with a graphite moderator, as discussed in Chapter 6. The reason is that the fast neutrons, as they slow down through the resonance energies, are in intimate contact with U^{238} nuclei and have ample opportunity to collide with them. Thus neutrons have little chance of proceeding on to thermal energies. One is forced to isolate the moderating medium from the fissionable material by constructing a *heterogeneous* system, either using lumps or cylindrical slugs of uranium imbedded in the moderator. In such a lattice arrangement, the fission neutrons escape from the metal, slow down principally in the moderator, and eventually are absorbed as thermal neutrons in the slug. As discussed in Chapter 6, two modifications in the calculations of the multiplication constant must be made:

(1) The resonance capture that still exists after the lumping arrangement has been made must be evaluated. The heterogeneous nature of the system must be accounted for in the estimate of the resonance escape probability p appearing in the relation $k_\infty = \epsilon p \eta f$.

(2) Since the thermal neutron flux through the system is no longer uniform, with stronger absorption taking place in the slug than in the moderator, the calculation of thermal utilization f must include the proper weighting factors of the average fluxes in the fuel and the moderator, $\bar{\phi}_U$ and $\bar{\phi}_M$.

---

* Despite the simplifications, the method is highly technical, and the reader who is interested in the broader aspects of the nuclear energy field may do well to omit the section. This may be done without loss of continuity.

We shall review these two modifications and apply them to a specific design. Following the pattern set by the study of the gas cooled reactor, Chapter 11, we shall propose a use for the reactor and decide on its composition. Let us assume that we are interested in a relatively small, high-neutron flux unit for design studies on heat transfer with liquid metals, with anticipated extension of the design to a larger scale system. Practical use is to be made of the heat developed in the reactor. It is assumed that a turbo-generator operated by steam is to be coupled to the reactor through a heat exchanger. The requirement that the reactor should be small makes it necessary that the moderator have a small thermal-neutron absorption cross section. Heavy water would seem to be the ideal moderator. Its σ_a per molecule in pure form is 0.92 millibarns in comparison with σ_a for graphite of 4.5 millibarns; the logarithmic slowing down loss ξ in D_2O is the largest of all compounds except light water. The choice of slug size and lattice arrangement is arbitrary until there is evidence by actual calculation that the system will or will not multiply. We shall adopt for trial the dimensions of the Oak Ridge reactor, with 1.1 in. diameter slugs on 8-in. centers arranged as in Fig. 12.1. Since the moderator is to be liquid it will probably be desirable to contain it in a cylindrical tank as was done in the Chicago heavy water reactor CP-3.

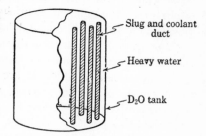

Fig. 12.1. Core of heterogeneous liquid-metal cooled reactor.

The physical arrangement of this latter reactor can be examined to give us a general model for our design. A 6-ft diameter aluminum tank, 8 ft 10 in. high, is filled with approximately $6\frac{1}{2}$ tons of heavy water. Suspended vertically in the tank are 120 natural uranium rods, each 6 ft long and 1.1 in. in diameter. The rods are arranged in a square lattice with centerline separation of $5\frac{3}{8}$ in. The heavy water is circulated, to serve as a coolant in addition to its normal function as moderator. The 300 kw of heat developed is removed by passing 200 gal/min of heavy water at around 35°C through a heat exchanger, in which the water is cooled about 8°C for the return to the reactor. A 2-ft thick graphite reflector surrounds the tank, followed by a 4-in. lead-cadmium alloy gamma-neutron shield, and an 8-ft concrete shield. Safety and control rods are made of tubular Al-Cd-Al sandwiches, $3\frac{1}{2}$ in. in diameter, supported from the lid of the tank at an angle of about 30° from the vertical. A rod is lifted "out" by raising the lower end to put the rod in a horizontal position.

12.2 Calculation of thermal utilization

Our first task will be the determination of the thermal utilization, which appears in the effective multiplication constant in two places: (a) directly in the four-factor formula $k_\infty = \epsilon p \eta f$ and (b) in the effective diffusion length L of the reactor system. In Chapter 6 we set down the essentials of the calculation method, which will be applied here. The most troublesome problem is not the computations, but the accumulation of correct or reasonable physical constants. This is particularly true if the reactor has a moderator that is a compound or mixture, if the uranium is enriched, or if use is made of an unusual material, for which experimental data are not available. Heavy water is a good example to illustrate this difficulty. One might well criticize the emphasis that we put on constants, on the ground that numbers for many standard materials are available in various references. Seldom is the method of arriving at them revealed, however, which puts the burden on the nuclear engineer to find the original constants.

The microscopic cross section for thermal neutron absorption per atom of deuterium is listed in AECU-2040 (see References) as $(\sigma_a)_D = 0.46 \times 10^{-3}$ barns. That for oxygen is quoted to be less than 0.2×10^{-3} barns. If we assume $(\sigma_a)_O$ to be negligible in comparison with $(\sigma_a)_D$, the macroscopic cross section is $(\Sigma_a)_{D_2O} = 2N_{D_2O}(\sigma_a)_D$ where the number of heavy water molecules per unit volume is $N_{D_2O} = (1.1/20)(6.023 \times 10^{23}) = 0.0331 \times 10^{24}$. We find $(\Sigma_a)_{D_2O} = 3.04 \times 10^{-5}$ cm^{-1}. Experimental measurements in Canada by Sargent, et al., yield a figure for the thermal neutron diffusion length in pure D_2O, $L = 171$ cm. At this point we must question the possibility of obtaining perfectly pure D_2O in the large quantities needed in a reactor, or having put it in the system, that it remains pure. It is a well known fact that the moisture in the air contaminates exposed heavy water rather rapidly. The hydrogen cross section is almost 1000 times that for deuterium, so a 0.1 per cent contamination would double the effective cross section. Glasstone and Edlund list figures that appear to be more realistic: $(\Sigma_a)_{D_2O} = 8.0 \times 10^{-5}$ and

$L = 100$ cm. Both of these data are consistent with those for pure D_2O if one assumes an H_2O content of about 0.23 per cent. In all further calculations, we will accept the *higher* cross-section data.

The second important constant to be found is the reciprocal diffusion length K_0 for natural uranium. The first thought would be to apply the formula from diffusion theory of Section 2.7 to the calculation of L. The theory does not apply, however, to strongly absorbing media, such as uranium, and a more rigorous formula from transport theory applicable to a heavy element must be used,

$$\frac{K}{\Sigma} = \tanh \frac{K}{\Sigma_s}$$

In this transcendental formula Σ_s is the scattering cross section, and Σ is the sum of Σ_s and Σ_a, the absorption cross section. Now $N_U = 0.0473 \times 10^{24}$, $\sigma_a = 7.42$ barns, and $\sigma_s = 8.2$ barns. Therefore,

$$\Sigma_a = 0.351 \text{ cm}^{-1}, \quad \Sigma_s = 0.388 \text{ cm}^{-1}, \quad \Sigma = 0.739 \text{ cm}^{-1}$$

For a *very strong* absorber $\Sigma_a \gg \Sigma_s$, K is simply equal to Σ, which gives a first trial value of 0.739. Repeated adjustments yield the value $K_0 = 0.70$ cm^{-1}. For D_2O, K will be taken as $1/L = 1/100$ or $K_1 = 0.0100$ cm^{-1}.

The procedure for calculating the thermal utilization of the reactor consists of examining the neutron balance in the cell, or smallest

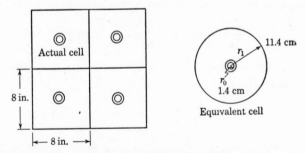

Fig. 12.2. Relation of actual and equivalent cells in a heterogeneous reactor.

unit of the array. The cell is taken as one line of slugs plus its "share" of the moderator. As shown in Fig. 12.2, for our example, this is a square 8 in. on a side and the length of the reactor. The study of one cell is made easier if we consider it as a cylindrical tube, of the same area as the square tube. The equivalent of an 8-in. square is a circle of radius $r_1 = 8/\sqrt{\pi} = 4.52$ in. $= 11.5$ cm. For the first trial calculations, we neglect any cooling channel, and assume the slug has a radius $r_0 = 0.55$ in. $= 1.40$ cm. We may now apply the formulas of Section 6.6 for computing $1/f$, the reciprocal of the thermal utilization for a heterogeneous reactor

$$\frac{1}{f} = 1 + \frac{V_1 \Sigma_1}{V_0 \Sigma_0} \frac{\phi(r_0)}{\bar{\phi}_0} + \delta$$

where

$$\frac{\phi(r_0)}{\bar{\phi}_0} \simeq 1 + \frac{(K_0 r_0)^2}{8} - \frac{(K_0 r_0)^4}{192}$$

and

$$\delta \simeq \frac{(K_1 r_1)^2}{2} \left(\log_e \frac{r_1}{r_0} - \frac{3}{4} \right)$$

Now

$$K_0 r_0 = (0.70)(1.40) = 0.98$$
$$K_1 r_1 = (0.0100)(11.5) = 0.115$$

and

$$\frac{r_1}{r_0} = 11.5/1.40 = 8.2$$

Thus

$$\frac{\phi(r_0)}{\bar{\phi}_0} \simeq 1 + \frac{(0.98)^2}{8} - \frac{(0.98)^4}{192} = 1.115$$

$$\delta \simeq \frac{(0.115)^2}{2} \, (\log_e 8.2 - 0.75) = 0.0089.$$

The volume ratio V_1/V_0 is the same as the area ratio

$$\frac{\pi r_1^2 - \pi r_0^2}{\pi r_0^2} = \left(\frac{r_1}{r_0} \right)^2 - 1 = 66.2$$

The ratio of cross sections is $\Sigma_1/\Sigma_0 = 8.0 \times 10^{-5}/0.351 = 2.28 \times 10^{-4}$. Substituting in the equation for $1/f$,

$$\frac{1}{f} = 1 + (66.2)(2.28 \times 10^{-4})(1.115) + 0.0089$$

$$\frac{1}{f} = 1 + 0.0168 + 0.0089 = 1.0257$$

or

$$f_1 = 0.9749$$

This high thermal utilization might have been expected from the choice of a moderator with low absorption cross section. We label it f_1 because it is a first approximation.

12.3 Corrections for absorption in coolants and ducts

We may regard the thermal utilization just computed as a basic value, which must be corrected for absorption by coolant, the metal duct, by fission product poisons that will be trapped in the slug, and for temperature changes. Elaborate methods are available for incorporating these effects into the original analysis of the flux distribution. Since it is important for the designer and the engineer to appreciate the magnitude of the various effects, we shall consider only the relative sizes rather than seeking absolute accuracy. The procedure amounts to a rough "perturbation" method.

Absorption by coolant. Instead of adopting the diamond-shaped coolant channels of our prototype, the Oak Ridge reactor, let us replace them by cylindrical annuli of the same area, and fill the resultant tubes with liquid sodium instead of air. Assume that the diamond with sides $1\frac{3}{4}$ in. just fits a 1.1-in. diameter slug. By noting that the area of such a figure is the product of the length of a side and the diameter of the inscribed circle $(1.75)(1.1) = 1.925$ in.^{2}, we obtain the following data:

Slug area: $(\pi/4)(1.1)^2 = 0.950$ in.$^2 = 6.13$ cm^2
Coolant cross-sectional area:
$$(1.925) - (0.950) = 0.975 \text{ in.}^2 = 6.29 \text{ cm}^2$$
Outside radius of coolant duct: $\sqrt{1.925/\pi} = 0.783$ in. $= 1.99$ cm
Annulus thickness: 0.233 in. $= 0.59$ cm

Assume that the neutron flux through the coolant is practicall_ the same as that at the surface of the slug $\phi(r_0)$, and add another absorption term to our previous result $1/f_1$. The corrected value $1/f_2$ will be

$$\frac{1}{f_2} = \frac{1}{f_1} + \frac{V_{Na}\,\Sigma_{Na}\,\phi(r_0)}{V_0\,\Sigma_0\,\bar{\phi}_0}$$

The ratio of sodium volume (per unit length of slug) to that of uranium is

$$\frac{V_{Na}}{V_0} = \frac{6.29}{6.13} = 1.026$$

From cross-section tables, Σ_{Na} is computed to be 0.012, making the ratio $\Sigma_{Na}/\Sigma_0 = 0.012/0.351 = 0.0342$. The flux ratio is already known to be 1.115. The change in $1/f$ is

$$\left(\Delta \frac{1}{f}\right)_{Na} = (1.026)(0.0342)(1.115) = 0.0391$$

Thus,
$$\frac{1}{f_2} = \frac{1}{f_1} + \left(\Delta \frac{1}{f}\right)_{Na} = 1.0257 + 0.0391$$
$$= 1.0648$$

and
$$f_2 = 0.9391$$

Absorption by ducts. A similar approach may be used to correct for metal absorption. The chart of liquid metal corrosion with various metals, Section 9.4, Table 9.6, shows that iron is safe for use up to 800°C with liquid sodium. We shall choose thin-walled iron tubes for ease in calculating the absorption, although some alloy such as stainless steel would probably be better for structural strength and to withstand corrosion. The microscopic cross section of iron, 2.43 barns, is relatively high, which requires that the ducts be very thin. As a probable minimum safe thickness, we assume $\Delta r = 1/64$ in. (15.6 mils or 0.0397 cm). The metal volume per unit length is $2\pi r \Delta r = 2\pi(2.01)(0.04) = 0.505$ cm^2; the volume ratio is $V_{Fe}/V_0 = 0.505/6.13 = 0.0824$. With the macroscopic cross section of iron of 0.205, $\Sigma_{Fe}/\Sigma_\theta = 0.205/0.351 = 0.584$. Thus

$$\left(\Delta \frac{1}{f}\right)_{Fe} = (0.0824)(0.584)(1.115) = 0.0537$$

Now let
$$\frac{1}{f_3} = \frac{1}{f_2} + \left(\Delta \frac{1}{f}\right)_{Fe}$$
$$= 1.0648 + 0.0537 = 1.1185$$

and
$$f_3 = 0.8940$$

It is surprising to note that the thin duct of iron contributed more to the absorption loss in f than did the $\frac{1}{4}$-in. annulus of coolant. If stainless steel had been used, $\Sigma_a = 0.253$, the effect of duct would have been some 20 per cent larger. This points up the need to study the properties of coolant and container simultaneously. A coolant of relatively high cross section that will not corrode some available metal of very low cross section may turn out to be the preferable choice. It will be observed that no provisions for a jacket on the uranium slug have been made. Having discovered that the duct absorption is very high, we shall assume that a method will be developed for coating the slugs with an extremely thin layer of low absorption metal. If this is not possible, the absorption that is contributed by whatever canning system we adopt can be added in.

12.4 Absorption by fission product poisons

Fission products evolved in a homogeneous reactor may be continuously or periodically removed, to prevent a contribution of unwanted neutron absorption. Most of the products formed in the slug of a heterogeneous reactor must remain intimately mixed with the uranium. The strongest known absorber of thermal neutrons is the fission product Xe^{135}, for which σ_a is 3.5×10^6 barns. At the start-up of our reactor, there will be none of this isotope present. As time goes on, the concentration would build up to a level that may reduce k below unity were an excess of reactivity not put in the reactor originally. The very fact that Xe^{135} is a strong absorber means that it will be continually "burned out" by the neutron flux. An equilibrium level of Xe concentration will be reached, where formation and loss by absorption are balanced. We shall now develop the working formulas for estimating the amount of Xe^{135} poisoning at equilibrium. The principal decay chain that yields Xe^{135}, labeled with the various half-lives, is the following:

$$_{52}Te^{135} \underset{\beta,\ 2\ min}{\rightarrow} \ _{53}I^{135} \underset{\beta,\ 6.7\ hr}{\rightarrow} \ _{54}Xe^{135} \underset{\beta,\ 9.2\ hr}{\rightarrow} \ _{55}Cs^{135} \underset{\beta,\ 2.1 \times 10^6\ yr}{\rightarrow} \ _{56}Ba^{135} \quad (stable)$$

We shall not be concerned with the relative amounts of xenon that are formed directly or result from the decay of iodine, but assume a yield fraction of Xe^{135} in fission of $y = 0.059$ (see Fig. 3.1). The rate of Xe atom formation is $y\Sigma_f\phi$, where Σ_f is the macroscopic fission cross section of uranium. There are two ways the xenon is lost: (a) by radioactive decay, at a rate $-\lambda N$, where the decay constant λ is 2.1×10^{-5} sec^{-1} and N is the number of atoms of Xe^{135}/cm^3; (b) by burn-out at a rate $-N\sigma\phi$, where σ is the thermal absorption cross section of xenon, 3.5×10^{-18} cm^2. At equilibrium, formation plus loss equals zero or

$$y\Sigma_f\phi - \lambda N - N\sigma\phi = 0$$

from which we obtain

$$\Sigma = N\sigma = \frac{y\Sigma_f}{1 + \lambda/\sigma\phi}$$

for the equilibrium value of macroscopic absorption.

We may now estimate the change in $1/f$ due to this poisoning in one slug.

$$\left(\Delta \frac{1}{f}\right)_{\text{Xe}} = \frac{\Sigma}{\Sigma_{\text{U}}} = \frac{y\,\Sigma_f/\Sigma_{\text{U}}}{1 + \lambda/\sigma\phi}$$

Putting in numerical values, including the ratio $(\sigma_f/\sigma_a)_{\text{U}} = 3.92/7.42$ $= 0.528$

$$\left(\Delta \frac{1}{f}\right)_{\text{Xe}} = \frac{(0.059)(0.528)}{1 + \dfrac{2.1 \times 10^{-5}}{3.5 \times 10^{-18}\,\phi}} = \frac{0.0312}{1 + \dfrac{6.0 \times 10^{12}}{\phi}}$$

The maximum possible change in $1/f$ is 0.0312, corresponding to a flux much greater than 6.0×10^{12}. The minimum change is of course zero at zero flux. At a point in the reactor where the flux is 6.0×10^{12}, $\Delta(1/f)$ would be half the maximum. At this stage, we do not know the reactor size, the power density, or the flux, so we cannot make a good choice. If we attained the CP-3 flux value of 10^{12}, the poisoning would be much smaller than if the flux were 5.8×10^{13}, as in the Chalk River reactor NRX. Until flux data are available we shall arbitrarily take $\Delta(1/f)_{\text{Xe}} = 0.01$. The new $1/f_4$ is thus 1.1285, and $f_4 = 0.8861$. The fractional change in k_∞ produced by the poisoning is approximately equal to the fractional change in $1/f$, as proved below. Treating the correction as if it were of differential size, $d(1/f) = (1/f^2)\,df$, but since $dk/k = df/f$, then

$$\frac{dk}{k} = f\,d\left(\frac{1}{f}\right) = \frac{d(1/f)}{1/f}$$

The maximum effect on k is thus $0.01/1.1185$ or 0.9 per cent. The excess reactivity provided at the start would be accommodated by control rods.

Distributed absorption. Since the xenon absorption depends on neutron flux, which in turn is a function of position in the reactor, the amount of poisoning differs from one slug to another. This situation has not arisen before, because the coolant or duct absorptions bore a constant ratio to the moderator or uranium absorption regardless of position. A method of perturbation that was first used in quantum mechanics may be applied to obtain the correct overall effect on the multiplication constant. It may be shown that the $\Delta(1/f)$ should be *weighted* according to ϕ^2 rather than according to ϕ as one would expect.

The more general expression, applicable to any localized or non-uniformly distributed absorber is

$$\frac{dk}{k} = \frac{\int \Delta\Sigma_a \, \phi^2 dV}{\int \Sigma_a \, \phi^2 dV}$$

where $\Delta\Sigma_a$ is the added macroscopic absorption cross section and the integration is to be taken over the reactor coordinates. To illustrate the use of the formula, let us find the effect of replacing the single short slug at the geometric center of a cubical reactor by one that has an absorption cross section higher by an amount $\Delta\Sigma_a$. Now the flux at this point is ϕ_c, while that at any point (x,y,z) is

$$\phi = \phi_c \sin \frac{\pi x}{s} \sin \frac{\pi y}{s} \sin \frac{\pi z}{s}$$

The integral in the numerator is

$$\int \Delta\Sigma_a \, \phi_c^2 \, dV = v\Delta\Sigma_a \, \phi_c^2$$

where v is the volume of the one slug. ($\Delta\Sigma_a$ is zero everywhere else in the reactor but in the volume v.) The denominator may be found by noting that all integrals of the type $\int_0^s \sin^2 (\pi x/s) \, dx$ are equal to $s/2$. Thus

$$\frac{dk}{k} = \frac{v\Delta\Sigma_a \, \phi_c^2}{\Sigma_a \, \phi_c^2(s/2)^3} = \frac{8v\Delta\Sigma_a}{V\Sigma_a}$$

where V is the total reactor volume. Compare this result with that from distributing the absorber uniformly through the system, with an amount $v\Delta\Sigma_a/V\Sigma_a$ per unit volume. The fractional change in k would then be

$$\frac{dk}{k} = \frac{v\Delta\Sigma_a}{V\Sigma_a} \frac{\int \phi^2 \, dV}{\int \phi^2 \, dV} = \frac{v\Delta\Sigma_a}{V\Sigma_a}$$

We find the remarkable fact than an absorber is *eight times as effective* when located in the center of a reactor as when distributed uniformly throughout it.

12.5 Calculation of resonance escape probability

The ratio of cross sections "Σ_U"/"Σ_M" that appears in the mathematical form of the factor p for a homogeneous reactor

$$p = e^{(-"\Sigma_U"/"\Sigma_M")}$$

resembles the ratio that appears in the thermal utilization

$$\frac{1}{f} = \frac{\Sigma_M}{\Sigma_U} + 1$$

This fact suggests the possibility of formally applying the method of calculation of $1/f$ to the resonance problem, as if the high energy neutrons formed a flux that diffused, and were "absorbed" either by actual capture in U^{238} or by equivalent scattering. On the basis of such an analogy, one may invent a resonance utilization $1/f_r$ from which p is calculated using

$$p = e^{-(1/f_r - 1)^{-1}}$$

The constants "Σ_U" and "Σ_M" for these neutrons are readily evaluated from the formulas of Section 6.5. The logarithmic width of the resonance region is 5.6 corresponding to $E_2/E_1 = 270$ where E_2 and E_1 are the boundaries of the energy range. If E_2 were 54 ev, just beyond the prominent peaks on the uranium cross-section graph, see Fig. 12.4, the lower limit is $E_1 = 0.2$ ev, which is just below the weak resonance peak. The scattering cross section of D_2O over most of this region is $(\sigma_s)_{D_2O} = 10.5$ barns. Thus

$$(\Sigma_s)_{D_2O} = (0.0331)(10.5) = 0.348 \text{ cm}^{-1}$$

The factor ξ should be thought of as a weighted average quantity for the *molecule*, dependent on the relative scattering cross sections and logarithmic energy losses of deuterium and oxygen. Now $\xi_D = 0.726$ and $\xi_O = 0.121$; $(\sigma_s)_O$ for the energy range is 3.8 barns, requiring that $2(\sigma_s)_D$ be 6.7 barns. Thus

$$\begin{aligned}
\xi_{D_2O} &= \frac{\xi_D 2(\sigma_s)_D + \xi_O(\sigma_s)_O}{(\sigma_s)_{D_2O}} \\
&= \frac{(0.726)(6.7) + (0.121)(3.8)}{10.5} \\
&= 0.507
\end{aligned}$$

Thus
$$\begin{aligned}
\text{"}\Sigma_M\text{"} &= \frac{\xi_{D_2O}(\Sigma_s)_{D_2O}}{5.6} \\
&= \frac{(0.507)(0.348)}{5.6} = 0.0315 \text{ cm}^{-1}
\end{aligned}$$

This is found to check rather well with the figure of 0.0313 quoted by Glasstone and Edlund. Now

$$\text{``}\Sigma_U\text{''} = (N_U)(9.25/5.6)\left(1 + 2.67\frac{S}{M}\right)$$

$$= (0.0473)(9.25/5.6)\left[1 + 2.67\,\frac{2}{(1.4)(18.7)}\right]$$

$$= 0.0941 \text{ cm}^{-1}$$

The value of K in the moderator is given by

$$K_1 = \sqrt{3\text{``}\Sigma_M\text{''}\Sigma_t}$$

where $\Sigma_t = \Sigma_s(1 - \overline{\cos\theta})$

$$= (0.348)(1 - 0.228) = 0.269 \text{ cm}^{-1}$$

The value of $\overline{\cos\theta}$, which will be abbreviated as μ, is computed from $2/(3M)$ using *atomic* masses for deuterium and oxygen. (See Section 2.7.)

$$\mu = \frac{\mu_D 2\sigma_D + \mu_O \sigma_O}{\sigma_{D_2O}}$$

$$= \frac{\dfrac{2}{(3)(2)}(6.7) + \dfrac{2}{(3)(16)}(3.8)}{10.5} = 0.228$$

The result, $K_1 = \sqrt{3(0.0315)(0.269)} = 0.159$ compares favorably with the 0.155 quoted by Glasstone and Edlund. An empirical value of the reciprocal diffusion length K_0 for natural uranium is quoted to be 0.022ρ, i.e., $K_0 = (0.022)(18.7) = 0.411$. We may now collect the necessary constants: the subscripts 0 and 1 for the metal and moderator are applied as before, remembering that the constants now refer to the *resonance capture*.

$K_0 r_0 = (0.411)(1.4) = 0.575$

$K_1 r_1 = (0.159)(11.5) = 1.83$

$r_1/r_0 = 8.2$

$\Sigma_1/\Sigma_0 = 0.0315/0.0941 = 0.335$

$V_1/V_0 = 66.2$

The resonance utilization $1/f_r$ is computed by direct analogy with $1/f$ in the thermal problem. Now

$$\frac{\phi(r_0)}{\bar{\phi}_0} = 1 + \frac{(0.575)^2}{8} - \frac{(0.575)^4}{192}$$

$$= 1 + 0.0413 - 0.00057 = 1.0407$$

$$\delta = \frac{(1.83)^2}{2} (\log_e 8.2 - 0.75) = 2.27$$

$$\frac{1}{f_r} - 1 = (66.2)(0.335)(1.0407) + 2.27$$

$$= 23.08 + 2.27 = 25.35$$

$$\left(\frac{1}{f_r} - 1\right)^{-1} = 0.0394$$

The resonance escape probability is thus

$$p = e^{(-0.0394)} = 0.9613$$

The fast fission factor ϵ from Fig. 6.9 is 1.031; the average number of neutrons per absorption η is 1.32. Thus we find

$$k_\infty = \epsilon p f \eta$$

$$= (1.031)(0.9613)(0.8861)(1.32) = 1.159$$

Thus the reactor can be made critical, if enough material is assembled.

12.6 Temperature effects

A reactor that is to be operated at a high temperature will have a slightly different multiplication constant from one that stays near room temperature. Two of the effects that take place as the temperature of the system increases are:

(1) Increase in resonance capture (reduction in p) due to increased neutron energy, and due to the change in metal temperature.

(2) Decrease in thermal utilization due to changes in flux distribution.

A qualitative graphical analysis may help to understand the resonance effect. Only if neutrons were produced at low energy and if there were zero absorption would the neutron energy distribution coincide with that of the moderator as in the curve A, Fig. 12.3. A real system has absorption that is stronger for the lower energy neutrons than for the higher ($1/v$ absorption). The system also contains a certain fraction of neutrons that have not yet become thermal. The lower velocity side of the maxwellian distribution is depressed, the high energy side increased as in curve B, Fig. 12.3. This has the net effect of giving an *apparent* new maxwellian distribution of a higher energy. For some purposes it may be useful to think of it as such and merely state that the neutron temperature is higher than that for the medium. Whatever the distribution, the effect of heating the moderator is to shift the typical neutron velocity to a higher value, curve C in Fig. 12.3. The total cross-section curve for uranium

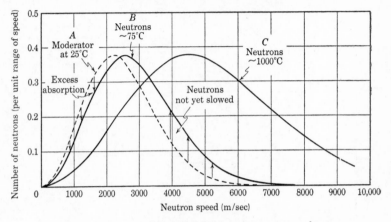

Fig. 12.3. Neutron velocity distributions in reactor moderators.

is shown in Fig. 12.4. The rate of neutron absorption in metallic uranium per unit volume is given by

$$\int_{v=0}^{v=\infty} dn\, vN\sigma(v)$$

The difference in absorptions for two temperatures could be estimated by numerical integrations if one knew the detailed *absorption* cross-section curve for U^{238}. "Doppler broadening" is an additional effect that becomes important in metal slugs that are heated to temperatures much higher than the moderator. The cross section for capture of neutrons of energy E by a nucleus having one resonance level at E_r is given by the formula of Breit and Wigner as

$$\sigma(E) = \frac{\sigma_r}{1 + [2(E - E_r)/\Gamma]^2}$$

where σ_r is the peak cross section, at the energy value E_r, and Γ is the width of cross-section peak at $\sigma_r/2$. As the metal heats up, its nuclei have speeds that are not negligible in comparison with neutron speeds. For E one must use the relative kinetic energy E', which is approximately equal to $\frac{1}{2}m(v - v_N)^2$, where v and v_N are the neutron and nucleus speeds. The latter have a separate maxwellian distribution over which an average must be taken. Bethe* has derived the expression for the effective cross section for neutrons of energy E

$$\sigma(E) = \sigma_r \psi$$

where ψ is a function of the relative energy E', the neutron energy E, the temperature of the medium and the width of the cross-section

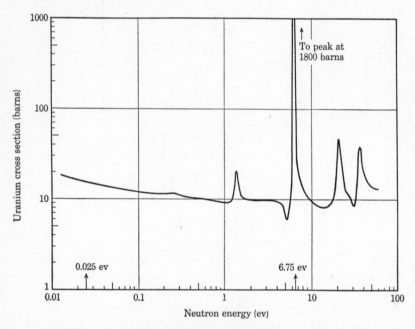

Fig. 12.4. Natural uranium cross section as a function of energy,
$$\sigma = \sigma_a + \sigma_s.$$

peak. The new σ must be substituted in the formula for total absorption in uranium per unit volume in order to estimate the effect on resonance capture. This effect has been found experimentally to vary with $1/T$. Resonance capture thus depends on both the metal and the moderator temperature. It increases with average neutron energy, because of the shift of the distribution toward the first

* H. A. BETHE, "Nuclear Physics." *Rev. Mod. Phys.*, **9**, 69 (1937).

resonance near 7 ev. Experiments show that the effective cross section varies almost linearly according to

$$"\sigma_U" = ("\sigma_U")_0(1 + \alpha T)$$

where T is the temperature in °C above room temperature and α is the temperature coefficient, with a numerical value of approximately 10^{-4} per °C. Since the moderator of our reactor is aqueous, it will be presumed that its temperature must be kept below the boiling point by air space insulation between the outer coolant duct and the moderator, or by circulation and external heat removal from the reactor. Let us assume that the maximum moderator temperature during operation is 80°C. The fractional change in $"\sigma_U"$ is thus $\alpha(\Delta T) = (10^{-4})(80° - 20°) = 0.006$. This results in a decrease of p by about 0.02 per cent. At the reactor start-up, when the moderator is cool, there will be a slight excess reactivity of about the same amount.

The effect of temperature on thermal utilization can be explained in terms of the fundamental definition:

$$f = \frac{V_U \Sigma_U \bar{\phi}_U}{V_M \Sigma_M \bar{\phi}_M + V_U \Sigma_U \bar{\phi}_U}$$

In a homogeneous reactor, where $\bar{\phi}_U$ and $\bar{\phi}_M$ are one and the same flux, and if absorbers are of the $1/v$ type, f remains essentially constant with neutron temperature. The flux ratio $\bar{\phi}_M/\bar{\phi}_U$ is not constant with T in a heterogeneous system, however, even with $1/v$ variation of cross section, because of the way diffusion lengths change with temperature. In most low absorbing moderators, the characteristic K varies as $\sqrt{3 \Sigma_a \Sigma_t}$ while the K for natural uranium is roughly $\Sigma_a + \Sigma_s$. With the different dependence on Σ_a and thus on neutron speed, the flux ratio is variable with temperature. For the D_2O reactor, we shall assume that the 60° rise in moderator temperature results in a negligible change in multiplication. This would not be true for reactors composed of solid moderator that were allowed to run at several hundred degrees excess.

12.7 Reactor dimensions

The critical size of the reactor may now be found by applying the condition

$$k_{\text{eff}} = \frac{k_\infty e^{-K^2 \tau}}{1 + K^2 L^2} = 1$$

For the cylindrical shape, the appropriate size shape factor is

$$K^2 = \left(\frac{2.4048}{R}\right)^2 + \left(\frac{\pi}{H}\right)^2$$

where R is the radius and H is the height. The leakage from a bare reactor is a minimum when $H = 1.8475R$. If we adopt this height to radius ratio, we find

$$K^2 = \left(\frac{2.9453}{R}\right)^2$$

The age τ in a heterogeneous reactor is not appreciably different from the age in the moderator material, since the scattering by uranium nuclei in the slugs results in practically no energy loss. We shall adopt the value $\tau = 120$ cm². The slugs do affect the thermal diffusion length L however. Since the square of the diffusion length is proportional to $1/\Sigma_a$, we may write

$$\frac{L^2}{L_M^2} = \frac{(\Sigma_a)_M \bar{\phi}_M}{(\Sigma_a)_R \bar{\phi}_R}$$

where the subscript M refers to moderator only and R to the whole reactor, and the average fluxes serve as proper weighting factors. Now

$$(\Sigma_a)_R \bar{\phi}_R = \frac{V_M \Sigma_M \bar{\phi}_M + V_U \Sigma_U \bar{\phi}_U + V_P \Sigma_P \bar{\phi}_P}{V_R}$$

where P stands for all "poisons," including coolant and duct materials, and V_R is the reactor volume. A little rearrangement yields the result

$$L^2 = L_M^2(1 - f_1)(f/f_1)(V_R/V_M)$$

where f_1 is the first thermal utilization that was computed, dependent only on moderator and slugs. Note that if $V_R \simeq V_M$ and $f \simeq f_1$, this reduces to the result for a homogeneous reactor. The ratio V_R/V_M is merely $\pi r_1^2/(\pi r_1^2 - \pi r_0^2) = [(V_1/V_0) + 1]/(V_1/V_0)$ which for our problem is $67.2/66.2 = 1.015$. Also $f/f_1 = 0.8861/0.9749 = 0.9089$; $1 - f_1 = 0.0251$. L_M is taken as 100 cm, $L_M^2 = 10^4$ cm². Thus

$$L^2 = (10^4)(0.0251)(0.9089)(1.015) = 231.5 \text{ cm}^2$$

A first approximation comes from an approximate formula for small K^2.

$$K^2 = \frac{k_\infty - 1}{L^2 + \tau} = \frac{1.159 - 1}{231.5 + 120} = 4.52 \times 10^{-4} \text{ cm}^{-2}$$

Substitution of this number and one slightly lower, 4.00×10^{-4} for example, back in the more general formula gives two values for interpolation.

K^2	4.52×10^{-4}	4.00×10^{-4}	4.33×10^{-4}
k_{eff}	0.9938	1.0110	1.0001

$$R = \frac{2.9453}{K} = \frac{2.9453}{\sqrt{4.33 \times 10^{-4}}}$$

$$= 141.5 \text{ cm} = 55.7 \text{ in.} = 4.64 \text{ ft}$$

$$H = 1.8475R = 261.4 \text{ cm}$$

$$= 103 \text{ in.} = 8.58 \text{ ft}$$

Several other properties immediately fall out:

Reactor volume V_R:

$$\pi R^2 H = \pi (4.64)^2 (8.58) = 580 \text{ ft}^3$$

Heavy water requirement $V_R/(V_R/V_M)$:

$$580/1.015 = 571 \text{ ft}^3$$

At a density of $(1.1)(62.4) = 68.6 \text{ lb/ft}^3$, this is $39,200$ lb $= 19.6$ tons.

Uranium requirement $(r_0/r_1)^2 V_R$:

$$580/(8.2)^2 = 8.63 \text{ ft}^3$$

At a density of $(18.7)(62.4) = 1167 \text{ lb/ft}^3$, this is $10,070$ lb, or 5.0 tons.

Number of slug channels: The reactor cross-sectional area is $\pi R^2 = 67.64 \text{ ft}^2$, and the cell area is $(8 \text{ in.} \times 8 \text{ in.})/144 = 0.444 \text{ ft}^2$. Thus $N = 152$.

We have arrived at the physical size of the reactor, which is just half of the problem, since the heat removal must yet be analyzed.

12.8 Heat transfer with non-uniform flux in reactor

The assumption made in Chapter 10 that the rate of heat generation is the same along the line of slugs is incorrect in a bare reactor, since the flux is represented by a sine function, of the form

$$\phi = \phi_c \sin \frac{\pi x}{L}$$

as shown in Fig. 12.5a. Note that L is now used in place of H. The modification of the analysis made previously is straightforward.

The amount of heat dq developed in a length dx at a distance x from the coolant inlet will also be proportional to the flux at x:

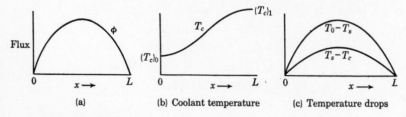

Fig. 12.5. Flux and temperature variations along coolant flow channel.

$dq = A \sin (\pi x/L)\, dx$ where A is a constant to be determined. The total heat Q generated per unit time in the line of slugs is the sum of all the infinitesimal contributions or the integral

$$Q = \int_{x=0}^{x=L} dq = A \int_0^L \sin \frac{\pi x}{L}\, dx = \frac{2AL}{\pi}$$

Thus $\qquad A = \dfrac{\pi Q}{2L} \quad$ and $\quad dq = \dfrac{\pi Q}{2L} \sin \dfrac{\pi x}{L}\, dx$

The rise in coolant temperature by the time it reaches x will be such that

$$T_c = (T_c)_0 + \int_0^x \frac{dq}{cM}$$

$$= (T_c)_0 + \frac{\pi Q}{2LcM} \int_0^x \sin \frac{\pi x}{L}\, dx$$

Integration leads to the result

$$T_c = (T_c)_0 + \left(\frac{\pi Q}{2LcM}\right)\left[\frac{-L}{\pi} \cos \frac{\pi x}{L}\right]_0^x$$

$$= (T_c)_0 + \frac{Q}{2cM}\left(1 - \cos \frac{\pi x}{L}\right) \tag{12.1}$$

which is plotted in Fig. 12.5b. Note that when $x = L$, we obtain $T = (T_c)_0 + Q/cM$ as expected.

The temperature difference between the coolant and slug surface will vary from point to point, because the heat that is to be transferred is also given by the sine function. Thus,

$$dq = hS\,dx(T_S - T_c) = \frac{\pi}{2}\frac{Q}{L}\sin\frac{\pi x}{L}\,dx$$

or
$$T_S - T_c = \frac{\pi Q}{2hSL}\sin\frac{\pi x}{L} \tag{12.2}$$

Figure 12.5c shows this sine variation of $T_S - T_c$.

The temperature drop between the center of the slug and its surface will also vary with position. The heat developed in a unit length, $\pi Q/2L \sin \pi x/L$ is transferred through the slug of conductivity k and with a temperature drop

$$T_0 - T_S = \frac{\alpha(\pi Q/2L)\sin(\pi x/L)}{4\pi k} \tag{12.3}$$

α is a factor close to unity that corrects for the fact that the neutron flux drops from the slug surface to the center. It may be shown (see Appendix) that a good approximation for α is

$$\alpha = 1 - \tfrac{1}{16}(K_0 r_0)^2$$

where K_0 is the reciprocal diffusion length in uranium and r_0 is the slug radius. Since $K_0 r_0 = 0.98$ for the D_2O reactor under study, $\alpha = 0.94$. The above temperature drop is plotted as a

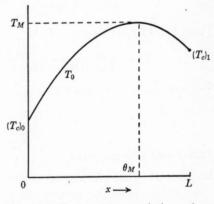

Fig. 12.6. Temperature variation along line of slugs.

function of position in Fig. 12.5c. Adding Eqs. 12.1, 12.2 and 12.3 together yields

$$T_0 - (T_c)_0 = \frac{Q}{2cM}\left(1 - \cos\frac{\pi x}{L}\right) + \frac{\pi Q}{2L}\left(\frac{1}{hS} + \frac{\alpha}{4\pi k}\right)\sin\frac{\pi x}{L}$$

We may simplify this expression by letting $\pi x/L$ be an angle θ and writing a "resistance"

$$R = \frac{1}{hS} + \frac{\alpha}{4\pi k}$$

$$T_0 = (T_c)_0 + \frac{Q}{2cM}(1 - \cos\theta) + \frac{\pi Q}{2L} R \sin\theta \qquad (12.4)$$

A plot of the central slug temperature T_0 is shown in Fig. 12.6. The temperature does not reach a maximum at the coolant exit end, as was found in the case of uniform flux, but somewhat beyond the middle of the reactor. Physically, the reason is that less and less heat is generated as one passes the center of the reactor, and the metal temperature approaches that of the coolant. The maximum available reactor power will be limited by the highest metal temperature, $(T_0)_M$. The angle θ_M at which T_0 has its maximum may be found by differentiating T_0 with respect to θ. Thence a relation between $(T_0)_M$ and Q may be obtained.

$$\frac{dT_0(\theta)}{d\theta} = \frac{Q}{2cM}\sin\theta + \frac{\pi Q}{2L}R\cos\theta = 0$$

or
$$\tan\theta_M = -\frac{\pi cMR}{L} \qquad (12.5)$$

From Eq. 12.4,

$$Q = \frac{(T_0)_M - (T_c)_0}{(1/2cM)(1 - \cos\theta_M) + (\pi/2L)\ R\ \sin\theta_M} \qquad (12.6)$$

We combine Eqs. 12.5 and 12.6 to obtain

$$Q = \frac{cM[(T_0)_M - (T_c)_\theta]}{(1 - \sec\theta_M)/2} \qquad (12.7)$$

12.9 Total reactor power

We showed in the previous section that the maximum slug temperature occurs somewhat toward the outlet end of the coolant duct. Further, we know that the channel along the central axis of the reactor is exposed to the highest average flux and therefore must have the greatest amount of heat removed from it. Let us now specify the coolant, its flow rate, the inlet temperature, and the important quantity, the maximum allowable uranium metal temperature in the system. The heat removal in the central channel may then be deduced, and then the total reactor power. In practice, one would actually start with the total power and work back to the flows and duct sizes, but the analysis is less straightforward. Methods developed in Chapter 10 and those in the immediately preceding sections will be applied. The specifications taken as primary are listed:

Liquid sodium coolant, inlet temperature $(T_c)_0$: 250°F.
Maximum uranium metal temperature $(T_0)_{max}$: 1000°F.
Coolant flow velocity v:

$$10 \text{ ft/sec} = 3.60 \times 10^4 \text{ ft/hr}$$

Length of line of slugs L: 8.58 ft (Section 12.7).
Annulus width $D/2$: 0.233 in. = 0.0194 ft.
Coolant duct cross section A:

$$0.975 \text{ in.}^2 = 6.77 \times 10^{-3} \text{ ft}^2 \text{ (Section 12.3)}$$

Slug surface area per foot S:

$$2\pi(0.55)/12 = 0.288 \text{ ft}^2 \text{ (Section 12.3)}$$

Uranium thermal conductivity k_U: 19 Btu/hr-°F-ft.

The density and heat capacity of liquid sodium vary with temperature, which is yet unknown. We shall estimate that the average coolant temperature is 400°F. Thus four new properties of the coolant may be tabulated:

Density ρ: 53.3 lb/ft³.
Heat capacity c: 0.305 Btu/lb-°F.
Conductivity k_c: 41.2 Btu/hr-°F-ft.
Mass flow rate M: $\rho v A$ = 13,000 lb/hr.

We may now compute the heat transfer coefficient h, using the annulus relation from Section 10.5

$$N_N = 5.8 + 0.02(N_{Pe})^{0.8}$$

$$N_{Pe} = \frac{Dv\rho c}{k_c}$$

$$= \frac{(0.0388)(3.60 \times 10^4)(53.3)(0.305)}{41.2} = 551$$

$$(N_{Pe})^{0.8} = 156, \qquad N_N = 8.9$$

$$h = \frac{k_c N_N}{D} = \frac{(41.2)(8.9)}{0.0388} = 9450 \text{ Btu/hr-°F-ft}^2$$

All the necessary data are available to find the point in the central line of slugs at which the maximum metal occurs, and the cooling capacity in this line. Referring to Section 12.8,

$$R = \frac{1}{hS} + \frac{\alpha}{4\pi k_U}$$

$$= \frac{1}{(9450)(0.288)} + \frac{0.94}{4\pi(19)} = 4.34 \times 10^{-3}$$

$$\tan \theta_M = \frac{-\pi c M R}{L}$$

$$= \frac{-(\pi)(0.305)(13000)(4.34 \times 10^{-3})}{8.58} = -6.30$$

The angle θ_M is thus 99°. The point at which the maximum temperature occurs is $(99/180)(8.58) = 4.72$ ft from the inlet, or about 5 in. beyond the center. Now $\sec \theta_M = -6.38$ and the rate of heat removal from the axial slugs is, from Eq. 12.7,

$$Q = \frac{cM[(T_0)_M - (T_c)_0]}{(1 - \sec \theta_M)/2}$$

$$= \frac{(0.305)(13000)(1000 - 250)}{3.69}$$

$$Q = 8.06 \times 10^5 \text{ Btu/hr}$$

$$= 2.36 \times 10^5 \text{ watts} = 0.236 \text{ mw}$$

The calculations just completed referred only to the power available from a single line of slugs. We must now determine the total reactor heat, taking account of the variation of flux through the reactor, perpendicular to the axis of coolant flow. We showed in Chapter 6 how the flux varied with position in homogeneous reactors according to a modified sine curve in a sphere, as a product of sine curves for a rectangular parallelepiped, and as a sine function times a Bessel function for a finite circular cylinder. The same smooth curves represent the effective flux through the heterogeneous reactor even though there are local variations in flux through the slug and surrounding moderator. Let us assume that the reactor has a cylindrical shape, with height L, radius R, and for simplicity, has no reflector. We suppose of course, that these dimensions are large enough to make the reactor critical. The neutron flux level can be raised to a point where the line of slugs running along the central axis generates the heat Q that we have computed previously. If the average flux along the axial line is labeled ϕ_0, the other channels off the axis will have a flux given by

$$\phi = \phi_0 J_0(2.405r/R)$$

and thus the heat they produce is

$$\phi = QJ_0(2.405r/R)$$

The *average* power of a line is calculated from the average value of the zero-order Bessel function over the reactor, i.e.,

$$\frac{\int^R QJ_0(2.405r/R)2\pi r \, dr}{\pi R^2} = 0.43Q$$

The total reactor power is thus the product of $0.43Q$, and the number of slug channels, N. Thus for our reactor

$$Q_T = 0.43 \, Q \, N$$
$$= (0.43)(0.236)(152) = 15.4 \text{ mw}$$

Many more estimates of the type described in Chapter 11 on the homogeneous reactor could be made. We shall be content to find only the neutron flux at the very center of the reactor and the average over the machine. The average power density along the central line of slugs is Q/V where V is the volume $\pi r_0^2 L$. Thus the peak power density is $(\pi/2)(Q/V)$. See Section 5.2. For our reactor this is

$$\frac{\pi(2.36 \times 10^5 \text{ watts})}{2(6.13 \text{ cm}^2)(261.4 \text{ cm})} = 231 \text{ watts/cm}^3$$

Now since $\phi = Pc/\Sigma_f$ (see Section 6.4), where Σ_f for natural uranium is $N_U (\sigma_f)_U = (0.0473)(3.92) = 0.185$, the peak flux in the metal is $3.75 \times 10^{13}/\text{cm}^2$-sec. The average over the reactor is smaller than this by the factor $(0.43)(2/\pi) = 0.27$, i.e., $\bar{\phi} = 1.0 \times 10^{13}$. We may go back to check our assumption on xenon poisoning in Section 12.4. At the center, the change in $1/f$ is

$$\Delta(1/f)_{\text{Xe}} = 0.0312/(1 + 6.0 \times 10^{12}/3.75 \times 10^{13}) = 0.027$$

Our assumption of 0.01 (average) would probably turn out to be low by a factor of two.

Power distribution with reflector. The effect of a reflector on a large heterogeneous reactor can be represented approximately by assuming that the flux goes to zero at a distance equal to the diffusion length L

beyond the edge of the core, as shown in Fig. 12.7. A useful corollary is that the reflected reactor will be critical with a dimension smaller than the bare reactor by approximately L. The flux in the active part of the system, i.e., that in which fission and heat generation take

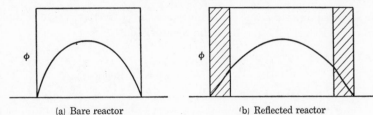

(a) Bare reactor   (b) Reflected reactor

Fig. 12.7. Effect of reflector on flux distribution.

place, might be called a "chopped sine" distribution, in the case of a square or rectangular reactor, and in the radial direction might be called a "chopped Bessel function" distribution in the case of our cylindrical reactor. The advantage of a reflector is evident. The average flux is closer to the maximum flux, and since the latter fixes the "hot spot" in the system, a higher total power per unit volume may be obtained. One may re-examine both the axial and radial power distributions by a simple extension of the methods already presented in light of the change in shape of the generation curve. Two slightly different cases are of importance:

(1) reflector on sides only,
(2) reflector on all surfaces.

The first is applicable if the chosen method of loading and unloading the reactor makes an end reflector impractical.

12.10 Reactor designs

The reader may find it instructive to look into the feasibility and characteristics of one or more of the different reactor types listed below. This list is pure invention, such as any reader could devise from the principles of reactors that have been presented. Many of the reactors are probably impractical, others may by chance be similar to those under consideration within the Atomic Energy Commission. It is suggested that analysis of the physical arrangement, nuclear properties, and heat transfer features be followed by block diagrams, layout sketches and estimates of material requirements. Comments on problems requiring further investigation and development should be made.

Experimental reactors:

(1) Homogeneous, heavy-water moderated and reflected; partially depleted uranium. Cooled by circulating D_2O in ducts through the core. SUGGESTION: find the lowest U^{235} isotopic concentration with which the reactor will be critical at any size, and consider the variation with concentration of the D_2O and uranium weights needed.

(2) Heterogeneous, natural uranium sealed in containers that melt far above the melting point of uranium, so that no restriction on slug temperature is needed. Coolant, liquid metal; moderator, beryllium. SUGGESTION: examine the expansion effects that may affect the stability of the system.

Power reactors:

(3) Heterogeneous, circulating fuel, composed of enriched uranium dispersed in a low-absorption liquid metal. D_2O filled tubes as moderator. SUGGESTION: consider the special question of the transient behavior of the reactor with some delayed neutrons emitted outside the reactor core, as the fuel flows in its circuit. Also look into possible interaction of critical and subcritical portions of the system.

(4) Heterogeneous, natural uranium, light-water moderated, with the central portion of the reactor containing partially or highly enriched slugs. SUGGESTION: investigate the relative importance of locating strong absorbers at different places in the reactor.

(5) Heterogeneous, natural uranium, high pressure light-water steam as coolant, D_2O as moderator, turbo-generator driven by steam. SUGGESTION: specify first the power output, and the appropriate steam pressure and temperature at the turbine, and work back to the reactor design.

(6) Heterogeneous, enriched uranium, beryllium moderator, mercury cooled. Direct coupling of coolant with turbine. SUGGESTION: the amount of mercury that can be allowed will be small because of the high cross section.

Breeder reactors:

(7) Heterogeneous, U^{235} slugs canned with a thin layer of thorium around each. SUGGESTION: look into the rate of production of U^{233} with different geometrical arrangements.

(8) Heterogeneous, spherical lumps of plutonium, depleted (e.g.

0.6 per cent U^{235}) uranium blanket, cooled and moderated by circulating light water. Use for hot water supply at about 200°F. Suggestion: consider relation between losses of neutrons by absorption in water with the ability to achieve thermal neutrons, and cooling requirements.

Problems

12.1 Using the distributed poison formulas, make an estimate of the effect on multiplication constant of a cadmium rod with radius 1.4 cm running the length of the central axis of a 23-ft cubical reactor containing 1248 slug channels. NOTE: the flux varies along its length.

12.2 Estimate the thermal utilization "temperature coefficient" from the first approximation to the thermal utilization

$$\frac{1}{f} = 1 + \frac{V_1 \Sigma_1}{V_U \Sigma_0} \cdot \frac{\phi(r_0)}{\bar{\phi}_0}$$

for a heterogeneous natural uranium-graphite reactor with slug radius 1.4 cm, cell radius 11.4 cm. Assume that both the absorbers obey the $1/v$ law.

12.3 Sketch the "chopped sine" flux distributions given by $\phi = 0$ for $0 < x < a$ and $L - a < x < L$; $\sin(\pi x/L)$ for $a < x < L - a$. Derive a working formula analogous to Eq. 12.7 for the maximum heat removal from a line of slugs with this type of flux.

12.4 Set up the accurate calculation of the Xe poisoning, $\Delta(1/f)_{Xe}$, from formulas of Section 12.4 and the known distribution of flux through the reactor.

12.5 Find the average heat developed in a reactor with square cross section in terms of that removed from the axial line of slugs. Keep in mind that the flux varies sinusoidally along all axes.

12.6 Compare $\Delta(1/f)_{Fe}$ due to ducts with the change in $1/f$ that would be experienced if aluminum of the same thickness were used. Repeat for zirconium.

12.7 Moderator and fuel is available in sufficient quantities to build a heterogeneous power reactor. From what has been learned about neutron leakage, critical size and the distribution of power through a reactor, which shape would you choose—cylindrical or cubical? What other practical considerations are involved in the decision?

12.8 Plot a semi-log graph of the scattering cross section of hydrogen using the following data:

Neutron energy (ev)	σ_s (barns)	Neutron energy (ev)	σ_s (barns)
0.025	36	10^3	20
0.1	26	10^4	20
1.0	22	10^5	13
10	20	10^6	4.5
10^2	20	2×10^6	3

Estimate ξ_{H_2O} from the atomic constants for hydrogen and oxygen, using the average ordinate of the semi-log plot for $(\sigma_s)_H$ and assuming that σ_s for oxygen is constant at 3.8 barns over the energy range.

12.9 How much error in L, the diffusion length, would have been incurred if the approximate formula $L^2 = L_M^2 (1 - f)$ had been used in Section 12.7?

12.10 Estimate the change in multiplication constant of the reactor if the D_2O is contaminated by an additional 0.05 per cent of light water. How much water does this actually imply?

12.11 Investigate the question of how much additional power can be obtained from a bare cubical reactor if a side reflector is added. Consider the two effects of reflector (a) to reduce the critical size and thus the number of power producing slugs, (b) the "flattening" of the flux distribution.

12.12 Compute the change in resonance escape probability for the graphite BEPO reactor of Section 6.5 if the moderator temperature is allowed to run up to 500°F.

References

THE AEC NEUTRON CROSS SECTIONS ADVISORY GROUP, *Neutron Cross Sections*, AECU-2040. Washington, D. C.: Office of Technical Services, U. S. Department of Commerce, 1952.

SARGENT, B. W., D. V. BOOKER, P. E. CAVANAGH, H. G. HEREWARD, and N. J. NIEMI, "The Diffusion Length of Thermal Neutrons in Heavy Water." *Can. J. Res.*, A25, 143 (1947).

GLASSTONE, S. and M. C. EDLUND, *The Elements of Nuclear Reactor Theory*. New York: D. Van Nostrand Co., 1952.

GOODMAN, C., Ed., *The Science and Engineering of Nuclear Power*. Cambridge, Mass.: Addison-Wesley Press, 1949, Vols. I, II.

GUGGENHEIM, E. A. and M. H. L. PRYCE, "Uranium-Graphite Lattices." *Nucleonics*, February (1953) p. 50.

BONILLA, C. F., *An Up-to-Date Review of the Principles of Heat Transfer, with Particular Application to Nuclear Power*, M-4476. Gibbs and Cox, Inc., 1949.

LYON, RICHARD N., Ed., *Liquid Metals Handbook*, 2d Ed. Washington, D. C.: U. S. Government Printing Office, June, 1952.

JAHNKE, E. and F. EMDE, *Tables of Functions with Formulae and Curves*. New York: Dover Publications, 1945.

CHAPTER 13

RADIATION HAZARDS

The problem of guaranteeing protection from the unseen danger of radiation from chain reactors or from their products is faced at one time or another by almost every person in the nuclear field. The workers in a plant who process radioactive chemicals, the designer who specifies reactor shielding, and the scientist who does research with neutrons or nuclear reactions, all meet different aspects of the radiation hazard problem. We shall review in this chapter the fundamentals of the relation between radiation and body health.

13.1 The principles of health physics

There are two ways the human body may be exposed to danger from radioactive emanations: (a) externally, by direct bombardment of rays or particles, or (b) internally, through breathing, ingestion, or cuts in the skin. In each case the ultimate effect on the body is cell damage, produced by the interaction of the penetrating rays or particles with the atoms constituting the body tissue.

We shall first reiterate the processes that occur in the stopping of particles in general and their effect on the human body. Gamma rays, high energy photons, lose energy in three ways as described in Chapter 1. In the photo-electric effect, dominant at low gamma energy, electrons are ejected from atoms by the absorption of the light. These electrons in turn cause ionization of other atoms. If the energy of the gamma is as large as 1 mev, it may be converted bodily by the pair production process into a positive electron and a negative electron. For higher gamma energies, the excess over 1 mev is given to the electron and positron as kinetic energy. Fast neutrons are stopped in the body by the same elastic collision processes that occur in a reactor moderator. Hydrogen, which constitutes a large part of the atoms in the body, was found to be the best element for slowing neutrons in a reactor. From the point of view of safety, hydrogen is the worst or "most dangerous" element in that the atoms gain the maximum recoil energy on being struck by a neutron. The recoiling

257

proton is a highly ionizing particle. Relatively little neutron absorption takes place at high energy, as evidenced by the $1/v$ cross-section variation. In the absorption of thermal neutrons in the body, it is the associated gamma rays that are harmful. Absorption in hydrogen by the reaction $H^1(n,\gamma)H^2$ yields a 2.2-mev gamma. Deuterium is not radioactive, fortunately. With reference to the other main body elements, the absorption of neutrons in C^{12} yields stable C^{13}; the reaction $N^{14}(n,p)C^{14}$ with its ionizing protons dominates the (n,γ) event; oxygen has a negligible cross section. Alpha particles and beta particles are highly ionizing in their own right. The danger from all particles, including the above two rays and gamma rays, fast neutrons, and slow neutrons, is thus seen to be the secondary-charged particle ionization, which may lead to the destruction of living cells.

Health physicists are those specialists who estimate amounts of exposure, analyze the dangers of radiation, and specify precautionary procedures for working with or near sources of radiation. They have developed technical terms to express their findings and recommendations. We shall define terms that are essential to an appreciation of the health problem, at some expense of exactness.

When x-rays first became widely used, a measure of the absorption of their energy called the *roentgen* (r) was devised. It is the amount of x-radiation that would ionize air to the extent of creating one statcoulomb of charge per cubic centimeter of air.* An alternative definition better for some purposes is that a roentgen is the radiation dose that will release 83 ergs of energy in a gram of air. The equivalence of the definitions can easily be demonstrated by making use of the fact that the energy needed to create an ion pair in air is approximately 32.5 ev. Measurement of radiation dosage may be accomplished by use of an ionization chamber, consisting essentially of two plates at different potentials. Ions are formed in the gas between the plates by an x- or gamma ray beam, and are swept out and observed as a current. Conversion of the currents observed to roentgens is necessary, of course.

13.2 Maximum permissible external dosage

For a number of years (after 1936), the amount of radiation that was believed to result in no permanent damage to the body was taken as

---

* In a free air chamber at standard temperature and pressure, and in which all ionization by secondary electrons is included.

0.1 r per 8-hr day, and the protective practices of the atomic energy project were based on that number. Later (1949), the maximum permissible dose (m.p.d.) was reduced by international agreement to 0.3 r per week. In order to visualize this radiation, one may use these rough figures: a diagnostic x-ray may involve about 1 r; a dose of 25 r is commonly applied to local growths on the body; a lethal dose is around 450 r.* It is evident that the definition of the roentgen above is rather abstract in that it is based on effects in air, which does not have absorption properties identical to those of body tissue. In fact, an amount of radiation that releases 83 ergs in a gram of air will give about 93 ergs in a gram of tissue. In performing calculations of tolerance radiation flux the larger figure is used. The colloquial term "tolerance" is a misnomer, in that all efforts are made to keep the radiation level to zero, rather than *allowing* a certain amount. A person who does research with radioactive materials or works near a reactor has a choice of two methods of being sure the maximum dose will not be exceeded. The first, and most dependable method, is to employ a detector, calibrated in roentgens, to survey the area. The second approach, if the activity and type of emanations are known, is to compute the relation between the radiation flux present and the dosage. Such analyses are important in shielding design and in providing specifications on safe work areas. We may illustrate by estimating the flux of 1-mev gamma rays that results in the m.p.d. in average body tissue. Visualize a cubic centimeter of tissue irradiated on one face by a gamma ray flux $\phi(\text{cm}^{-2} \text{ sec}^{-1})$. The (absolute) number of gammas absorbed in a thickness Δx will be

$$\Delta \phi = \mu \phi \Delta x$$

This may be derived by differentiation from the exponential attenuation law for all light radiation,

$$\phi = \phi_0 e^{-\mu x}$$

where μ is the absorption coefficient for these rays. If each gamma ray has an energy ϵ, and the thickness Δx is 1 cm, the rate of energy absorption in the cube is

$$E \text{ (mev/cm}^3\text{-sec)} = \epsilon \text{ (mev)} \ \mu \text{ (cm}^{-1}) \ \phi \text{ (cm}^{-2} \text{ sec}^{-1})$$

* This is colloquial terminology. Half the individuals exposed to 450 r will die This dose is called "LD-50," i.e., lethal dose, 50 per cent mortality.

The value of the m.p.d. energy E_m depends on the units used and the exposure time assumed. Let the week consist of five work days, and for the sake of being conservative, assume constant 24-hr irradiation. The maximum energy is thus

$$E_m = \frac{(0.3\text{r/week})(93 \text{ erg/g-r})}{(5 \text{ days/week})(8.64 \times 10^4 \text{ sec/day})(1.6 \times 10^{-6} \text{ erg/mev})}$$
$$= 40.4 \text{ mev/g-sec}$$

The absorption coefficient μ is taken as the total μ_t less the effect due to Compton scattering σ_s, in which the gamma rays are redirected, but with negligible energy loss. Figure 13.1 shows the variation with

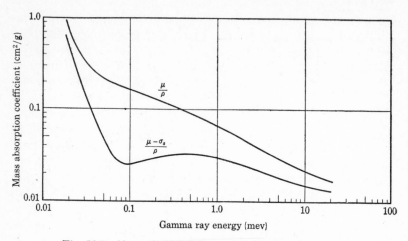

Fig. 13.1. Absorption coefficients of tissue for gamma rays.

gamma energy of μ_t/ρ and $(\mu_t - \sigma_s)/\rho$ where ρ is the material density for tissue, taken as $\simeq 1.0$ g/cm³. From the graph we find that $\mu = 0.03$ cm⁻¹. Equating energies E and E_m and solving for ϕ,

$$\phi = \frac{(40.4 \text{ mev/cm}^3\text{-sec})}{(1 \text{ mev})(0.03 \text{ cm}^{-1})} \simeq 1350/\text{cm}^2\text{-sec}$$

This compares fairly well with the standard of 1300 1-mev gammas/cm²-sec as used by the Oak Ridge National Laboratory. It is unnecessary to compute such numbers with a high degree of accuracy, since operations must not be conducted in a deliberate attempt to match this level. Note may be made of the assumption of 24-hr exposure. A higher and thus less safe flux value by a factor of 3 would have been derived if normal 8-hr work day exposure were used.

To this point, we have dealt only with external gamma ray exposure, for which tolerances are obtained in this straightforward manner. For other radioactive particles, alphas, betas, neutrons, and protons, modified definitions are used. The term *roentgen equivalent physical* (rep) is defined as the amount of radiation that will cause 93 ergs of energy to be released in tissue. It appears at first glance that this is almost the same as the roentgen. There are two differences (a) the definition is based on absorption in *tissue*, not air, with a numerical value that is 11 per cent higher, and (b) the term is applicable to all other particles besides x-rays or gammas. A typical comment might be made as follows. "Exposure for 5 min to the beam of thermal neutrons from this reactor thermal column will result in a total body dose of 4 rep." This means that in each cubic centimeter of tissue exposed to the beam 4 × 93 ergs of energy are released. The *dosage rate* may be deduced from the number of rep and the time of exposure. For our illustration the rate is 0.8 rep/min, or 48 rep/hr.

It has been found that *energy release* is not the best criterion to use in establishing the m.p.d. for particles other than gamma rays. The study of the mechanisms of interactions of the different particles with living cells is still under way, but it is known that each type of particle has its particular "relative biological effectiveness" (RBE) in destroying cells. A dose of alpha particles, for instance, is about 20 times as dangerous as gamma rays, even if the energy releases are identical. Beta particles are as effective as gamma rays. The value of the RBE is approximately proportional to the square root of the specific ionization of the radiation. A rough check is provided by

TABLE 13.1

RELATIVE BIOLOGICAL EFFECTIVENESS OF RADIATIONS

Radiation	RBE	Radiation	RBE
x or gamma	1	fast neutron (2 mev)	10
beta	1	protons	10
thermal neutron (0.025 ev)	5	alpha	20

these data on ionization per centimeter in air: alpha, 20,000; beta, 50. Table 13.1 collects the known facts on the RBE, using a scale in which the RBE of gammas is 1. Now if we accept the fact that 0.3 r per week is the upper limit on dosage for gammas, we must *scale down* the tolerances for other particles. We can thus construct a new list of m.p.d. values, as in Table 13.2. Each of the values of m.p.d. cor-

TABLE 13.2

RADIATION LIMITS FOR EXTERNAL EXPOSURE

Radiation	Maximum Permissible Dose (rep/week)	Equivalent Flux (/cm²-sec)
x or gamma	0.3	1300 (1 mev)
beta	0.3	32 (1 mev)
thermal neutron	0.06	600 (0.025 ev)
fast neutrons	0.03	22 (2 mev)
protons	0.03	
alpha	0.015	0.0016 (5 mev)

respond to a standard of 0.3 rem/week where rem stands for roentgen equivalent man. Thus rep = rem/RBE. The approximate flux values that yield the m.p.d., if the exposure is based on five 24-hr days per work week, are listed in this table for convenience.

13.3 Internal exposure

The outer layer of the skin serves as some protection for the body from alpha and beta particle bombardment because of the weak penetration of these particles. When radioactive substances emitting these particles enter the body, however, they are in contact with sensitive cells and thus damage may be severe. Several factors determine the ultimate danger to the organism:

Amount taken in. It would naturally be expected that the more of an active isotope that enters the body, the greater would be the hazard. In addition, the time factor enters the problem. If the material is taken in continuously in small quantities, the body may be capable of replacing destroyed cells fast enough to keep the body in essentially normal health. A single large dose however, might destroy the function of the cell-forming tissues.

The chemical nature of the material. This is important in that it affects the rate of elimination from the body. One may classify substances as follows: (a) those that are chemically inert, such as the "noble gases," argon, xenon and krypton. These gases may be inhaled, remain in the lungs for a short while and perhaps be suspended in the blood stream, but never form compounds that are a part of the body. If all other factors including half-life were equal, these gases would be least dangerous internally. In the same category are substances not normally utilized. (b) Those that constitute a normal intake of the body. The compound water and elements such as sodium and chlorine that go to make salt, have a rapid turnover in the body, and thus do not remain in the system for indefinitely long periods. (c) Those that have a particular affinity for some vital organ of the body, such as iodine, which concentrates in the thyroid gland. Strontium, calcium, and plutonium settle in the bone tissues, and destroy the marrow that manufactures blood cells. Iron constitutes a necessary ingredient of the red blood corpuscles. A convenient description of the rate at which length of time substances stay in the body is the "biological half-life." The analogy to radioactive half-life is self-evident.

The size of the particles. It has been found that particles of size greater than 10 microns have difficulty in getting farther than the nasal passages, which protects the more vital lungs and organs fed by the blood stream from the lungs. Foreign bodies composed of an only slightly soluble material can be taken orally and eliminated without permanent damage.

The radioactive half-life, and energy and type of radiation. Elements that decay rapidly with half-lives of the order of minutes or hours will give an initial burst of radiation, but soon disappear, perhaps before being deposited in a vital organ; those that have very long half-lives, with the limiting case a stable element, do little damage because of the low activity. It is the "intermediate half-lives" of the order of years, that must be guarded against, since they irradiate the cells of the body at an essentially constant level for the individual's lifetime.

The radiosensitivity of the tissue. One of the most important factors is the sensitivity of the organ to damage by radiation. Blood and blood-forming cells are more seriously impaired than are nerve cells, for example.

Table 13.3 lists selected isotopes and maximum permissible amounts that may be present in the body, with the reasons for the specifications whenever possible. The data refer to plant personnel and should be reduced by a factor of at least 10 for the general population.

Radioactive materials may enter the body and be fixed there in **a**

TABLE 13.3. LIMITS ON EXPOSURE TO RADIOISOTOPES*

Element	Half-life	Radiations (type, energy in mev)	Maximum amount fixed in body (μc)	Maximum air concentration (μc/liter)	Maximum drinking water concentration (μc/liter)	Remarks
Ra^{226}	1620 yr	α, 4.8	0.1	8×10^{-9}	4×10^{-5}	Almost permanent retention. Anemia, damage to bone.
Pu^{239}	2.4×10^4 yr	α, 5.2	0.04	2×10^{-9}	1.5×10^{-3}	Almost permanent retention.
Sr^{89}	53 days	β, 1.5	2.0	…	…	
Sr^{90}	25 yr	β, 0.54	1.0	2×10^{-7}	8×10^{-4}	Intermediate half-life.
Po^{210}	138 days	α, 5.3	0.005	…	…	
H^3	12.5 yr	β, 0.019	10	0.05	0.4	Rapid turnover as water.
$C^{14}(CO_2)$	5720 yr	β, 0.155	…	1×10^{-2}	…	Low energy betas.
Na^{24}	14.9 hr	β, 1.4; γ, 2.8, 1.4	15	…	8	Rapid turnover as salt.
P^{32}	14.3 days	β, 1.7	10	…	0.2	
Co^{60}	5.2 yr	γ, 1.2, 1.3	1.0	7×10^{-6}	0.01	
I^{131}	8.0 days	β, 0.60; γ, 0.36	0.3	3×10^{-6}	0.03	Concentration in thyroid.
A^{41}	1.8 hr	β, 1.25; γ, 1.3	…	1×10^{-3}	…	
Xe^{133}	5.3 days	β, 0.32; γ, 0.085	…	0.01	…	
Xe^{135}	9.2 hr	β, 0.9; γ, 0.25	…	3×10^{-3}	…	
U^{238}	4.5×10^9 yr	α, 4.2	…	1.7×10^{-8} (natural U)	…	Natural U hazard is mainly chemical. Enriched U has higher γ activity. Concentrations of U^{234} above natural (0.0058%) are dangerous.
U^{235}	8.8×10^8 yr	α, 4.4; γ, 0.16	…	…	…	
U^{234}	2.7×10^5 yr	α, 4.8	…	…	…	

* Based on recommendations of International Commission on Radiological Protection, 1950.

264

. variety of ways. The two ways most commonly considered are by inhalation of contaminated air, as in a radioactive laboratory, or in drinking contaminated water.

13.4 Calculation of maximum permissible concentration

In order to illustrate the method of analysis, let us derive maximum permissible concentrations, abbreviated m.p.c., for two isotopes A^{41} and Sr^{89}, the first for air contamination, the second for drinking water activity. These estimates are based on knowledge of the half-life, the chemical affinity for particular body organs, the type of radiations and the energy of radiations. This radioisotope A^{41} is formed by neutron absorption in an air cooled reactor of the Oak Ridge, Brookhaven, or British type. The A^{40} content of the air is small, 0.94 per cent, and air itself is tenuous, but with a high thermal flux the activity produced is appreciable. Special ventilating equipment, high discharge stacks and monitoring instruments must be provided. Let us formulate a general expression for the concentration of such isotopes in air that results in danger to the body. The lungs will certainly be directly exposed to the radiation. We shall neglect other effects such as blood damage because of the uncertainty in their magnitude. In a large "cloud" of contaminated air, the rate at which beta and gamma rays are emitted by the isotopes in a unit volume will be almost exactly equal to the rate they are absorbed. (By *large* is meant much bigger than the particle range.) Let the unknown maximum safe activity in the air be A_m(d/sec-cm^3). The energy release is thus $A_m E$, where E is the total disintegration energy in mev. This is equal, however, to the energy absorption rate, which can be converted to roentgens by recalling that 1 r corresponds to 83 ergs/g.

$$1\ r = \frac{(83\ \text{ergs/g})(0.001293\ \text{g/cm}^3)}{(1.6 \times 10^{-6}\ \text{erg/mev})} = 6.7 \times 10^4\ \text{mev/cm}^3$$

We shall assume the individual breathes the air continually. His lungs will be exposed to radiation for the full 168 hr in a week. We shall insist that the dosage rate is no greater than 0.3 r per week, or

$$\begin{aligned}
(0.3)/(168 \times 3600) &= 5.0 \times 10^{-7}\ \text{r/sec} \\
&= (5.0 \times 10^{-7})(6.7 \times 10^4) \\
&= 0.034\ \text{mev/sec-cm}^3
\end{aligned}$$

Equating the energy release in air to that for the tolerance,

$$A_m E = 0.034 \quad \text{or} \quad A_m = 0.034/E(\text{d/sec-cm}^3)$$

our general relation is thus

$$A_m = \frac{0.92 \times 10^{-6}}{E} \cdot \frac{\mu c}{cm^3}$$

Let us apply this formula to A^{41}, which emits a beta particle of maximum energy 1.25 mev and a gamma ray of 1.3 mev. The average beta energy is $\frac{1}{3}$ that of the maximum so that the total beta plus gamma energy release is $0.42 + 1.3 = 1.72$ mev. Thus

$$A_m = 0.92 \times 10^{-6}/1.72 = 5.3 \times 10^{-7} \ \mu c/cm^3$$

This is about half of the value of 1×10^{-3} $\mu c/$liter listed in Table 13.3. It will be remarked that plant personnel are not likely to be exposed for 168 hr per week. If one assumes a 40-hr work week, this m.p.c. can be scaled up by a factor $168/40 = 4.2$.

The formula giving A_m in terms of d/sec-cm^3 as a function of E is convenient for estimating the sensitivity of detectors that are needed to recognize an excessive concentration. The number of disintegrations per second per unit volume of air containing the m.p.c. of argon $0.034/1.72 = 0.020$. The counting rate per unit volume of detector is around 1.2 per minute. A rather large volume chamber would be needed.

The maximum permissible concentration of a radioactive substance in air or drinking water is extremely low for an element that lodges in a particular organ. We shall analyze this problem from a general point of view and then apply it to an example. Let us imagine that an individual has been drinking contaminated water for such a long time that the element has built up to an equilibrium concentration in the organ. Let N_w be the number of active nuclei per cubic centimeter in the water, V the daily volume intake of water, and f the fraction retained in the body. The rate of deposit of active elements is thus $N_w V f$. Now, let N be the number of nuclei in the organ, λ be the radioactive decay constant and λ_B be the "biological decay constant" or fraction eliminated from the body per unit time. The total rate of loss is thus $N\lambda + N\lambda_B$. Equilibrium means that the rates of gain and loss are in balance. Thus

$$N_w V f = N(\lambda + \lambda_B)$$

If the deposit is uniformly distributed throughout an organ of weight W and the range of particles is short, the rate of energy absorption from the emanations is $N\lambda E/W$, where E is the energy, in mev. The energy absorption for a tolerance dose, however, is 0.3 r/168-hr week or 5.0×10^{-7} r/sec (from the A^{41} problem). Now in tissue,

$$1 \text{ r} = 93 \text{ ergs/g} = 5.8 \times 10^7 \text{ mev/g}$$

The tolerance energy absorption amounts to

$$(5.0 \times 10^{-7})(5.8 \times 10^7) = 29 \text{ mev/sec-g}$$

Equate these rates of energy absorption

$$\frac{N\lambda E}{W} = 29$$

Substitution in the equilibrium condition yields

$$N_w = \frac{29W}{\lambda E} \cdot \frac{(\lambda + \lambda_B)}{Vf} \text{ atoms/cm}^3$$

This result may be used to find the m.p.c. in water for S^{89}, a 53-day half-life, 1.5 mev beta emitter, that has an affinity for bone tissue. The water intake of a "standard man" is agreed to be 2200 cm³/day. Let us assume the bones weigh 7000 grams, the biological half-life is 250 days, and that 40 per cent of the intake is deposited in the bones. Now $\lambda_B = 0.0027$ day^{-1}, $\lambda = 0.0131$ day^{-1}, and $E = \frac{1}{3} \times 1.5$. Thus

$$A_w = \frac{(7.8 \times 10^{-4})(7000)(0.0158)}{(0.5)(2200)(0.4)} = 2.0 \times 10^{-4} \text{ }\mu\text{c/cm}^3$$

If the water is consumed for only 40 hours each week, as in the case of plant personnel, this m.p.c. could be increased by a factor of 4.2 to 8.4×10^{-4} μc/cm³. The method above may be applied equally well to the intake of radioactive isotopes by breathing or by eating.

13.5 Reactor radioactivity

A logic similar to that used to derive the m.p.c. for A^{41} may be applied to the determination of the safe distance from a reactor if it should suddenly release all its accumulated fission products. Such a catastrophe is hard to visualize, but the predictions based on its occurrence can assist in deciding where a reactor may be located. The elements constituting the fission fragments cover such a wide range in the periodic table that it would be very tedious to analyze their composite formation in the reactor and decay after release. It is preferable to make use of theoretical relationships for the number and energy of fission product radiations, devised by Way and Wigner, or experimental measurements based on absorption. The rough rules are

$$\gamma \text{ mev/sec-fission} = 1.26t^{-1.2}$$

$$(\beta + \gamma) \text{ mev/sec-fission} = 2.66t^{-1.2}$$

where t is in seconds and the formulas are good for the interval 10 sec to 100 days after fission. The cumulative activity may be deduced. Assume that a reactor had been operating for a long time, effectively infinitely long in terms of the half-lives of the fission products. In Fig. 13.2, the time scale is laid out. For all times up to $t = 0$,

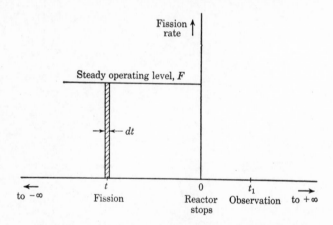

Fig. 13.2. Time scale for computing fission decay activity.

the fission rate is constant at a value F fissions/sec. In an infinitesimal time interval dt at t, the number of fissions is $F\ dt$. Note that this t is *negative* on our scale. Now assume that at time $t = 0$, the reactor stops, and all the fission products are released. At some later time t_1, we observe the energy release of those isotopes formed at the earlier time t. The *elapsed* time is $t_1 - t$ and their infinitesimal beta and gamma energy contribution is

$$dE = 2.66(t_1 - t)^{-1.2}F\ dt$$

To obtain the total energy, we may integrate from $t = -\infty$ to 0. The result is

$$E = 2.66F \int_{-\infty}^{0} (t_1 - t)^{-1.2} \, dt = -2.66F \frac{(t_1 - t)^{-0.2}}{-0.2} \Bigg]_{-\infty}^{0}$$

or

$$E = \frac{13.3F}{t_1^{0.2}} \text{ mev/sec}$$

As a specific example of the application of this relation, let us find the exposure of an individual one mile from a reactor operating at 1 mw that suddenly releases a spherical cloud of 100 ft radius containing all of its radioactivity. Imagine that the cloud drifts undisturbed in the wind at a speed of 5 mph. The fission rate F before the event was

$$(10^6 \text{ watts})(3 \times 10^{10} \text{ fissions/watt-sec}) = 3 \times 10^{16} \text{ fissions/sec}$$

The time required for the cloud to traverse the distance is one-fifth of an hour or 720 sec. Thus

$$E = (13.3)(3 \times 10^{16})/(720)^{0.2} = 1.07 \times 10^{17} \text{ mev/sec}$$

This energy is distributed throughout the sphere, the volume of which is easily computed to be 1.19×10^{11} cm^3. The energy "density" will thus be 9.0×10^5 mev/sec-cm^3. Since $1 \text{ r} = 6.7 \times 10^4$ mev/cm^3, the radiation dosage in the cloud would be 13 r/sec. If the cloud were now to stop, the daily exposure would be extreme; if instead it moved on at the same speed of 5 mph, the time for the cloud to pass would be about 27 sec, which would result in exposure of around 350 r. This is about three-fourths of the LD-50. It is clear that many assumptions have to be accepted to obtain an estimate on the question of the space needed around a reactor.

Problems

13.1 Show that the two definitions of the roentgen (Section 13.1) are the same. NOTE: electronic charge, 4.8×10^{-10} statcoulombs; density of air, 1.29×10^{-3} g/cm^3.

13.2 Estimate the maximum permissible 2-mev gamma flux.

13.3 Plot a graph of tolerance gamma flux as a function of photon energy in the range 50 kv to 5 mev.

13.4 How long would it take an experimenter who stood within 6 in. of a millicurie source of Co^{60} to receive a tolerance dose?

13.5 Determine the m.p.c. of I^{131} in continuously used drinking water, assuming that the biological half-life is one month and that the thyroid gland weighs 20 grams.

13.6 Compute the maximum safe deposit of Pu^{239} (in micrograms) in the body. The alpha particles have a 5-mev energy; the half-life is 2.4×10^4 years.

13.7 Estimate the heat energy released by the fission products produced by a day's operation of a reactor at 100 mw, one hour after the reactor has been shut down.

13.8 A reactor is operated for 24 hr only. How much error is incurred by assuming that it had operated for an infinitely long time in estimating the energy release 10 hr after shut-down?

References

LAPP, R. E. and H. L. ANDREWS, *Nuclear Radiation Physics*, 2d Ed. New York: Prentice-Hall, Inc., 1954, Chaps. 16, 17.

SNYDER, W. S. and J. L. POWELL, *Absorption of Gamma Rays*, AECD-2739. November 25, 1949.

Lecture Notes: Health Physics Training Lectures, 1948–1949, AECU-817. Health Physics Division, Oak Ridge National Laboratory, September 29, 1950.

LANSING, N. F., Ed., *The Role of Engineering in Nuclear Energy Development*, TID-5031. December, 1951. Section by K. Z. Morgan, p. 176.

MORGAN, K. Z., et al., *Health Physics Insurance Seminar*, TID-388. March 12, 1951.

"Recommendation of International Radiation Commission." *Nucleonics*, January (1951).

Safe Handling of Radioactive Isotopes, No. 42, September, 1949:

Recommendations of the International Commission on Radiological Protection and the International Commission on Radiological Units, 1950, No. 47, June 29, 1951:

Recommendations for Waste Disposal of Phosphorus-32 and Iodine-131 for Medical Users, No. 49, November 2, 1951:

Radiological Monitoring Methods and Instruments, No. 51, April 7, 1952: National Bureau of Standards Handbooks, U. S. Department of Commerce. Washington, D. C.: U. S. Government Printing Office.

KINSMAN, S. and D. J. NELSON, JR., Eds., *Radiological Health.* Cincinnati: Federal Security Agency, September, 1952.

PLOUGH, HAROLD R., "Radiation Tolerances and Genetic Effects." *Nucleonics*, August (1952) p. 16.

WIGNER, E. P. and K. WAY, *Radiation from Fission Products*, MDDC-48. May 6, 1946

CHAPTER 14

SHIELDING

Two situations arise in which shielding is necessary: (a) production or research operations in which gamma emitting radioisotopes must be handled. The uranium recovery system for plutonium producing reactors would be one example—a laboratory test of a process by the use of radioactive tracers would be at the other end of the scale so far as magnitude is concerned; (b) reactor operation, in which protection against fast neutrons, slow neutrons and gamma rays must be provided.

14.1 The shielding problem

A variety of emanations arise from radioactive decay and fission: alpha particles, beta particles, gamma rays, neutrinos, and neutrons. Only the gamma rays and neutrons require appreciable thicknesses to provide radiation protection. Alpha and beta particles are easily stopped by relatively thin sheets of metal, while the neutrinos, although highly penetrating, appear to have no physiological importance. The absorption of gamma rays is most favorable in a dense element of high atomic number, such as lead. As pointed out in the previous chapter, the gamma rays interact primarily with electrons. The combination of density and large numbers of electrons per atom is thus the requirement for a good gamma shield. Since there is relatively little absorption of neutrons except at low energies, one of the principal functions of a neutron shield is to provide targets for fast neutrons to be slowed down. For this purpose, materials with a large hydrogen content, particularly water, are best. The neutron can lose a large fraction of its energy in one collision with a hydrogen atom. The test of the effectiveness of a reactor shield is whether it reduces the particle flux far below the tolerance level. (As was emphasized in the previous chapter, the term "maximum allowable exposure" level is preferable.) The generally accepted tolerance figures, in terms of the particle flux, are reported here for reference:

	Flux (/cm²-sec)
1-mev fast neutrons	30
2-mev fast neutrons	22
1-mev gamma rays	1300
2-mev gamma rays	800
thermal neutrons	600

The numbers above correspond roughly to the figure of 0.3 rep/week.

In the description of shielding calculations to follow, we shall be content to provide rough rules that help to familiarize the student with sizes of numbers. A study of the detailed science of shielding is beyond the intent of this book.

14.2 Inverse square spreading

For small thicknesses of a gaseous medium such as air, or any distance in a vacuum, it is permissible to think of the flux of particles, either neutrons or gamma rays, in terms of straightline motion. The simple *inverse square law* is applicable. With a point source emitting n_0 particles per second, the flux density on the surface of an imaginary sphere of radius r surrounding the point is

$$\phi = n_0/4\pi r^2$$

Figure 14.1 illustrates the attenuation with distance. In comparing flux values at different radii, it follows that

$$\frac{\phi_2}{\phi_1} = \frac{r_1^2}{r_2^2}$$

This rule is remarkably simple, but of great importance in computing shielding protection. When there is plenty of space surrounding an installation that generates neutrons or gamma rays, one can save enormous amounts of material merely by restricting the distance of closest approach. As an illustration, let us find the minimum safe distance that one can remain from a 2-mev gamma source of 10-μc strength. The rate of emission n_0 is

$$(10)(3.7 \times 10^4) = 3.7 \times 10^5/\text{sec}$$

It may easily be checked that a distance of 6 cm serves to reduce the flux ϕ to 800/cm²-sec.

14.3 Attenuation of gamma rays in matter

The simplest law of absorption of light stems from the assumption that the reduction in intensity per unit path length is proportional to the intensity itself. The exponential attenuation formula is

$$\phi = \phi_0 e^{-\mu x}$$

for the flux ϕ at a distance x within a medium characterized by an absorption coefficient μ, where the incident flux is ϕ_0. Values of μ

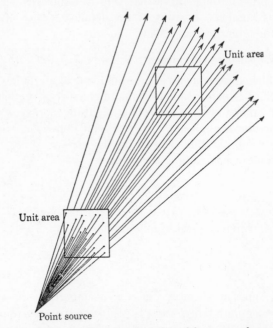

Unit area

Unit area

Point source

Fig. 14.1. Inverse square spreading of particles or rays from a point source.

depend on the material and on the energy of the incident rays in a manner that is complicated to determine theoretically. Figure 14.2 shows calculated curves of the three contributions to absorption in lead, and the composite effect. Illustrative values for different materials for 2-mev gammas are given in Table 14.1. It is very important to note that the absorption coefficients are defined in terms of a *beam* of gamma rays. Any event that causes the photons to be removed from the beam, either by true absorption or by scattering, which only changes their direction, is counted as absorption. Use of this total μ thus leads to over-estimates in attenuation, since the

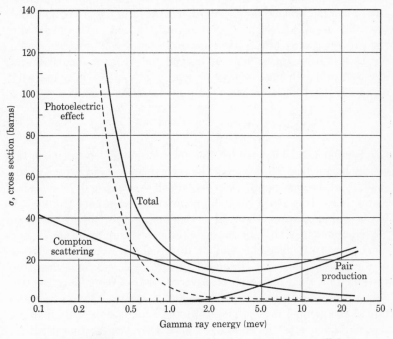

Fig. 14.2. Gamma-ray absorption in lead. Absorption coefficient
$$\mu = N\sigma.$$

scattered gamma rays are not actually lost. The mathematical complexity involved in the description of multiple Compton scattering is

TABLE 14.1

TOTAL ABSORPTION COEFFICIENTS FOR 2-MEV GAMMA RAYS

Material	μ (cm^{-1})	Material	μ (cm^{-1})
Water or body tissue	0.047	Lead	0.53
Concrete	0.09	Aluminum	0.12
Iron	0.35	Uranium	0.95

such that only high-speed electronic computers are capable of giving answers, and to date, only the simpler idealized geometries have been investigated to any degree of accuracy. The true state of affairs cannot be described by simple exponential attenuation formulas. Consider a single gamma ray of given high energy $h\nu$ incident on a shield surface. Its initial collision can occur anywhere in the material (with an exponential probability distribution of the form $e^{-\mu x}$). Assume that the collision takes place at a point x within the shield. If the gamma ray ionizes an atom with probability σ_P, we may consider the gamma ray as lost from the system. If instead the ray is scattered by an electron, probability σ_S, it may proceed in any direction ϕ and with an energy derivable from the Compton scattering formula

$$\lambda' - \lambda = \frac{h}{m_0 c} (1 - \cos \phi)$$

(see Section 1.2). The cross section for collision is dependent on the energy it now has. It may make its second collision anywhere in the shield, and the chance processes operate all over again, to be repeated many times. Because of the infinite variety of fates, each gamma ray has a unique history. Instead of answering the simple question, "What fraction of the photons gets through without collision?", one must answer "What is the number, direction and energy distribution of the photons that get through?" Below an energy of 1 mev, the threshold for the production of positron-electron pairs, only the two above processes characterized by σ_P and σ_S occur. Above 1 mev the fate of the gamma rays produced by the annihilation of the pair by recombination must be considered also. Designers are faced with a dilemma—they may estimate the amount of attenuation expected in their particular configuration by using addition processes based on sparse basic information, or they must set up experimental equipment that resembles the actual installation closely enough that attenuation data are meaningful. Neither choice is adequate. The solution of shielding problems will undoubtedly be one of the most pressing in reactor design for some time to come.

It is useful to retain the basic exponential relations for computations, but with the insertion of a correction form or "build-up" factor B. Thus instead of an intensity ratio $\phi/\phi_0 = e^{-\mu x}$ for attenuation of a plane beam in a slab of material, one writes

$$\phi/\phi_0 = Be^{-\mu x}$$

Goldberger quotes $B \simeq 3$ for 2-mev gammas in a thick water shield, and $B \simeq 1$ for energies up to about 1-mev in lead.* One may see from Fig. 14.2 that this is a reasonable choice since Compton scattering forms only a small part of the total absorption effect up to 1 mev.

Table 14.1 shows that μ increases with density of materials. This may be explained qualitatively by recalling that gamma ray stopping is an electron effect up to 1 mev, at least. We would expect μ to be proportional to the number of electrons per unit volume of the shield. However, since the number of atoms per cubic centimeter in a compound of density ρ is

$$N = \frac{\rho N_a}{M}$$

where N_a is Avogadro's number, and M is the molecular weight; the number of electrons per cubic centimeter is $\rho(N_a Z/M)$, where Z is the atomic number. Now Z/M is of the order of $\frac{1}{2}$ for most of the periodic table. Thus $\mu \sim \rho$ or $\mu/\rho \simeq$ constant. Experiments show that in the region around 2 mev, elements ranging in weight from aluminum to uranium have a value of μ/ρ of about 0.05 cm²/g. This number is convenient for rough computations.

In a medium in which there is both inverse square spreading of the beam and absorption, we may combine the two effects into one formula

$$\phi = \frac{r_0 e^{-\mu r}}{4\pi r^2}$$

where r is the radial distance from a point source. This relation glosses over the question of multiple scattering of gamma rays.

The magnitude of the shielding problem for nuclear reactors may be demonstrated by using this relation for the computation of the safe distance from an unshielded reactor of power as low as ten kilowatts. If there are five 2-mev gammas per fission, and 3×10^{10} fissions/sec correspond to one watt, the number of gammas emitted per second n_0 is 15×10^{14}. Let the flux at the safe distance r be ϕ_T. Letting $\mu/\rho = 0.05$ cm²/g, and $\rho = 1.29 \times 10^{-3}$ g/cm³, we find $\mu = 6.5 \times 10^{-5}$ cm⁻¹. The tolerance flux ϕ_T is 800 gammas/cm²-sec. Thus the equation to be solved for r is

---

* Also see U. Fano, "Gamma Ray Attenuation." *Nucleonics*, August (1953) Part I, Basic Processes, p. 8; September (1953) Part II, Analysis of Penetration, p. 55.

$$800 = \frac{15 \times 10^{14}}{4\pi r^2} e^{-(6.5 \times 10^{-5} r)}$$

By trial and error, we may find r to be around 5.8×10^4 cm, or 1900 feet. It would not be safe to remain within a *quarter of a mile* from the unshielded reactor. This example clearly shows the need for more substantial physical shielding. Let us check to see if a 6-ft thickness of ordinary concrete would be adequate to reduce such a flux to tolerance. Let $\mu = 0.09$ cm and $r = 183$ cm. Then

$$\phi = (15 \times 10^{14}) \frac{e^{-(0.09)183}}{4\pi(183)^2} = 250/\text{cm}^2\text{-sec}$$

Since this is close to the tolerance figure, one would have to increase the shield thickness considerably to achieve a good safety factor, or raise its density by the addition of a heavy element such as iron or lead. Lead in metal form, a conventional shield for x-ray machines, serves well in any system in which conservation of space is important. The thickness x_h of a layer of any material that will reduce the original intensity by a factor of 2 is easily estimated from

$$\tfrac{1}{2} = e^{-\mu x_h} \quad \text{or} \quad x_h = 0.693/\mu$$

The analogy to radioactive decay is apparent. The half-value layer x_h is comparable to the half-life t_H; the absorption coefficient μ is paralleled by the decay constant λ. For lead, with $\mu = 0.53$, the half-value layer is of thickness 1.3 cm. From a cost standpoint iron is preferable to lead even though greater thicknesses are needed for a desired attenuation factor.

14.4 Thermal neutron diffusion and absorption

It will be remembered that thermal neutrons have the ability to diffuse through any medium for an appreciable distance before being absorbed and thus must be treated by different methods from those applied to gamma rays.

The thermal neutron distribution in a non-multiplying medium can be estimated by application of diffusion theory. If a beam of thermal neutrons ϕ_0 is incident on a large flat surface of a very thick medium, diffusion theory predicts that the flux is given by

$$\phi = \phi_0 e^{-x/L}$$

For example, if a directed stream of 10^{10} neutrons/cm²-sec strikes a slab of water, for which $L = 2.88$ cm, the flux is reduced by $1/e = 0.37$ every 2.88 cm into the medium. Another idealized case is that of a point source of n_0 thermal neutrons per second in an infinite medium. This situation would be approximated in a large water tank with an artificial source in the center, if the original fast neutrons became thermal within a few inches of the source. The flux distribution is given by

$$\phi = \frac{3n_0}{4\pi\lambda_t r}e^{-r/L}$$

where L is the diffusion length, and λ_t is the *transport* mean free path. The reduction of flux with distance is seen to be exponential, but is proportional to $1/r$ rather than $1/r^2$. This can be attributed to the inherent difference between straightline motion of particles and the diffusion by many collisions. The net outward flow at any point r can be deduced from the current formula $j = (-\lambda_t/3)(d\phi/dr)$; the calculation of leakage from a finite sphere is precluded because the above flux distribution refers to an infinite medium. The solution of the diffusion problem becomes more complicated if there is a definite boundary to the system. The flux and current density formulas are listed (without proof) for a sphere of radius R with a point source at the center.

$$\phi = \frac{3n_0}{4\pi\lambda_t r} \frac{\sinh (R - r)/L}{\sinh R/L}$$

$$j_R = \frac{n_0}{4\pi RL \sinh R/L} \simeq \frac{n_0}{2\pi RL} e^{-R/L}$$

for large R. For example, let us put a point source of 10^6 thermal neutrons/sec in the center of a 4-ft diameter sphere ($R = 61$ cm) of water. The total number of neutrons escaping at the surface is $n = 4\pi R^2 j$ or

$$n \simeq n_0 \frac{2Re^{-R/L}}{L} = (10^6)\frac{122}{2.88} e^{-61/2.88} = 0.027$$

The water sphere would be predicted to be a very effective shield for the neutron source.

The neutron flux distribution from plane and point sources just presented are applicable to a medium for which the scattering cross section is much larger than the absorption cross section, and diffusion theory is applicable. The attenuation of thermal neutrons in an element such as boron or cadmium, for which $\sigma_a \gg \sigma_s$ must be treated differently. A thermal beam incident on a slab is attenuated exponentially, but according to

$$\phi = \phi_0 e^{-Kx}$$

where K is given by Σ_a. (This K is the limiting value derived from the transcendental formula given in Section 12.2.) The difference between forms $e^{-x/L}$ and e^{-Kx} can be attributed to the fact that absorption is so strong that scattering collisions and hence diffusion does not play an important part in the neutron distribution.

A useful method for finding the flux from a reactor surface is now presented. The number of neutrons that escape from a reactor can be estimated from the leakage factor $\mathcal{L}_t$ computed earlier. In order to be critical $k_{\mathrm{eff}} = k_\infty \mathcal{L}_f \mathcal{L}_t$ must be unity, implying that for every k_∞ starting fast neutrons, $k_\infty \mathcal{L}_f$ becomes thermal, and that $k_\infty \mathcal{L}_f - 1$ escape as thermal. This is easily shown to be equal to $(1/\mathcal{L}_t) - 1$ $= K^2 L^2$. The power level of the reactor determines the number of fission neutrons produced, or

$$P \text{ (watts) } c \left(\frac{\text{fissions}}{\text{watt-sec}} \right) \nu \left(\frac{\text{neutrons}}{\text{fission}} \right)$$

Let us find the leakage from a graphite reactor similar to that for which the critical size was computed in Section 6.2. For convenience we assume the material with $k_\infty = 1.10$ is built into a spherical shape rather than cubical. Further, we take the power level to be 1.0 mw. The number of fission neutrons produced is thus

$$(10^6)(3 \times 10^{10})(2.5) = 7.5 \times 10^{16}/\text{sec}$$

The critical radius R can easily be shown to be close to 250 cm and $K^2 L^2 = 0.0398$. The leakage *per fission neutron* is

$$K^2 L^2 / k_\infty = 0.0398/1.1 = 0.0362$$

The total thermal leakage is

$$(7.5 \times 10^{16})(0.0362) = 2.7 \times 10^{15}/\text{sec}$$

Assume that this crosses the reactor surface of area

$$4\pi R^2 = 4\pi (250)^2 = 7.85 \times 10^5 \text{ cm}^2$$

The current density will thus be

$$(2.7 \times 10^{15})/(7.85 \times 10^5) = 3.4 \times 10^9/\text{cm}^2\text{-sec}$$

A check on this figure can be provided by an evaluation of the neutron current density at the reactor surface, using the following facts:

(1) The flux distribution in a sphere is

$$\phi = \phi_c \frac{\sin \pi r/R}{\pi r/R}$$

(2) The ratio of average flux to central flux is

$$\frac{\bar{\phi}}{\phi_c} = \frac{3}{\pi^2}$$

(3) The relation between power and flux is

$$P \text{ (watts)} = \frac{\bar{\phi} \, \Sigma_f \, V}{c}$$

(4) The current density is given in terms of the transport mean free path $\lambda_t = 3 \Sigma_a/K^2$ by

$$j = -\frac{\lambda_t}{3} \cdot \frac{d\phi}{dr}$$

14.5 Fast neutron shielding

The biological danger of fast neutrons is many times higher than that of thermal neutrons, as discussed in the previous chapter. Further, it is relatively easy to remove low energy neutrons with a strongly absorbing element such as boron. Thus the neutron shielding problem evolves into one of reducing fast neutrons to low energy, in as short a distance as practical, without inducing any secondary processes. The cross sections for fast neutrons are rather small, of the order of that predicted from the nuclear radius, quoted in Section 1.3 as $r = 1.4 \times 10^{-13} \, A^{1/3}$ cm. For lead $A = 207$, the cross section would be estimated as $\pi r^2 = 2.2$ barns. This is not true absorption; sometimes neutrons are scattered inelastically. Collisions cannot be depended on to remove completely the neutron from the picture. The ideal substance for neutron shielding is water because of the slowing down properties of hydrogen nuclei. Unfortunately water is not a very good gamma shield, composed as it is of elements of low atomic number. On the other hand, heavy elements that stop gamma rays adequately are poor for reduction of neutron energy. It is clear that it is necessary, therefore, to mix a heavy element with the water, or vice versa, or to arrange the two types of matter in successive layers, if gamma rays are to be stopped along with fast neutrons. The difficulty that arises is that fast neutrons interact with heavy nuclei by inelastic scattering, in which a secondary gamma ray is produced. Only a shift from one undesirable component to another has been achieved. The new gamma rays always originate closer to the outer surface of the shield than did the fast neutrons, and thus have a thinner shield to penetrate. If the shield is thick enough, of course, both components eventually will be stopped. A point that should also be emphasized is that the great danger is from the few neutrons that by chance are repeatedly scattered through very small angles and thus preserve both direction and energy. The bulk of the neutrons lose energy rapidly and are removed; the "unusual" neutrons escape through the shield. An indication of shield thickness that will reduce most of the neutrons to low energies can be obtained from the age theory, used previously to calculate reactor sizes. In a medium that has a point source of n_0 fast neutrons of energy E_0 per second, the number that become thermal per second in a unit volume a distance r away is

$$q = \frac{n_0 e^{-(r^2/4L_f^2)}}{(4\pi L_f)^{3/2}}$$

where L_f is the fast diffusion length, and $L_f^2 = \tau$. A plot of this "slowing down density" for water and graphite is shown in Fig. 14.3. It is seen that practically no neutrons get beyond 30 cm in water. One may compute the average distance r at which neutrons become thermal, or more commonly the average square of the distance r^2. The latter, by the relation $\int r^2 q \, dV / \int q \, dV$, is found to be

$$\bar{r^2} = 6L_f^2$$

As an example, for graphite $L_f^2 = 300$ cm^2, $\bar{r^2} = 1800$ cm^2. The root mean square distance $r_{\text{rms}} = \sqrt{\bar{r^2}}$ is thus 42 cm. It is clear that a graphite shield must be much thicker than 42 cm to guarantee essentially complete thermalization. For water,

$$L_f^2 = 33 \text{ cm}^2, \quad 6L_f^2 = 198, \quad r_{\text{rms}} = 14 \text{ cm}$$

A water shield is thus much more effective than a graphite shield.

The proper way to estimate the effect of a shield is to calculate the flux of fast neutrons of all energies throughout the medium, and compute leakages as was done for thermal neutrons. This task is as difficult as the gamma-ray shielding theory, and it is preferable to develop semi-empirical formulas from experimental data.

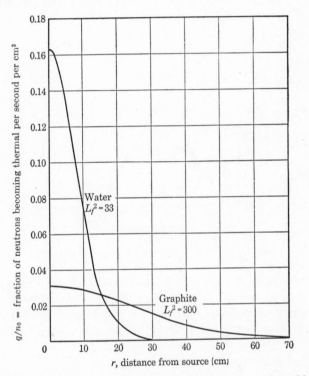

Fig. 14.3. Neutron slowing down distributions in water and graphite
$$q/n_0 = e^{-(r/2L_f)^2}/(4\pi L_f)^{3/2}.$$

It is conventional practice to describe the elimination of neutrons from the high energy range either by elastic collisions or inelastic collisions, or slowing and whatever absorption occurs by a "relaxation length" λ. This distance is analogous to L in the exponential attenuation relation for thermal neutrons. Thus we write a new attenuation formula for fast neutrons

$$\phi = \phi_0 e^{-x/\lambda}$$

The slope of the flux plotted against the distance on semi-log paper is

$$\frac{d(\log_{10} \phi)}{dx} = \frac{0.434 d(\log_e \phi)}{dx} = \frac{-0.434}{\lambda}$$

which is a constant. Thus a straight line plot would be found if experiment could be represented this simply. Figure 14.4 shows typical

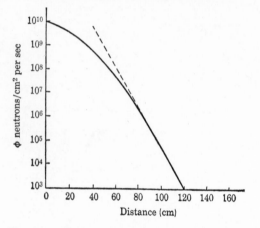

Fig. 14.4. Typical fast neutron attenuation curve.

data. Despite the deviation from linearity, the *effective* λ can be used. For ordinary concrete, density $2.0 - 2.5$ g/cm³, λ is about 11 cm. For a more dense concrete, such as 3.5 g/cm³, λ would be close to 7 cm. Let us make an estimate of the effect of a 6-ft thick shield of high density concrete on the fast neutron flux of 10^{11}/cm²-sec. The reduction factor in the distance of 183 cm is

$$e^{-183/7} = e^{-26} = 5.1 \times 10^{-12}$$

The flux escaping would be about 0.5 neutron/cm²-sec. If the 7-cm relaxation length is a reliable figure, the shield would have a safety factor of about 40.

Neutron-induced gamma rays. Thermal neutron capture by most elements is accompanied by the emission of a gamma ray, usually of high energy. Thus the elimination of neutrons by shield materials may create a new and equally serious hazard. This effect was overlooked by the legendary individual who suggested that a cadmium lined suit be designed for workers near reactors. Energies of gammas released upon (n,γ) reaction are listed below:

Element	Energy (mev)	Element	Energy (mev)
H	2.2	Fe	7.6
Be	6.8	Cd	7.5
C	4.9	Pb^{206}	6.7
Na	6.3	Pb^{207}	7.4
Al	7.7		

The absorption coefficients of such high energy radiations in shields are considerably lower than for fission gamma rays. For instance, the mass absorption coefficient for 2-mev gammas in water is 0.05 cm²/g whereas for 7-mev gammas it is only 0.025 cm²/g. A high-energy gamma flux may turn out to dominate the shield requirement, even though the initial amount of radiation may seem negligible. For example, assume that there is a thermal neutron flux of 10^{11} at the 1/16-in. stainless-steel core container wall of a homogeneous reactor. One may estimate that the number of absorptions per cm² per second is approximately

$$\phi \, \Sigma \, t = (10^{11}/\text{cm}^2\text{-sec})(0.206 \text{ cm}^{-1})(0.16 \text{ cm})$$

$$= 3.3 \times 10^9/\text{cm}^2\text{-sec}$$

Assume that of these about one-third or 10^9 give rise to 7-mev gammas. We found in Section 14.3 that in a power level of 10 kw, the total fission gamma emission was 15×10^{14}. With a surface area of 3000 cm², the number of gamma rays leaving the reactor per cm² per second (neglecting self-absorption) would be 5×10^{11}. We note that the induced flux is initially 1/500 of the fission flux. As one proceeds into a shield, however, the flux ratio changes according to

$$\frac{\phi(7)}{\phi(2)} = \frac{\phi_0(7)}{\phi_0(2)} \, e^{(\mu_2 - \mu_7)x} = e^{+0.025x}/500$$

At a distance of 6 ft into a water shield the flux ratio is down to about $\frac{1}{5}$ and at 8 ft the fluxes are *equal*.

The neutron-induced gamma rays must be accounted for in a shield throughout which thermal capture takes place. It is important to note that these gammas may be created right up to the external shield surface, where they constitute an immediate danger.

14.6 Practical shielding

The choice of shielding substances for a reactor will be based on which of the requirements listed is dominant:

(1) cost of materials or construction;
(2) physical space available;
(3) weight limitations.

A stationary installation for which there are no space or weight problems might best be protected by a shield of ordinary concrete of great thickness. Gains in gamma absorption could be provided by using iron ore or barium ore as part of the concrete aggregate. Since the cost of concrete goes up roughly as the cube of the thickness, an actual saving in cost might be achieved with reduced dimensions. The addition of special materials would be mandatory in the case of an airplane shield where both size and weight are important. The way in which a spherical shield size depends on the two variables density ρ and thickness r, favors the dense shield as now shown. In order to achieve a given attenuation, suppose r/λ has to be some known constant, neglecting the inverse square effect. The total shield weight W is proportional to the volume and thus ρr^3. But also

$$\lambda \sim 1/\rho, \quad r \sim 1/\rho, \quad W \sim 1/\rho^2$$

This shows that the denser the shield, the lighter can be the system as a whole. There are two ways of increasing density, of course; by adding a heavy element, or by choosing a mixture that is inherently more closely packed.

Whether the shield should be laminated or the constituents should be uniformly mixed is a matter to be determined only by experiment. Every combination of materials and geometry behaves differently and, as yet, simple engineering formulas for making predictions are apparently not available. Some success has been met in the use of the stochastic (Monte Carlo) approach, in which the histories of many individual neutrons are traced and the fraction that gets through is estimated. The theory of some idealized situations such as the slowing down of neutrons in moderators of relatively large mass number, neglecting absorption and assuming constant scattering properties, has been derived analytically.

Factors that must be considered in a complete evaluation of shielding problems are the following:

(1) Reactor radiation consists of neutrons and gamma rays of a variety of energies.

(2) There is a three dimensional motion from the reactor.

(3) The reactor sources and the regions of possible exposure are finite volumes, not points.

Partial or "shadow" shielding may be employed for installations where the reactor operators can remain in a fixed location. In an airplane, for example, only the side of the reactor facing the crew needs to be heavily shielded for direct radiation. Some shielding from particles scattered by the air would be needed, of course. To discover how much, resort may be made to calculations or experiments.

As a simple illustration of the complexity of the analysis of combined geometric and physical shielding, consider the problem of neutron scattering in air from a pencil of thermal neutrons of starting

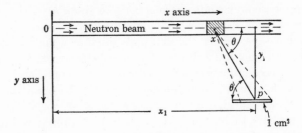

Fig. 14.5. Geometry for analysis of air scattering of neutrons from beam.

flux ϕ_0 as observed at a point at the side of the beam; see Fig. 14.5. The flux of neutrons in the beam at any point along its path is

$$\phi = \phi_0 e^{-\Sigma x}$$

where Σ is the total (absorption plus scattering) cross section of air. The number scattered in a thickness dx at coordinate x is $\phi \Sigma_S \, dx$, which serves as a new source of neutrons. The flux across a surface of unit area parallel to the beam at a point $P(x,y)$, due to this contribution is thus

$$(\phi \, \Sigma_S \, dx) \frac{e^{-\Sigma r}}{4\pi r^2} \cos \theta$$

The total number of neutrons crossing the surface is the sum over all scattering sources:

$$\int_{x=0}^{x=\infty} \frac{\phi_0 e^{-\Sigma x} \Sigma_S \, dx \, e^{-\Sigma r} \cos \theta}{4\pi r^2}$$

where $\qquad r^2 = (x_1 - x)^2 + y_1^2$

and $\qquad \cos \theta = \dfrac{x_1 - x}{r}$

This integral may be evaluated by numerical methods.

The requirement on fixed shields, for reactors, cyclotrons, or "hot" laboratories differ considerably from those for mobile systems such as the nuclear powered aircraft. The weight factor that is all-important for vehicles is essentially eliminated, to be replaced by the factors of cost and volume. In this section we shall describe several types of concrete and other cheap materials.*

As discussed earlier, the ideal shield would consist of a light element to slow neutrons without the production of gamma rays by inelastic scattering; it would include a strong neutron absorber, again without secondary gamma rays, it would contain a heavy dense element to stop gamma rays; finally the materials mixture would be very inexpensive and easy to fabricate. No one substance satisfies all these conditions, so compromises must be made. One approach is to find cements with a high water content. Figure 14.6 shows the water contents of several high water cements. Of these, magnesium oxychloride appears to be the best in that its hydrogen content approaches that of water itself. The Brookhaven reactor shield was constructed of "MO," a mixture of magnesium oxychloride, steel punchings and shot. Rockwell points out however, that ordinary Portland cement can be made to retain many times the expected water content by the use of a porous aggregate and a paint coating of the structure.

Regardless of the type of aggregate used, the density that can be achieved depends on the distribution of sizes of the component particle. In general, the gradation should be such that the interstices of the largest particles are filled by smaller particles.

Several aggregates have been found successful in neutron gamma shields. At the Argonne National Laboratory, mortar was first poured in forms, and steel punchings 1 in. in diameter and 0.5 in. thick were vibrated into place. Scrap metal, in the form of proper metal turn-

---

* A few definitions may be necessary. *Cement* is the bonding material, *aggregate* consists of heavier inert chunks of stone, metal or ore that gives weight and strength, *concrete* is the product mixture of cement and aggregate.

ings, has been found advantageous in conjunction with punchings at Oak Ridge. A few of the ores that have been used are listed in Table 14.2.

TABLE 14.2

ORES FOR SHIELD AGGREGATES

Name and Source	Composition (%)	Density g/cm³
Limonite (Alabama)	50 Fe	3.3
Magnetite (Adirondacks)	60 Fe	5.1
Barytes (Tennessee, Georgia)	95 BaSO₄	4.3
Galena (Missouri)	80 Pb	7.5
Colemanite (California)	44 B₂O₃	. . .

In many instances handling techniques unfamiliar in the concrete field must be used. In tests prior to the construction of the Raleigh

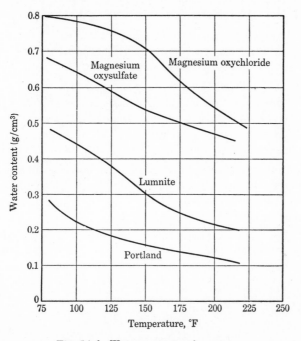

Fig. 14.6. Water contents of cements.

reactor shield, it was found that the slight water solubility of the boron ore, colemanite, resulted in failure of the mixture to harden.

The method of preparing the concrete that was developed to eliminate the difficulty was to mix only the cement and barytes aggregate, with a minimum of water, and allow it to stand for half an hour. Water was thus partially committed to the cement, and later addition of colemanite did not affect the setting properties. Another special method that has been used for reactor shields involves first filling the forms with aggregate and then pumping in the fluid mortar at high pressure.

Problems

14.1 What would be the safe distance from an unshielded reactor with power level 28 mw, as in the Brookhaven reactor?

14.2 Find the thickness of a water shield that will bring a 2-mev gamma flux from a 2.5-mw reactor down to the tolerance level.

14.3 If the relaxation length of fast neutrons in water is 10 cm, find the shield thickness for an initial flux of $10^{13}/cm^2$-sec.

14.4 It is not obvious at first glance which is the cheaper shield for a point source emitter: (a) a spherical shield that surrounds the source; or (b) a spherical shell at some distance away from the source. Compare these two cases.

14.5 Find the total number of neutrons of energy above 5 mev that are emitted each second in a 10-megawatt reactor. (See Section 3.2 for fission neutron energy distribution). Compute the maximum current density at the surface of the 3-ft diameter core.

14.6 Determine the amounts of material and costs of two shields: lead (20¢/lb) and iron (5¢/lb) for a 0.3-curie source of 2-mev gammas that will reduce the flux to 50 gammas/cm^2-sec. What conclusion can you draw from this estimate?

14.7 Two different methods for finding the flow of neutrons from a spherical reactor were given in Section 14.4. Verify *analytically* that the two are equivalent.

14.8 Find out what weight of colemanite (see Table 14.2) should be added to each cubic yard of a concrete mix yielding 215 lb/ft^3 in order to achieve 1 per cent boron by weight.

14.9 A water solution of zinc bromide ($ZnBr_2$, molecular weight 225.2, density 4.22 g/cm^3) is used for gamma-neutron shields. The effective cross section of each atom for 2-mev gamma rays is 5 barns.

Find the minimum thickness of a slab shield for a *plane* gamma beam of 10^{12} gammas/cm²-sec, if the solution is 20 per cent by weight of $ZnBr_2$. Will this thickness be adequate to reduce a beam of 10^{12} fast neutrons/cm²-sec, to tolerance?

14.10 Find the thickness of a layer of boron carbide (B_4C, density 2.5 g/cm³), that will reduce the thermal leakage from the spherical reactor of Section 14.4 to 60 neutrons/cm²-sec.

References

ENGBERG, C. J., Ed., *Radiation Shields and Shielding. A Bibliography of Unclassified AEC Report Literature*, TID-3032. Oak Ridge, Tenn.: Technical Information Service (AEC), September (1952). 130 annotated references.

DAVISSON, C. M. and R. D. EVANS, "Gamma Ray Absorption Co-efficients." *Rev. Mod. Phys.*, *24*, 79 (1952).

TITTLE, C. W., *The Slowing Down and Diffusion of Neutrons in Hydrogenous Media*, NP-1418 (AEC) M.I.T. Nuclear Shielding Studies, I, August 31, 1949.

LEVIN, J. S., J. W. WEIL, and C. GOODMAN, *Gamma Ray Ionization in Spherical Geometry*, NP-875 (AEC). M.I.T. Nuclear Shielding Studies, II, June 15, 1949.

DACEY, J. E., R. W. PAINE, JR., and C. GOODMAN, *Shielding Proper-ties of Various Materials against Neutrons and Gamma Rays*, NP-1243 (AEC). M.I.T. Nuclear Shielding Studies, III, Octo-ber 20, 1949.

ROCKWELL, THEODORE, III, *Construction of Cheap Shield: A Survey*, AECD-3352. Oak Ridge National Laboratory, January 16, 1950.

UECKER, D. F., K. R. FERGUSON, D. G. SEAY, and C. B. WEBSTER, *Test of Concrete with Iron Punchings for Cave Construction*, AECD-3013. Argonne National Laboratory, July 11, 1949.

PAVLISH, A. E. and J. C. WYND, *Concretes for Pile Shielding*, AECD-3007. Battelle Memorial Institute, August, 1948.

TIRPAK, EDWARD G., "Report on the Use of Barytes Aggregate in Concrete for Shielding Purposes." *Civil Engineering*, *21*, 451 (1951).

GOLDBERGER, M. L., *The Shielding of Nuclear Reactors*, MDDC-806. Argonne National Laboratory, March 24, 1947. (See also GOOD-MAN, C., Ed., *The Science and Engineering of Nuclear Power*. Cambridge, Mass.: Addison-Wesley Press, 1949, Vol. II, p. 196.)

RUDDY, JOHN M., *Gamma Ray Shielding for Engineering Reference*, AECU-1211. Brookhaven National Laboratory, February 15, 1951.

ARON, W. A., B. G. HOFFMAN, and F. C. WILLIAMS, *Range-Energy Curves*, AECU-663. University of California Radiation Laboratory, December 2, 1949.

SOODAK, HARRY and E. C. CAMPBELL, *Elementary Pile Theory*. New York: John Wiley & Sons, 1950.

BALDERSTON, J. L., J. J. TAYLOR, and G. J. BRUCKER, *Nomograms for the Calculation of Gamma Shielding*, AECD-2934. Kellex Corp., November 15, 1948.

CHAPTER 15

RADIOACTIVE WASTE DISPOSAL

The process waste-disposal problem is common in industry. The smoke that is released by steel mills is a typical example—without some measure of control, smoke can cause a health problem for the surrounding population. Wastes from atomic energy installations not only constitute a potential chemical hazard, but also a more important radiation hazard. In this section we shall estimate amounts of waste, classify their types, indicate their principal sources, and describe briefly the modes of safe handling.

15.1 Amounts of radioactive wastes that must be handled

Two different situations are encountered in the treatment of radioactive material. The first is the disposal of a true waste, in which no attempt is made to salvage any particular element. The second is one in which a valuable element or radioactive isotope must be isolated and purified. An example of the latter is the extraction of plutonium and uranium from the dissolved slugs of a Hanford-type reactor. We are not able to estimate the amount of material that must be processed, since the details of the Hanford plant are not available. It is clear, however, that the natural uranium slugs, after neutron irradiation, contain plutonium, fission products, and uranium. Stringent recovery requirements must be set because of the inherent power value of plutonium and its potential hazard to human beings. One gram, properly administered, could cause the disability or death of thousands of people. It is clear also that uranium that is contaminated by fission products produced in a reactor is effectively worthless. For each pound of plutonium produced, about the same weight of U^{235} will be converted into fission products (see Section 5.2). The weight of fission products to be removed is small but the radioactivity is extremely high. The total gamma energy yield from a pound of gross fission products at various times after irradiation can be estimated from the $t^{-1.2}$ formula (Section 13.5). Inspection of

Fig. 15.1 shows that the activity of the accumulation remains high for hundreds of days. One may compute the radiation from this pound by making the rough assumption of 1-mev energy per particle,

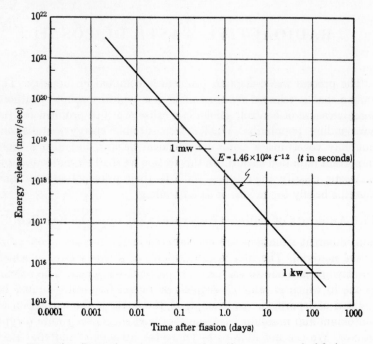

Fig. 15.1. Rate of gamma energy release from one pound of fission products. 1 mev/sec = 1.6 × 10⁻¹³ watt.

and using the approximation that one roentgen corresponds to a flux of around 1000 gammas per cm²-sec. If a worker were to stand 10 ft from a pound of fresh (0.1 day) fission products, he would receive a lethal dose ($\simeq$ 450 r) in about 10^{-3} sec.

By-products of the chemical processes in the nuclear energy program are classified according to their state of matter when the disposal problem is met, that is, gaseous, liquid, or solid.

15.2 Gaseous wastes

Materials that are normally gaseous can most easily result in atmospheric contamination. One example that was described earlier (Section 13.4) was the radioactive argon A^{41} produced in an air cooled reactor. The half-life of around two hours is so high that temporary holding is impractical, in view of the flow rates needed to cool reactors. In this instance, the air is filtered before and after going through the machine to remove particles and stop most of the impurities, and then is released to the atmosphere through tall stacks 200–300 ft high.

With discharges of this type the science of meteorology plays an important part in determining the safety of operation. When there is a strong wind, or strong lapse conditions exist (a normal variation of temperature with altitude, with the temperature lower at higher levels) released gases will be readily dispersed by turbulence. If, however, an inversion is present (with air near the ground cooler than it is higher up) streams of material can be carried along for many miles without much dispersal. On occasion, the inversion may break down, bringing large concentrations of active material to the ground along its path. In practice, continuous observations and classifications are made of weather conditions, estimates of possible danger at populated locations are made regularly, and under questionable conditions the operations are stopped.

The remaining sources of gaseous wastes are more conventional in nature. Radioactive dusts are produced in the mechanical preparation of metallic ores, and fumes and gases are released in the chemical processing. Characteristic industrial equipment such as electrostatic precipitators, filters, and scrubbing towers are used to prevent contamination of the air breathed by plant personnel and the surrounding population. Uranium is probably more hazardous from the standpoint of chemical toxicity than it is from its radioactivity because of its long half-life.

The chemical separation of fission products from uranium and plutonium at the Hanford plant results in the liberation of active elements such as iodine, strontium, yttrium, columbium, ruthenium, cesium and cerium. Because of the potential health hazard if excessive amounts are deposited at any one point, these dissolving operations are shut down if weather conditions are unfavorable. As a result of measurements of activity in vegetation surrounding the production area, it was found necessary at Hanford to install special decontamination equipment to remove the radioactive materials prior to the dilution by air and the exhaust through a high stack. In the research laboratories that produce gaseous effluents, the main precaution that is taken is to provide high-speed high-capacity ventilation. Much of the work that involves hazardous fumes or gases is carried out in sealed boxes, handled with protective gloves or by remote control.

15.3 Liquid wastes

Two widely different practices are used in dealing with liquid wastes. One is dilution, usually by copious quantities of water, and subsequent release. The other is concentration to small volumes and storage. The dilution method has the advantage of resulting in minimum handling but has the chance of contamination of areas into which the water passes if the dilution factor is not adequate. Rules with reference to three widely used isotopes have been formulated:

(1) Radioiodine, I^{131}, may be discharged from an installation to a main sewer if each millicurie is mixed with 1 g of potassium iodide and if the concentration in water is less than 10 μc/liter.

(2) Radiophosphorus, P^{32}, may be discharged into a sewer if 10 g/mc of an inert phosphorus compound is added and the concentration in water is less than 0.1 μc/liter. The maximum activity discharged per week is 200 mc.

(3) Radiocarbon, C^{14}, may be released to the atmosphere if the concentration is less than 0.01 μc/liter and if particles have previously been filtered from the air.

It will be noted that the allowable concentrations are of the order of the air and drinking water concentrations of Table 13.3. Thus no credit is taken for further dilution in the sewerage system. Specifications have not been provided for the discharge of all the isotopes that may be encountered. As a starting approximation, the drinking water and air limits can be used.

The induced radioactivity in the cooling water of the Hanford plant is held in basins and then discharged into the Columbia River. In the event of the failure of a slug coating that would add the high-fission product activity to the water, the flow is diverted and held separately.

Every laboratory that uses radioactive materials has small amounts of liquid wastes from cleanup operations. Known active wastes are normally held in special containers, so that the amount that gets into the drainage system will be relatively small, and diluted with large quantities of water. At larger installations such as Oak Ridge, Knolls Atomic Power Laboratory, Argonne, and Brookhaven, great quantities of radioactivity are produced. The system of handling fission products and uranium at Oak Ridge is characteristic of the facilities that are needed. Wastes containing uranium are stored indefinitely. Other radioactive materials are held, converted into large insoluble aggregates, and allowed to settle in a series of tanks. The residual liquid is sent to underground retention tanks and then to White Oak Lake, which is located in the restricted area. This in turn feeds the Tennessee Valley water system. Activity surveys of vegetation and mud in the neighborhood of the lake are made frequently to determine the amount of radioactivity released from government control. Measurements indicate that the level is below $5 \times 10^{-7} \mu c/cm^3$, which is of the order of the activity due to cosmic radiation in mountainous areas and much less than the content of certain mineral water.

Whenever the dilution treatment is undesirable because of the isotope handled, concentration methods are practiced. Several different treatments for reducing the fluid volume have been proposed and tested. The most common methods are evaporation, ion exchange, flocculation, adsorption, and biological treatment methods.

Evaporation. This is the simplest and surest method of handling dilute liquid radioactive wastes but it has the disadvantage of associated high costs. At the Knolls Atomic Power Laboratory a forced circulation-type evaporator with a capacity of 500 gal/hr was used. This evaporator system was provided with de-entrainment apparatus to prevent contamination of the condensate. Decontamination factors as high as 10^7 were obtained, with a reduction in volume of 98 per cent. (The decontamination factor is defined as the ratio of the initial activity per milliliter to the final activity per milliliter.) The cost of operation of this unit when operated at a rate of 100,000 gal per month was $0.138/gal of waste.

This method of treatment is not suited for the concentration of liquid wastes that contain volatile radioactive materials. Radioactive iodine is volatile in acid solutions, but evaporation can be used by carrying out the process at high pH (11 to 12).

Ion Exchange. Certain solid resins have the property of exchanging some of their non-radioactive ions for radioactive ions as water flows through a finely-divided resin medium. Such resins are used to reduce the activity of large amounts of water containing very small amounts of radioactive ions. (If the solution contains both radioactive cations and anions they can be removed by first passing the solution through a cation exchanger and then through an anion exchanger or by passing the solution through a monobed exchanger containing both cation and anion exchange resins.) After the exchanger has been exhausted, the radioactive ions may be removed by regeneration, giving a concentrated solution of the radioactive ions. If the exchanger cannot be regenerated, the resin may be burned leaving a small volume of ash to be disposed of as a solid radioactive waste.

If the solution contains oils, soaps, greases, and precipitates, these may clog or coat the resin and prevent ion exchange. At the Knolls Atomic Power Laboratory a Dowex 50 resin was used to remove cerium from a 2 per cent solution of cerous chloride in the presence of soap, organic solvent, and oil. Even with these substances involved the decontamination factor was greater than 10^5.

Solutions may contain phosphates, citrates, tartrates or other compounds which form complexes with the radioactive elements. If these complexes are ions, they can be removed by ion exchange, but neutral or un-ionized complex molecules cannot be removed. However, some of the neutral complexes are unstable and may be broken down into ions by adding some reagent. An ion exchange resin may then be used successfully. Some complexes are stable only over a limited range of acidity and thus may be broken by changing the pH of the solution.

Flocculation. Conventional water treatment techniques have been used for the removal of radioisotopes from large volumes of water. One of these, flocculation, involves the addition of certain chemicals such as aluminum sulfate, ferric chloride, and sodium phosphate plus calcium hydroxide, to the water. These cause coagulation of material into clusters which are removed by sedimentation. The supernatent is then filtered to remove the smaller particles which did not settle out. Ferric chloride is superior to aluminum sulfate in the removal of plutonium. Phosphate precipitation at high pH is more effective than either aluminum sulfate or ferric chloride. The value of the flocculation method depends upon the radioisotope present. About 70 per cent of the radioactive materials may be removed from a fission product mixture by coagulation, sedimentation and filtration.

Adsorption. Some materials, such as activated carbon, activated silica, clays, celite, kaolin and pumice, with very high surface area per unit volume, have a tendency to adsorb on their surface certain molecules and ions. This phenomenon has been used for the removal of radioactive materials from solutions. Activated carbon has proved to be the best adsorbent, having the additional advantage that after separation from the solution by filtration or sedimentation the activity adsorbed can be concentrated by burning.

Adsorbents may be used alone or added along with the coagulation agent in the flocculation process. Clays used in conjunction with phosphate coagulation, sedimentation, and filtration have removed as much as 99 per cent of the radioactivity from a fission fragment mixture at the Oak Ridge National Laboratory. The flocculation method removed very little of radioiodine I^{131}, but the addition of activated carbon removed 26 per cent of the iodine.

Biological treatment methods. The activated sludge process is particularly suited for the removal of radioactive substances from dilute solutions. This process is a biochemical oxidative reaction by an activated sludge containing massive colonies of zoogloeal bacteria. The bacteria form gelatinous matrices with very large surface areas which are capable of adsorbing radioactive materials. Food such as domestic sewage must be supplied to perpetuate the colonies of bacteria. If this is not available, minerals, carbohydrates and proteins may be added. At Los Alamos 95 per cent of a long-life alpha emitter in concentrations up to 1.4 μg/liter was successfully removed by the activated sludge process.

The biological trickling filter is similar to the activated sludge process in that the colonies of bacteria are grown in the filter medium of rock and coarse gravel. This method of removal of radioactive materials is particularly suited to wastes that contain large amounts of foaming agents such as soap, because no aeration is required as in the activated sludge process. The trickling filter was used at Los Alamos for the removal of plutonium from laundry wastes.

In all the above processes, the necessity for remote handling increases the technological problems several fold. Repairs and replacements of components must be achieved both conveniently and safely.

15.4 Solid wastes

Some of the sources of solid radioactive matter are contaminated clothing, trash, biological specimens, scrap metal and discarded equipment, including materials of construction of buildings. Liquid wastes evaporated to dryness and sedimentation from the flocculation process obviously contribute additional sources. One method of handling consists of incineration in a closed cycle system, and subsequent burial of the ash. Other non-combustible materials must be buried directly. Much discussion has centered about the problem of achieving "adequate" storage. Radioactive substances buried in isolated guarded vaults may appear to be very secure in terms of a few years, but the nature of radioactive decay implies that protection must be guaranteed for hundreds or even thousands of years.

One of the recommendations of an Atomic Energy Commission meeting in 1948 was that isotopes may be buried in ground owned by the user if the minimum depth is five feet and if they are diluted with an inert isotope of the same element. The degree of dilution must be such that the energy release is less than 4.15 ergs/g-day. As an illustration, let us find the amount of sodium necessary to mix with a millicurie of Na^{24} (decay constant 1.29×10^{-5} sec^{-1}, total energy 5.5 mev). Let M be the necessary weight of inert material, A the activity, and E the energy per disintegration. Then the energy release per day per gram in the new mixture is

$$4.15 \text{ ergs/g-day} = \frac{A \text{ (d/sec)} \ E \text{ (ergs/d)} \ 8.6 \times 10^4 \text{ (sec/day)}}{M \text{ (g)}}$$

Taking $A = 3.7 \times 10^7$ d/sec, and $E = 8.8 \times 10^{-6}$ ergs/d, we find M to be 6750 kg. We see from this number that it is impractical to bury amounts of radioactivity greater than a few microcuries. The alternative method is to store the radioactivity in well sealed containers. Many suggestions on storage have been proposed, such as setting aside a large tract of land in the middle of the desert or burial at sea in containers that will remain intact for a very long time. The latter method has been used by the University of California. Wastes were mixed with cement, sealed in oil drums, and dumped in the ocean 30 miles off the coast. The danger that is always present is that sea plants and animals that utilize minerals from water will concentrate the active material in their bodies, and the radioactivity may ultimately reappear in sea food consumed by human beings.

15.5 Decontamination

Objects and areas which have been contaminated by radioactive materials may be cleaned or decontaminated by conventional methods and techniques. The radioactivity need not be removed completely but only reduced to a level where it will be safe for personnel working in the vicinity. Whenever economically feasible, decontamination that renders a piece of equipment usable is attempted.

The most common methods of surface decontamination are vacuum cleaning, abrasion, and washing with water, steam, detergents, complexing agents, organic solvents, acids, and caustics. After the activity of the object has been reduced by cleaning or by natural decay, the residual radioactivity may be sealed in by coating the surface with some semi-permanent material. Asphalt may be applied to roads and flat surfaces, paints and plastics to buildings and small objects, and grout to concrete surfaces.

The problem of decontamination may be reduced by the choice of structural materials and surface coatings that can be easily cleaned. These materials should be smooth and nonporous and have a high resistance to corrosion and heat. The U. S. Naval Radiological Defense Laboratory has prepared a chart listing the different methods of decontamination of paint, asphalt, concrete, brick, tile, wood and soil.* There are several approaches to the decontamination problem in systems where the activity is prohibitive. One rather obvious method that eliminates work is to throw away the equipment when it breaks down or is no longer useful. This is necessary with intricate equipment, or even in the case of long pipes that are contaminated on the inside. It is clear that such a practice is expensive, but decontamination operations may be more costly than the apparatus itself. At many of the atomic plants there are large "graveyards" of contaminated equipment, which contain various levels of activity, some dangerously high, others safe but having radiations that would be costly nuisances if the materials found their way into commercial channels, such as the photographic industry. Another is to devise mechanical robot control systems that perform washing, scrubbing and flushing operations that would be done manually if the activity were low. Such a system is expensive to set up and maintain. A third method that requires careful design is one in which the facilities for contamination are built into the equipment originally. A simple

* See *Nucleonics*, November (1951).

example would be the provision of extra lines to supply acid, water, and to drain the system. Before replacing or repairing the apparatus, repeated decontaminations "in place" may be performed.

In spite of the relative newness of the disposal problem, and the tremendous quantities of radioactive materials that suddenly had to be handled in the atomic energy project, the situation has been dealt with very capably. It is encouraging to note that efforts to develop better methods and controls are keeping pace with the growing problem of waste disposal.

References

"Symposium on Radioactive Wastes." *Ind. Eng. Chem.*, *43*, 1499 (1951). Nine comprehensive papers on different methods of handling wastes.

Handling Radioactive Wastes in the Atomic Energy Program. Washington, D. C.: Atomic Energy Commission, U. S. Government Printing Office, August, 1951.

STRAUB, C. P., R. J. MORTON, and O. R. PLACAK, "Studies on Removal of Radioactive Contaminants from Water." *J. Am. Water Works Assoc.*, *43*, 773 (1951).

RUCHHOFT, C. C., "The Possibilities of Disposal of Radioactive Wastes by Biological Treatment Methods." *Sewage and Ind. Wastes*, *21*, 877 (1949).

STRAUB, C. P., "Removal of Radioactive Waste from Water." *Nucleonics*, January (1952) p. 40.

BEERS, N. R., "Stack Meteorology and Atmospheric Disposal of Radioactive Waste." *Nucleonics*, April (1949) p. 28.

TOMPKINS, P. C. and O. M. BIZZELL, "Working Surfaces for Radiochemical Laboratories—Glass, Stainless Steel and Lead." *Ind. Eng. Chem.*, *42*, 1469 (1950).

TOMPKINS, P. C., O. M. BIZZELL, and C. D. WATSON, "Working Surfaces for Radiochemical Laboratories—Paints, Plastics and Floor Materials." *Ind. Eng. Chem.*, *42*, 1475 (1950).

"Decontamination Chart—U. S. Naval Radiological Defense Laboratory." *Nucleonics*, November (1951).

NEWELL, J. F. and C. W. CHRISTENSON, "Radioactive Waste Disposal." *Sewage and Ind. Wastes*, July (1951).

Radioactive Waste Disposal: A Bibliography of Unclassified Literature, TID-375. Oak Ridge: Technical Information Service, AEC, August, 1950.

CHAPTER 16

DETECTORS AND CONTROL
INSTRUMENTS*

The design, construction and maintenance of radiation detectors and associated circuits is as important a function in the nuclear engineering field as is reactor design and operation. Not only must accurate and dependable instruments be provided for measurement of neutron flux and for reactor control, but there are a host of detectors needed for the monitoring of radioactive operations, and for experimental nuclear physics and chemistry. In this chapter we shall restrict our attention to the more elementary, descriptive aspects of instrumentation, with the main emphasis on the detection of neutrons and the criteria for instruments to achieve safe reactor control. We must realize that a thorough understanding of the circuit operation involves a prerequisite of training in electronics, although it is hoped that from our discussion the non-specialist in this field will derive some appreciation of the functions that control systems serve, while the specialist observes new applications and special requirements of basic instruments.

16.1 Types of detectors

The basic process in most charged particle detectors is that of ionization. Consider two thin parallel metal electrodes enclosed in a gas filled chamber, as in Fig. 16.1. A high-speed charged particle or gamma ray enters the space between electrodes, which have a difference of potential between them. The incoming particle ionizes the gas, and the electrons and positively charged ions are swept by the electric field to their respective electrodes. The potential drop developed across the resistor due to the current flow is the signal sent on to the detector and recording circuit. Such a system, called an *ionization chamber*, is particularly useful for large steady incident beams of gamma rays or for highly-ionizing heavy particles, which

---

* The suggestions made by Joseph Lundholm, Jr. on parts of this chapter are gratefully recognized.

create individual pulses. A variety of adaptations of the ionization chamber with different physical arrangements of electrodes, gases, pressures and applied potentials have been devised for particular functions. We shall merely list the important features of several such detectors.

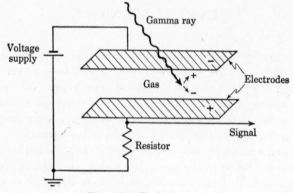

Fig. 16.1. Basic detector.

In the *proportional counter*, advantage is taken of the ability of secondary ions to create further ionization if they are given enough energy between the electrodes. The positive electrode or anode consists of a thin wire, while the negative cathode is a concentric shell. In the vicinity of the wire, the electric field is very high, allowing electrons to produce an ionization avalanche in that region. A current pulse is thus registered. The magnitude of the pulse is proportional to the amount of original ionization, and hence highly ionizing particles like alpha particles or fission fragments can be distinguished from weaker ionizing agents such as gamma rays. The time that is needed for the electrons resulting from one primary particle to be completely removed from the space and for the counter to recover completely is very short, of the order of 100 μsec. This is the "dead time," during which no further incoming particles can be detected. This is not a serious limitation, since the circuit normally cannot handle more than 10^4 consecutive particles per second. Corrections for statistical effects involving coincidental particles can readily be made.

The physical arrangement of electrodes in the *Geiger-Muller* (G-M) *tube* is similar to that in the proportional counter except that the potential difference between electrodes is higher. In this region, an incident particle sets off a discharge that is independent of the ionizing ability of the particle. The negative electrode may be a glass cylinder with very thin walls, covered with a metal film, or may have a mica window thin enough to allow the transmission and detection of beta particles. A typical gas used in the chamber is argon, with added alcohol vapor to assist in quickly cutting off the discharge, a process called "quenching." By proper construction, G-M tubes may be made efficient enough to detect gamma rays. Electrons ejected from the metal cathode by the gamma rays—the photo-electric effect—initiate the discharge, rather than the electrons released in the gas.

No mention has yet been made of the possibility of detecting neutrons with any of these devices. The fact that a neutron has no electrical charge and thus does not ionize makes it necessary to introduce an intermediate step in the sequence of events that yield currents. One way is to fill an ionization chamber with the gas boron trifluoride, BF_3. Slow neutrons are absorbed by the boron, especially the isotope B^{10}, to initiate the nuclear reaction

$$_0n^1 + {}_5B^{10} \rightarrow {}_2He^4 + {}_3Li^7$$

The alpha particle is capable of producing the necessary ionization in the chamber. The efficiency of such a detector for thermal neutrons is reasonably high because of the large boron absorption cross

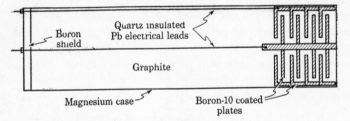

Fig. 16.2. Parallel circular plate ionization chamber for neutron detection.

section. Since boron is a $1/v$ absorber, its cross section is too low for useful detection of fast neutrons. An alternative to the BF_3 detector is made by coating the internal surfaces of the electrodes of an ionization chamber with boron or B^{10}. Neutrons absorbed in the lining release alpha particles that do the ionizing. One effective design, labeled "PCP" (parallel circular plates) is sensitive to both neutrons and gamma rays. It consists of several circular metal plates, coated with B^{10}, and strung on a central insulating rod. See sketch, Fig. 16.2. The polarity of alternate plates is the same, making the system effectively one large parallel plate chamber. By the use of large plate area and small volume of chamber, the gamma sensitivity is made relatively small.

The *fission chamber* is an ionization chamber operated in the proportional region with a layer of purified U^{235} on the electrode surfaces. Thermal neutrons are strongly absorbed and the energetic fission fragments create ionization that results in pulses. A typical fission chamber consists of a small nickel tube, about 4 in. long and $\frac{3}{4}$ in. in diameter. U^{235} is electroplated on its inner surface. The collecting electrode is a thin ($\frac{1}{8}$-in.) rod down the center. Highly purified argon flows slowly but continuously through the tube. Argon free of oxygen must be used because of the strong affinity of free electrons for oxygen molecules. If the thermal component of the beam is screened out by a boron or cadmium shield, normal uranium or uranium depleted in U^{235} could be used in a fission chamber for fast neutrons, by the reaction with U^{238}. Only neutrons above one mev can be detected effectively, however, because of the threshold of fast fission in U^{238}.

Fast neutrons may also be detected by a proportional counter filled with hydrogen gas or a hydrocarbon such as methane. The neutrons give up a large portion of their energy to the hydrogen atoms, which recoil as protons to ionize and set off the electron avalanche. A method that is useful for measuring neutron energies consists of bombarding a thin paraffin or polyethylene window with a ray of fast neutrons. The recoil protons may be detected as they traverse the tube and distinguished according to their direction and range.

The radiation to which a detector is exposed in or near a reactor consists of two components—neutrons and gamma rays. A large fraction of the latter come from fission products accumulated over previous operation, and thus their measurement does not yield a good index of the reactor power level. The *compensated ionization chamber* as used in the Raleigh reactor system is able to isolate the neutron component. It contains two volumes: (a) coated with boron, sensitive to both neutrons and gamma rays; (b) not coated, responsive only to gamma rays. With the circuit sketched in Fig. 16.3, the difference in currents across the two regions, namely that due to neutrons only, is observed. The volume ratio is adjustable, to achieve proper compensation for gammas.

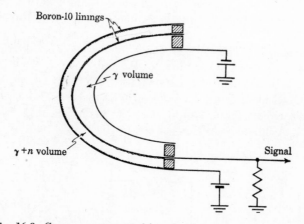

Fig. 16.3. Gamma-compensated ion chamber (schematic cross section of cylinder).

The method by which alpha particles were detected in Rutherford's scattering experiments (Section 1.2) consisted of observation of the flashes of light on the phosphor zinc sulfide. The *scintillation counter* is one device which registers such flashes electronically. Chemical compounds such as naphthalene, anthracene and scheelite ($CaWO_4$) are used for beta particle and gamma ray detection. Light due to fluorescence in the crystalline material is allowed to fall on a light sensitive surface of a photo-multiplier tube. Such tubes are specialized versions of the photocell (see Section 1.2) that are sensitive to minute light signals. Neutrons may be detected by the recoil protons in anthracene; slow neutrons can be detected by the secondary reaction in phosphors containing boron or lithium. The particular advantage of scintillation counters over G-M tubes is that there is practically zero recovery time, since the fluorescence is due to individual atoms. The lifetime of the excited atomic states is around 10^{-8} sec.

16.2 Electronic equipment

The function of the electrical circuit following the particle detector or "sensing element" is to respond quickly to variations in flux and to present an accurate picture of conditions on meters or recording instruments. We shall isolate a number of components and describe their principles of operation in rather non-technical terms. In Section 16.3 systems built from these components and detectors will be discussed.

Pulse amplifier. The voltage signal from a counting device such as a fission chamber is very low, of the order of a few tenths of a millivolt. If a mechanical register is used eventually to record the counts, a considerable total amplification of the voltage is necessary. The basic circuit for a typical stage in an amplifier is shown in Fig. 16.4. A burst of electrons swept to the central wire of the de-

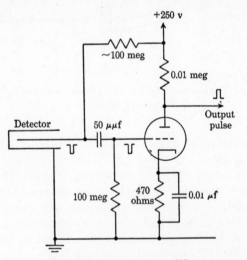

Fig. 16.4. Single tube amplifier.

tector reduces its potential, i.e., gives a negative pulse. The subsequent change in grid potential in the vacuum tube results in an amplified pulse in the plate circuit. Many such amplifier stages in series yield the needed gain.

Cathode follower. Most detectors in reactor research are located at some distance from the amplifiers, scalers, and recorders. This means that the resulting pulses must be transmitted over a length of coaxial cable. Such a cable has an inherent capacitance, distributed over its length, that must be charged up very quickly if the pulse of short duration is to preserve its height and shape.

If the original pulse amplitude is sufficient, then one may use a simple cathode follower circuit located at the detector for driving the coaxial cable. This consists of a one tube circuit with a resistor placed in the cathode connection to ground and the plate voltage connected directly to the plate without the usual plate resistor. Although the gain or amplification of a cathode follower circuit is slightly less than 1, its output impedance is only a few hundred ohms. Thus a low impedance source is provided which can supply the necessary power for quickly charging a length of coaxial cable.

If the pulse produced by the detector, such as a fission chamber or B^{10} thermal neutron detector, is not of sufficient amplitude for feeding directly into the main amplifier, it is usually desirable to use a *pre-amplifier* located at the detector for the necessary additional amplification factor of about 20. It consists of two amplifier stages as discussed previously, feeding the cathode follower.

In order to improve the characteristics of this pre-amplifier, as well as all amplifiers as used in pulse counting, it is customary to provide inverse feedback stabilization from the output of the cathode follower to the first amplifying stage. The principle of feedback is reviewed briefly. A voltage proportional to the output of an amplification circuit is fed back in series with the input voltage. Inverse feedback, the type in which the signal returned tends to reduce the input, serves to correct for non-linearities, to reduce certain kinds of electrical noise, and in general to stabilize the circuit against power supply fluctuations and tube aging. In the pre-amplifier, an improvement of frequency response is realized, which helps maintain the voltage pulse shapes.

Scaler. The purpose of this circuit is to transform a large number of pulses to a small number of signals that serve as a faithful measure of the original counts. A relatively slow mechanical register cannot keep pace with a counting rate of the order of thousands per second. The basic unit of a scaler consists of two vacuum tubes coupled in such a way that only every other pulse from the detector is transmitted. With two such units in series every fourth count is noted, with three in series every eighth count, etc. Scales of 32, of 64 and 128 are in common use.

Rate meter. Instead of counting individual pulses, it is often desirable to display a signal that is proportional to the number of counts per unit time averaged over a long period relative to the time between individual counts. This is achieved by allowing successive voltage pulses to charge a condenser, as shown in Fig. 16.5. The stage pre-

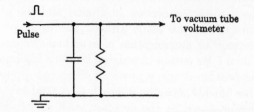

Fig. 16.5. Integration circuit of count rate meter, linear scale.

ceding the condenser serves to convert pulses of random shape and size into pulses that provide a fixed amount of electric charge. The leakage current through a resistance shunt to ground and the voltage drop thus developed are measures of the counting rate. A vacuum tube voltmeter may be used to measure the average potential.

A count rate meter is needed to obtain suitable signal voltages from pulse circuits to actuate reactor *trip circuits.* If the power level exceeds a pre-determined value, and the counting rate becomes excessive, the machinery is set in operation for a shut-down of the reactor.

Logarithmic amplifier. A reactor with an excess multiplication has been shown in Chapter 8 to rise in neutron density or power by factors of hundreds and thousands in short times. Even during normal start-up, the power level is raised from the order of watts to hundreds of kilowatts, i.e. through several "decades." A meter with a linear scale cannot handle such variations with equal sensitivity. A property of electron motion in a vacuum tube is put to advantage to overcome this difficulty. A diode vacuum tube is the main component of the logarithmic amplifier, the output of which is proportional to the logarithm of the input current. The electrons emitted by a heated cathode are approximately described by a maxwellian distribution—those of high velocity can cross the gap between cathode and plate in the vacuum tube even with a retarding potential. The fraction that do so is given by $e^{(-Ve/kT)}$ where V is the potential between electrodes and T is the cathode (and electron) temperature. Thus the current is given by

$$I/I_0 = e^{-Ve/kT} \quad \text{or} \quad V \sim -\log_e I \sim -\log_{10} I$$

A diode obeying this law may be inserted as the grid resistor in a circuit measuring small currents as shown in Fig. 16.6. The voltage

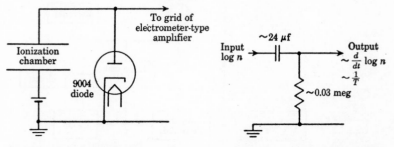

Fig. 16.6. Input circuit of logarithmic amplifier. Diode used as grid resistor.

Fig. 16.7. Differentiating circuit to obtain reactor period signal.

signal to the amplifier is proportional to the logarithm of the ionization chamber current rather than to the current itself. An increase of a factor of 1000 in the neutron flux and thus the current results in an increase of a factor of only 3 in the voltage. It is possible with certain tubes to achieve linear responses over a range of more than 10^6 in current.

Differentiating circuit. As was shown in Section 8.1, the reactor period T, the time for the power to increase by a factor e, is very sensitive to the excess reactivity δk. Knowledge of the period is a good index of how safely the reactor is being operated. The logarithmic amplifier discussed above yields a signal proportional to $\log n = \log n_0 e^{t/T}$. A differentiating circuit following the log circuit performs the function of taking the time derivative of $\log n$ electrically, i.e. giving $1/T$ or properly displayed, the period. Essentially it consists of a capacitor and a resistor of low values, as shown in Fig. 16.7. The output is zero if the neutron flux is steady; this corresponds to a period of $T = \infty$.

16.3 Start-up, control, and safety systems

The operating cycle of a reactor consists of three stages: (a) the approach to critical, (b) the rise to operating power, and (c) the steady operation. The first region is characterized by a low neutron flux. Detectors that observe the effects of individual particles and recorders that register them are needed. A slow, safe rise must be guaranteed by limits on the speed of control rod removal or by trip circuits. Figure 16.8 shows a standard start-up circuit for a low power machine

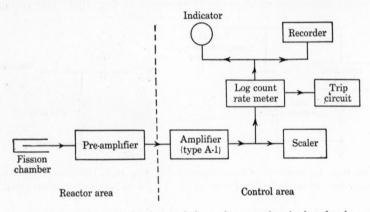

Fig. 16.8. Start-up circuit, used for pulse counting in low level operation.

such as the Raleigh reactor or the swimming pool reactor. The scaler is available for a direct measurement of counting rate in the early stages and for plotting $1/C$ versus mass graphs of the type discussed in Section 8.2. Since the counting rate from the fission chamber increases very rapidly from the start to the critical point, it is more convenient to measure and display its logarithm. The log-count rate meter uses a logarithmic diode in place of the resistor shown in Fig. 16.5. Once the basic fuel accumulation has been made, under controlled conditions, future start-up procedures are considerably abbreviated. The mass of uranium is no longer a variable quantity, as it was in the initial assembly, and the control rod or rods serve as a means of adjustment.

As the power level increases in the second stage, the neutron flux at the fission chamber becomes excessive from two standpoints: (a) the number of counts per second is larger than the amplifier can handle and (b) excessive fission-product activity is induced in the chamber. One technique is to pull the chamber farther from the core, to a region of lower flux. It may be preferable, however, to rely on current-measuring instruments. In Fig. 16.9 a circuit for the rise to power is shown. Each of the components has been discussed previously, and its arrangement in sequence is readily understood. The period indicator must have a special scale running from infinity down to some small value of the order of seconds. In conjunction

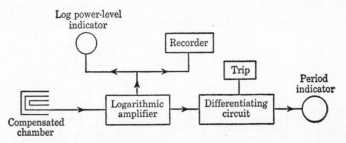

Fig. 16.9. Log n, period circuit for rise to power.

with the period meter, a trip circuit may be used. A signal from it opens the control-rod magnet circuit. Thus if T gets too short, the rod will be released.

Whether a reactor is used for commercial power or as an experimental neutron source, it is necessary to provide automatic control to eliminate excessive attention by an operator and maintain constant, steady, flux levels. A system linking neutron detectors and the control rod for this third stage operation is shown in Fig. 16.10. The detector observes the neutron flux; the voltage signal from the amplifier is balanced against a standard but adjustable voltage from the potentiometer. The *difference* signal actuates the motor that drives the control rod. If the neutron signal is too small, the rods are raised; if too large, the rods are lowered. The automatic system can be disconnected to allow for manual push-button control of the rods. In the event of a sudden change in nuclear characteristics of the reactor, or a mis-operation of the control system, a rapid rise in power level may be experienced. The system must be equipped with trip circuits that release the safety rod. A distinction may be made here between the various signals that assist the operator and protect the machine from damage:

(1) The *interlock* consists of a combination of relays that must be actuated if the reactor is to be turned on. For instance, control rod power is locked out if there is no reactor coolant flow.

(2) The *alarm* consists of a signal from a buzzer or bell, a visual indication on a panel of light bulbs. A change in reactor temperature or the failure of one instrument may thus be brought to the operator's attention.

(3) The *trip* refers to a circuit linked with a reactor safety mechanism such as rod magnets or a solution dump valve. A sharp rise in neutron flux as recorded by an instrument may actuate a trip.

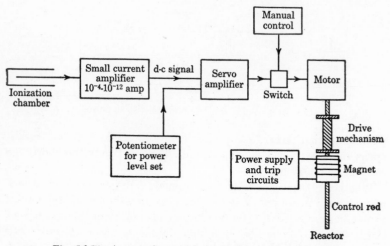

Fig. 16.10. Automatic control circuit, for steady operation.

(4) The *emergency signal* is the last line of defense, consisting of a manually operated lever or button that shuts down the reactor, including rod drops, and sounds a loud horn or siren demanding evacuation of the immediate area of the reactor.

Reactor instrumentation has grown from the special electronic circuits used in experimental physics for particle detection. In recent years, however, the demand for equipment has become so great that commercial concerns now supply many standard components and matched systems. Since the construction is practically on a mass production basis and the best available designs are used, the commercial units are reliable and usually superior to experimental models. The first step in planning reactor instrumentation is to find out what "on the shelf" components are available.

The above summary of the stages of operation has presupposed that circuit and control rod designs are compatible. We shall now examine this relation in somewhat more detail. In Chapter 7, the role of the rod and general trend of the power versus rod position was discussed briefly. The general reactor has several sources of negative reactivity that must be compensated by removal of the absorbing control rod. For instance, the separate sources of $\delta k/k$ for the swimming pool type are quoted by T. E. Cole to be the following:

	$\delta k/k$
Operation	0.003
Temperature	0.00375
Fuel depletion and fission products	0.0015
Xe poisoning	0.0045
Total	0.01275
Experimental	0.02

The total rod value is a function of the size, shape and composition of both the rod and the reactor. Computations of rod value of the same type as that given in Section 7.5, but more elaborate, are made to be sure the necessary total $\delta k/k$ is available. We now make estimates of typical contributions to the reactivity that must be controlled.

The δk to balance Xe^{135} poisoning in steady operation can be estimated by the same formula as that given in Section 12.4 for the heterogeneous natural uranium reactor except that the ratio $(\sigma_f/\sigma_a)_U = 0.528$ is replaced by the proper value for U^{235}, 0.845. The average flux in the swimming pool is around 5.8×10^{11} at 100 kw. Thus

$$\Delta\left(\frac{1}{f}\right) = \frac{0.0498}{1 + (6.0 \times 10^{12})/\phi} = 0.0044$$

We take $\Delta(1/f)$ as being of the order of $\delta k/k$ (see Section 12.4), with fair agreement with the quotation. The Xe^{135} effect is ten times as great in the high flux (around 10^{14}) Materials Testing reactor at Arco, Idaho. The control system must be able to accommodate this 4.7 per cent decrease in reactivity that arises during the approach to power. The rate of change of δk due to Xe with time during the approach to full power is governed by the unbalance of several factors: the growth of I^{135}, its decay into Xe^{135}, the burn-out of Xe^{135}

with time by the time-varying neutron flux, and the decay of radio-active Xe^{135}. Figure 16.11 shows the trend in poisoning with time during the start-up for a reactor with flux of 10^{14} reached at time zero.

A new important effect in reactor control arises when a high flux

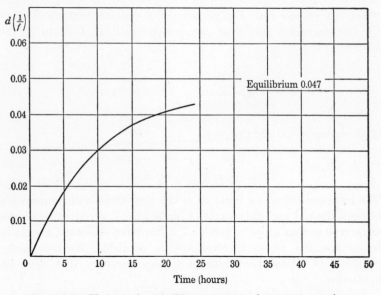

Fig. 16.11. Xenon poison build-up at start of reactor operation.
Average flux = 10^{14}.

reactor is shut down. The parent iodine, formerly at its equilibrium concentration, continues to supply Xe^{135} poison, which is no longer burned out by the flux. The Xe concentration rises above its equilibrium value to a point where decay ($t_H = 9.2$ hr) takes over. The drop in reactivity is severe, of the order of 20 per cent in the MTR after twelve hours have elapsed. Extending results of Section 12.4, the equations for the trends in the number of atoms/cm³ of the two fission products are

$$I = I_0 e^{-\lambda_1 t}$$

$$\frac{dX}{dt} = -\lambda_2 X + \lambda_1 I$$

$$X = X_0 e^{-\lambda_2 t} + \frac{\lambda_1 I_0}{\lambda_2 - \lambda_1} (e^{-\lambda_1 t} - e^{-\lambda_2 t})$$

where the equilibrium concentrations of I^{135} and Xe^{135} (just before shut-down) are

$$I_0 = \frac{y_1 \Sigma_f \phi}{\lambda_1}, \quad X_0 = \frac{y \Sigma_f \phi}{\lambda_2 + \sigma_2 \phi}$$

Here, y_1 is the fractional fission yield of iodine directly, 0.056, and y is the sum of y_1 and y_2 (the direct yield of Xe^{135}, 0.003). Figure 16.12

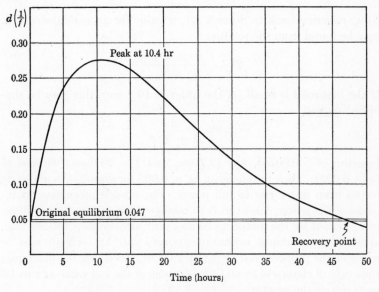

Fig. 16.12. Xenon build-up after reactor shut-down.
Average flux = 10^{14}.

shows the poisoning in terms of $\Delta(1/f)$ after shut-down of a reactor with 10^{14} flux. It can be seen that if provisions for control of all of the large (27 per cent) negative reactivity are not available, a delay of an hour or two will make it impossible to start up the reactor again, and it will be necessary to wait about four days for recovery by the decay process.

We accept the fact that a reactor just critical can run at any power level. In order to raise the level, however, it is necessary to have a temporary excess reactivity, i.e., be slightly supercritical, within the δk range 0 to 0.00755, as discussed in Section 8.1. The choice of excess must be governed by the speed with which the change is desired, and the degree of safety expected. Suppose that it is planned to go from 1 watt to 100 kw, a factor of 10^5, in a reactor of the swimming pool type in a time of 5 min = 300 sec. If we ignore short-lived transient effects, the dominant reactor period T should be such that

$$n/n_0 = e^{300/T} = 10^5 = e^{11.5}$$

or $\qquad\qquad T = 300/11.5 = 26.0 \text{ sec}$

Now, referring back to Section 8.1, a value for an *instantaneous* δk may be found from the relation

$$T = \frac{l + (\beta - \delta k)\bar{\tau}}{\delta k}$$

If the lifetime l is small (of the order of 10^{-4} sec), this may be simplified to read

$$\delta k \cong \frac{\beta}{1 + T/\bar{\tau}}$$

Inserting $\beta = 0.00755$, $\bar{\tau} = 12.2$ sec, and $T = 26.0$ sec, we find δk to be 0.0024. Thus the choice of $\delta k = 0.003$ for *operation* is adequate for an even faster rise to full power. The normal procedure for increasing the power, however, is to remove a rod at a certain uniform rate, limited by the motor speed and gear arrangement, rather than attempting an almost instantaneous removal. An estimate can be made of the proper speed of withdrawal by specifying the maximum time rate of change of δk and a knowledge of the rod value at various positions in the reactor.

Control rod sensitivity. Variations in rod value may be found by use of the theorem discussed in Section 12.4: that the importance of an absorber at a point in the reactor is proportional to the *square* of the flux. Consider a bare rectangular or cylindrical homogeneous reactor of height H, with a small axial control rod inserted an arbitrary depth x. As a first approximation, assume that the *shape* of the flux is not disturbed, but that the rod absorbs out neutrons that would otherwise help maintain the cycle. (A rod composed of nonfissionable material with the same absorption properties as the core would fit this assumption.) Now assume that the δk value of the rod is given by

$$\delta k \sim \frac{\int_{\text{rod}} \phi^2 dV}{\int_{\text{reactor}} \phi^2 dV}$$

The integral in the numerator, taken only over the *inserted* volume of the rod, is

$$A \int_0^x \phi^2 dx$$

This assumes that the flux does not vary much radially because of the small rod size and thus $\int \int dy \, dz = A$, the rod area. Were the rod all the way in, the maximum effectiveness would be a similar quotient, but with integration over the larger volume. Form the ratio

$$\frac{\delta k}{(\delta k)_{max}} = \frac{\int_0^x \phi^2 dx}{\int_0^H \phi^2 dx}$$

noting that areas have cancelled, as well as denominators. Substituting $\phi = \phi_0 \sin \pi x/H$ for the axial flux, and integrating, we obtain

$$\frac{\delta k}{(\delta k)_{max}} = \frac{x}{H} - \frac{\sin 2\pi x/H}{2\pi}$$

This ratio is plotted as a function of x/H in Fig. 16.13. The S-shaped

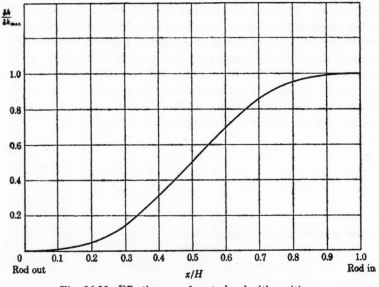

Fig. 16.13. Effectiveness of control rod with position.

$$\frac{\delta k}{\delta k_{max}} = \frac{x}{H} - \frac{\sin 2\pi x/H}{2\pi}$$

curve is found to agree with experimental data from the Los Alamos water boiler and from the ORNL graphite reactor. The maximum rate of change of δk with rod position occurs where $x = H/2$, at which point $\delta k = (\delta k)_{\text{max}}/2$. If a very quick response to a shift in operating conditions is desired, one should poise either a safety or control rod with its tip halfway in. Of course, for maximum overall suppression, the safety rod should be all the way out of the core. The rate of increase of δk as a rod is pulled out at a speed $v = dx/dt$ can easily be shown to be

$$\frac{d}{dt}(\delta k) = \frac{2v}{H}(\delta k)_{\text{max}}\left(\sin\frac{\pi x}{H}\right)^2$$

For small motions near the center of the core where this reduces to the largest rate of change of δk

$$\left[\frac{d}{dt}(\delta k)\right]_{\text{max}} = (\delta k)_{\text{max}}\frac{2v}{H}$$

Let us restrict this rate to a typical value of around 0.0001 per sec. In a reactor that is 60 cm high, about that for the swimming pool, with a total rod value of $(\delta k)_{\text{max}} = 0.005$, this implies a speed of 0.60 cm/sec. The time to withdraw the rods would be 100 sec. Another useful application of the above formulas is to the effect of a safety rod drop. Assume that an accidental increase in reactivity of amount δk_i occurs. One may ask: How quickly is the reactivity nullified by the rod, if free fall takes place? For example, assume that $\delta k_i = 0.01$, which is considerably above $\beta = 0.00755$, and as such the reactor is prompt critical. Let the maximum value of the rod be $(\delta k)_{\text{max}} = 0.05$. The fractional depth the rod must fall is given by

$$\frac{\delta k}{(\delta k)_{\text{max}}} = \frac{0.01}{0.05} = \frac{x}{H} - \frac{\sin 2\pi x/H}{2\pi}$$

which yields $x/H = 0.337$. If the reactor height is 60 cm, the necessary depth is 20 cm. The time required is obtained from

$$x = gt^2/2$$

where g is the acceleration of gravity. Thus

$$t = \sqrt{\frac{(2)(20)}{980}} = 0.20 \text{ sec}$$

For a 30-cm reactor, such as the water boiler, this time is reduced to 0.078 sec. To each of these must be added the time lapse between the neutron signal and the rod release, which may be around 0.050 sec. In a reactor with small temperature coefficient of reactivity to assist the control rod, the attendant power rise would be dangerous.

Reactor power flash-up with negative temperature coefficient. It is not realistic to consider only the safety rod effect in a homogeneous water-moderated reactor or the swimming pool type in which boiling will stop the reaction effectively. Let us estimate the expected instrument response if the safety rod were omitted from consideration (as if it did not fall), when the instantaneous excess reactivity is δk_i. Assuming responses that are so immediate that delayed neutrons may be ignored, we may use the simple neutron-density equation from Section 8.1.

$$\frac{dn}{dt} = n\,\frac{\delta k}{l}$$

where l is the neutron lifetime. It will be preferable to use the equivalent power form

$$\frac{dP}{dt} = P\,\frac{\delta k}{l} \tag{a}$$

If the reactor were operating at a steady power level P_0 when the event occurred, with a fixed rate of heat removal balancing that power, then there will be an excess of power $P - P_0$ available to heat up the reactor. Let the heat capacity of the core be C. The rate of temperature rise is thus

$$\frac{dT}{dt} = \frac{P - P_0}{C} \tag{b}$$

Dividing Eqs. (a) and (b),

$$\frac{dP}{dT} = \frac{CP\,\delta k}{(P - P_0)l} \tag{c}$$

The value of δk at any time is

$$\delta k = \delta k_i - |\alpha|T \tag{d}$$

where T is the temperature rise of the core and $|\alpha|$ is the temperature coefficient (absolute value), as discussed in Section 7.4. The temperature at which the temperature effect just cancels the initial δk_i is $T = \delta k_i/|\alpha|$. At the time this occurs, the power stops rising but there is still a large power difference that continues to heat the reactor to a higher temperature. Substitution of Eq. (d) in (c) and integration yields

$$\frac{P}{P_0} - 1 - \log_e \frac{P}{P_0} = \frac{C}{P_0 l}\left(T\delta k_i - \frac{|\alpha|}{2}T^2\right)$$

It may be deduced that T goes to a peak value equal to

$$T_{\max} = 2\frac{\delta k_i}{|\alpha|}$$

which is just twice the cancellation temperature. Taking $\delta k_i = 0.01$, and $|\alpha| = 2 \times 10^{-4}/°C$, the total temperature rise predicted is 100°C.

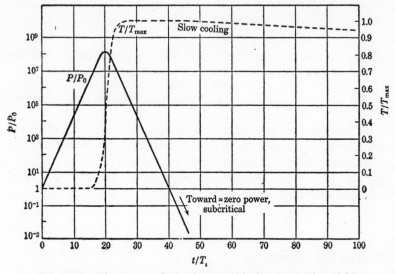

Fig. 16.14. First power flash of supercritical reactor. $\delta k_i = 0.01$; $l = 10^{-4}$ sec; $P_0 = 1$ watt; $|\alpha| = 2 \times 10^{-4}/°C$; $C = 56$ kw-sec/°C.

If the reactor started at room temperature, boiling would set in. Vapor bubbles give rise to an even stronger temperature coefficient, and the reaction would die down. The power level will have risen to a value of around

$$P \cong \frac{CT_{\max}}{4T_i}$$

where $T_i = l/\delta k_i$ the initial *period*. For a water boiler reactor with volume 14 liters and specific heat 0.95, the heat capacity is

$$C = (14{,}000 \text{ g})(0.95 \text{ cal/g-}^\circ\text{C})(4.186 \text{ joules/cal})$$

$$= 56 \text{ kw-sec/}^\circ\text{C}$$

Taking $T_i = 0.01$ sec, P goes to around 140 mw and then drops back. The time lapse for the power cycle is so short, however, that the radiation burst is not serious. A rough estimate of the time for P to reach its peak can be obtained by setting this calculated maximum equal to $P_0 e^{t/T_i}$, and solving for t. If P_0 were 1 watt, t would have to be about 20 periods or 0.2 sec. Assuming no safety rod drop, bursts would occur periodically, with the time between them dependent on the rate of cooling of the reactor from T_{max}. As soon as P gets back near P_0 the cooling rate is very small. Figure 16.14 shows the trend in P and T during the first burst.

16.4 Other instruments

Reactor start-up and control equipment by no means constitute all of the instrumentation needed for safe operation. Many miscellaneous devices assist in guaranteeing protection for working personnel and those nearby who are not connected with the reactor project. We shall merely enumerate the types of monitoring and appropriate instruments. *Personnel* can obtain an indication of daily radiation dosage by the use of pocket dosimeters, which are electroscopes charged at the start of the work period. The amount that they discharge is a measure of the exposure. A variety of film badges that indicate beta, gamma and neutron exposure, may be worn, depending on the radiation likely to be received. The various adaptations of the basic photographic technique involve special shielding, windows, and type of film. *Work area monitoring* is achieved by locating ionization chambers or Geiger-type tubes at different points in the rooms where radioactive material may be released. *Survey instruments* are usually small, portable detectors that may be brought near suspected active surfaces or particle beams. The instrument used is dependent on the particle to be detected: for low-level gamma activity or for alpha and beta particles, a G-M tube is used; for high-level gamma fluxes, an ionization chamber such as the "Cutie-pie"; for slow neutrons, a BF_3 or B^{10} detector; for fast neutrons, a proportional counter using the proton recoil principle. Other special instruments monitor activated reactor coolants, laboratory wastes or gaseous effluents.

Problems

16.1 The concept of cross section may be equally well applied to collisions of electrons with gas atoms as to neutron-nucleus interactions. If the collision cross section of argon is 10^{-15} cm^2, and the gas pressure is 0.2 atm, how much potential difference would be required to sweep out all electrons formed in a chamber with plate separation of 5 cm in 100 μsec?

16.2 Estimate the length of a BF$_3$ detector at pressure 12.5 cm Hg that is needed to give 95 per cent efficiency for a beam of thermal neutrons. Assume the boron is 90 per cent B^{10}.

16.3 What is the maximum counting rate that could be expected in a cylindrical BF$_3$ chamber with 1-in. diameter, 10-in. length, in a flux of 10^3/cm^2-sec of neutrons with energy 3 ev. Assume 90 per cent B^{10}.

16.4 What would the maximum counting rate be in a 10-cm^2 area fission chamber with plates coated with 10 mg of pure U^{235}? Using a range 7×10^{-4} cm consider whether the layer would stop many fission fragments. If the energy needed to create an ion pair is taken as 32.5 ev, test whether the 2 cm separation of plates is adequate.

16.5 The equivalent δk of a control rod of 10 in. effective length is 0.01. Examine the following problems:

(1) the effect of residual magnetism in the holding magnet on the speed of control of a sudden rise in reactivity of 0.01;

(2) the time of fall of the control rod from its central position to reduce δk to 0.005.

(3) the rate of removal of the rod to guarantee that δk increases less rapidly than 0.01 per cent per second, in the lower one-third of its motion.

16.6 Devise a scale for a period meter.

16.7 The thermal flux at the surface of a 1-ft diameter 30-kw reactor is 10^{11} neutrons/cm^2-sec, and drops off according to $e^{-0.02r}/r$, where r is in centimeters, in the graphite reflector. How far out must a B^{10} lined chamber rated at 100 μa per 10^{10} flux be pulled from the core to keep the current below 50 μa?

16.8 Estimate the relative gamma ray and thermal neutron flux values at a compensated ionization chamber located 2 ft from the reactor surface of Problem 16.7, when the reactor is first started.

HINT: it will be necessary to compute the gamma attenuation in graphite. Repeat for the case of reactor operation after a long time. HINT: Refer to Section 13.5.

16.9 A neutron source yielding 10^7 neutrons/sec is placed in the center of a 3-ft core. Assume the thermal leakage factor of a bare reactor to be $\mathcal{L}_t = 0.2$. Estimate the counting rate expected from a detector near the surface of the reactor that is of area 100 cm², efficiency 3 per cent at these various sub-critical mass levels: m/m_{critical} = 0.01, 0.1, 0.9, 0.9999. HINT: Refer to Sections 8.2 and 14.4 as needed.

References

LAPP, R. E. and H. L. ANDREWS, *Nuclear Radiation Physics*, 2d Ed. New York: Prentice-Hall, Inc., 1954.

BLEULER, ERNST and GEORGE J. GOLDSMITH, *Experimental Nucleonics*. New York: Rinehart & Co., 1952.

STAFF, M.I.T. DEPARTMENT OF ELECTRICAL ENGINEERING, *Applied Electronics*. New York: John Wiley & Sons, 1943.

ELMORE, WILLIAM C. and MATTHEW SANDS, *Electronics, Experimental Techniques*. New York: McGraw-Hill Book Co., 1949.

COLE, T. E., "Design of a Control System for a Low Cost Research Reactor." *Nucleonics*, February (1953) p. 32.

COCHRAN, D. and C. A. HANSEN, JR., "Instrumentation for a Nuclear Reactor." *Nucleonics*, August (1949) p. 6.

TRIMMER, J. D. and W. H. JORDAN, "Instrumentation and Control of Reactors." *Nucleonics*, October (1951) p. 60.

DUNLAP, G. W., "Detection and Measurement of Nuclear Radiation." *Electrical Engineering*, April (1948).

MEAGHER, R. E. and E. P. BENTLEY, "Vacuum Tube Circuit to Measure the Logarithm of a Direct Current." *Rev. Sci. Instru.*, *10*, 336 (1939).

GOODMAN, C., Ed., *The Science and Engineering of Nuclear Power*. Cambridge, Mass.: Addison-Wesley Press, 1949, Vols. I, II.

BECK, C. K., A. C. MENIUS, R. L. MURRAY, N. UNDERWOOD, A. W. WALTNER, and G. N. WEBB, *Further Design Features of the Nuclear Reactor at North Carolina State College*, AECU-1986. January (1952).

MOYER, BURTON J., "Survey Methods for Slow Neutrons." *Nucleonics*, April (1952) p. 14.

MOYER, BURTON J., "Survey Methods for Fast and High Energy Neutrons." *Nucleonics*, May (1952) p. 14.

ROSSI, B., *High-Energy Particles*. New York: Prentice-Hall, Inc., 1952.

ROSSI, B. and H. STRAUB, *Ionization Chambers and Counters*. New York: McGraw-Hill Book Co., 1949.

HARRER, J. M., "Reactor Operation." *Nucleonics*, June (1953) p. 35.

RYDER, J. D., *Electronic Fundamentals and Applications*. New York: Prentice-Hall, Inc. 1950.

KORFF, S. A., *Electron and Nuclear Counters*. New York: D. Van Nostrand Co., 1946.

WEINBERG, A. M., "Recent Advances in Reactor Technology." *Nucleonics*, May (1953) p. 18.

CHAPTER 17

NEUTRON EXPERIMENTS

A full description of the neutron studies that have been made since the 1930's would fill many volumes. We shall restrict our attention, therefore, to a few experiments that are closely related to the nuclear reactor. There are two classes of investigations. The first is the study of performance characteristics of the reactor itself, measurements of constants, and checks of the theory of rising or falling flux levels. The second type of experiment makes use of the reactor as a copious source of neutrons having a variety of energies. The advantage of a reactor over "artificial" sources for the neutron supply is that there are enough neutrons of a particular energy to make possible the detection of effects without exceptionally sensitive instruments. For example, the determination of the absorption cross section of an isotope in the vicinity of a resonance peak can be obtained by selecting neutrons of different speeds for bombardment of the sam · ple. In this section we shall describe five experiments as illustrative of the type of work that can be done with reactor neutrons.

17.1 Pile oscillator measurement of cross sections

The power level of a reactor is sensitive to the position of an absorbing control rod, as discussed in Section 7.5. The more of the material that is exposed to the neutron flux, the greater is the effect. This fact suggests that different absorbers could be inserted successively in a reactor and the shifts in power level compared as a measure of their respective cross sections. An alternative method used at Argonne and in England avoids uncertainties due to level drifts. The test sample is made to oscillate in and out of the reactive portion of the reactor, which causes a distinguishable fluctuation in power level. We shall describe briefly a third apparatus as used in the Oak Ridge reactor by Hoover and others. Advantage is taken of the fact that the neutron flux is depressed in the neighborhood of an absorbing sample. A cylinder containing a sample to be tested is caused, by a motor driven wire, to oscillate in a cavity in the reactor reflector (see Fig. 17.1). The effects on neutron flux are detected by a concentric boron-filled ionization chamber. The amplitude of the pulse observed is proportional to the cross section to be measured. The method is very sensitive, being able to detect total sample cross sections as low as 10^{-3} cm^2 (the product of the total number of nuclei

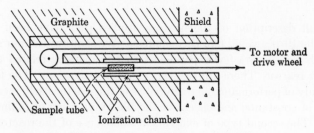

Fig. 17.1. Pile oscillator arrangement in Oak Ridge reactor.

in the sample and the microscopic cross section. For example, 5.5 grams of carbon, a very weak absorber, has a total cross section of 1.2×10^{-3} cm^2). Corrections can be made in the instrumentation to segregate the effects of scattering and absorption of neutrons. The cross sections of many stable isotopes, mass spectrographically separated, have been measured by Pomerance at Oak Ridge, using this equipment. A comparison is made with a standard such as gold, for which the absolute cross section is well known by other methods.

17.2 Neutron velocity selector

The function of this device, invented by Fermi, is to abstract those reactor neutrons having a common energy for the bombardment of samples or other experimental use. A circular cylinder is built up of alternate layers of aluminum and cadmium, and caused to rotate in front of the reactor thermal column, as shown in Fig. 17.2. Neutrons can get through this system only when the laminations are lined up with the flux from the column. Otherwise, the emergent stream will be absorbed by the lining of the projecting tube. Depending on the speed of rotation of the cylinder, pulses of neutrons are released from the cylinder at specified intervals. Since the time of travel down the tube is given by distance divided by velocity, the members of the pulse of different speeds arrive at the detector at different times. Instead of trying to isolate those of particular energy, the detector is cut off except for times corresponding to the arrival of the desired neutrons. This is achieved by a mirror-photocell arrangement linking the rotating cylinder with the instrument. In a later model, built at Brookhaven, all neutrons are detected, but their energies are distinguished according to arrival by a time analyzer. Cross sections

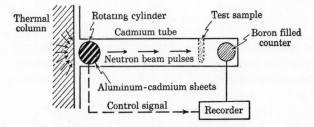

Fig. 17.2. Neutron velocity selector.

for neutrons of a small energy range may be measured by comparing pulses with and without an absorber in the path of the neutron beam.

17.3 Neutron diffraction

The dual nature of light as a particle and wave described in Section 1.2 was predicted to be applicable also to material particles by de Broglie and proved experimentally by Davisson and Germer. The wavelength associated with a particle of mass m, speed v is

$$\lambda = h/mv$$

where h is Planck's constant. It happens by coincidence that thermal neutrons have nearly the same λ (about 2×10^{-8} cm) as do x-rays produced by available potentials. Supplementary information on the structure of matter can be gained by an adaptation of the x-ray diffraction method to neutron waves. Although the wavelengths are similar, the mechanisms of interaction with the target material are different: x-rays are scattered by the electronic structure of the atom, while neutrons are scattered by nuclei. A further advantage of neutrons over x-rays is that they may be polarized by passage through a magnetized medium such as iron. The intrinsic magnetic moments of the neutrons in a beam are aligned by interaction with the directed magnetic fields in the iron. The technique of crystal diffraction has been used by Zinn and others at Argonne to separate neutrons of different energies and to measure cross sections. Wollan and Shull at Oak Ridge have extended the method. The Bragg x-ray formula gives the angle of reflection θ from a crystal for constructive interference of a neutron wave of length λ:

$$n\lambda = 2d \sin \theta$$

where d is the lattice spacing of the crystal, and n is the order of the interference pattern. A typical arrangement of the reactor, crystal and boron filled counter is shown in Fig. 17.3, quite schematically of

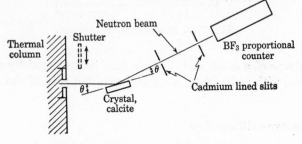

Fig. 17.3. Neutron crystal spectrometer.

course, since there must be many adjustment mechanisms for aligning the instrument accurately. Among the measurements made in the initial tests of the machine at Argonne were the energy distribution of neutrons from the reactor at several temperatures, the absorption cross section of boron as a function of neutron energy, and the shape of the resonance peak of cadmium around 0.2 ev.

17.4 Low energy neutrons

One method of obtaining low energy neutrons would be to allow them to slow down and diffuse through a medium at very low temperatures, such as liquid hydrogen. Anderson, Fermi, and Marshall at Argonne devised an alternative method of obtaining neutrons of energy as low as 18° absolute with apparatus maintained at ordinary room temperatures. The apparatus consists of a long shaft of graphite encased in a cadmium shield and extending from the thermal column

of the reactor as shown in Fig. 17.4. A cadmium sheet at the end of
the graphite column serves as a "shutter." Thermal neutrons from
the column are directed normally on the graphite tube because of the
absorption provided by the cadmium insert. They impinge on the
crystalline graphite at small angles, for which faster neutrons can

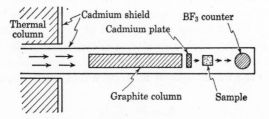

Fig. 17.4. Apparatus for obtaining "cold" neutrons by scattering in
graphite.

be scattered, but for which there can be no slow neutron scattering.
A study of the Bragg equation given in the previous section will
indicate these restrictions. The small angles have small sine, requiring that λ also be small and v large. The higher energy neutrons of
the thermal group are thus deflected to hit the cadmium wall of the
tube and be absorbed. Only the very low energy portion of the incident distribution, the "cold" neutrons, is transmitted. The shape of
the maxwellian distribution curve (see Section 2.2, Fig. 2.1) is such
that the number of neutrons remaining in the beam is rapidly reduced as the upper speed limit changes. The scattering and absorption cross sections for these neutrons in several materials were
measured. The low temperature of 18°K was deduced from the
change in the absorption by boron in Pyrex using the $1/v$ cross-section
property of boron. A check of the effect of chemical binding on the
scattering of the water molecule was also obtained.

17.5 Scattering of low energy neutrons

One of the important fundamental investigations in physics is the
determination of the range and nature of nuclear forces. One means
of attacking the problem is to make measurements of the scattering
of slow neutrons by protons. When a beam of neutrons strikes
a crystal containing hydrogen atoms in the lattice, two types of
scattering take place: (a) Bragg or *coherent* scattering, in which the

neutron waves can interfere as does light; (b) diffuse or *incoherent* scattering, due to effects of nuclear spin, differences between isotopes in the target element or to the random temperature fluctuations. There are no phase relationships in diffuse scattering. The two contributions must be isolated and distinguished to allow comparison of theory with experiment. A powerful technique has been developed that makes use of the phenomenon of *total reflection* of neutrons. Just as light may be internally reflected in a medium of higher index of refraction than air, such as water, neutron waves may be totally reflected from a liquid surface. The critical angle of reflection θ_c is related to the wavelength of neutrons λ and the scattering amplitude a by

$$\theta_c = \lambda\sqrt{Na/\pi}$$

where N is the number of nuclei per unit volume in the medium. The coherent scattering cross section is given by

$$\sigma = 4\pi a^2$$

Of particular fundamental interest is the sign and magnitude of the quantity a, which may be determined from measurements on reflected low-energy neutron beams. As shown in Fig. 17.5, a narrow beam of

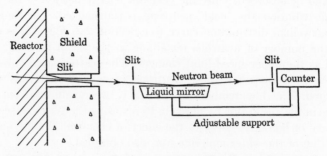

Fig. 17.5. Neutron reflection apparatus. The distance between the first and last slits is about 20 ft.

thermal neutrons from a reactor was allowed to fall at a glancing angle on the surface of a liquid hydrocarbon. The beam reflected from this "mirror" then passed through a slit in front of a set of counters. To each speed of neutrons and associated wavelengths there corresponds a critical angle given by the above formula. The fact that the maxwellian distribution curve drops rapidly with speed beyond its peak was used to obtain a unique wavelength. The scattering amplitude of hydrogen, a_H, was computed from observed critical angles and previously known carbon-scattering amplitudes by the relation

$$\theta_c = \lambda_c \left[\frac{N(a_C + 1.7a_H)}{\pi} \right]^{1/2}$$

where the factor 1.7 is the hydrogen to carbon ratio in the liquid. An amplitude a_H of $-3.78(\pm 0.02) \times 10^{-13}$ cm was obtained by this method by Burgy, Ringo and Hughes using the Argonne reactor.

17.6 The exponential pile

A measurement of the diffusion length L for a moderating medium or the size-shape factor K^2 for arrangements of moderator and fissionable material can be made by the "exponential" experiment. The term exponential is applied because the neutron flux in a medium falls off with distance z from a source according to $e^{-z/L}$ in a sub-

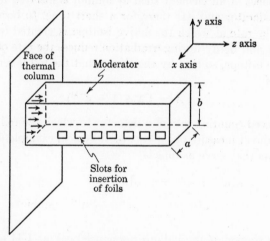

Fig. 17.6. Exponential experiment. Only a few of the many slots are shown.

critical (infinite slab) system. A large block of the moderator to be studied is mounted next to the exit end of a reactor thermal column, or artificial sources are located on one of its faces, as shown in Fig. 17.6. A flow of neutrons enters the block; the neutrons diffuse through the moderator. A steady distribution of neutron flux is set up, involving a balance of the constant source at one end, absorption in the medium and leakage from the sides. If the long axis of the system is labeled z and the other two axes are x and y, the theory of neutron diffusion predicts that the flux distribution along any line in the z direction that is not too close to a boundary is given by

$$\phi \sim e^{-l_{11}z}$$

where l_{11} is related to the dimensions of the block by

$$l_{11}^2 = \left(\frac{\pi}{a}\right)^2 + \left(\frac{\pi}{b}\right)^2 + \frac{1}{L^2}$$

The slope of the plot on semi-logarithmic paper of the measured flux as a function of distance along the z direction yields the constant l_{11}^2, from which L may be computed.

The *foil technique* by which the flux is measured is of sufficient interest and importance in other experiments to warrant a digression. A small sheet of an element such as indium is inserted in the body of the moderator and left there for a short time, to become radioactive. The rate at which the active isotope is created is the product $V\Sigma \phi$, and decay during irradiation reduces the rate of growth of the active isotope, so that by the time t that the foil is removed, the activity is

$$A = V\Sigma \phi (1 - e^{-\lambda t})$$

The observed counting rate of a detector to which the foil is exposed will be a direct measure of the flux ϕ. A typical example of reactions in elements that serve as foils is

$$_{49}In^{115} + _{0}n^{1} \rightarrow _{49}In^{116}$$

$$_{49}In^{116} \underset{54 \text{ min}}{\rightarrow} _{-1}e^{0} + _{50}Sn^{116} \quad (\text{stable})$$

The cross section at the indium resonance peak at 1.44 ev is 28,000 barns. Indium is commonly used as a foil in experiments involving neutron energy loss. The 1.44-ev point is well "marked" by the sharp resonance. Several factors complicate the problem—the disturbance by the foil of the flux to be measured, the corrections for the time to remove and count the foil, and the self-shielding of neutrons. In the exponential experiment, only relative fluxes are important for different points in the system, which eliminates the need to know the counter efficiency.

The exponential method may also be employed in the measurement of K^2 for a moderator "loaded" with uranium. The nuclear properties of an actual reactor to be studied may thus be obtained without actually building the final system and without possible danger. The same relations between flux and position and between the constants hold for this case as for the diffusion length experiment, except that $1/L^2$ is replaced by $-K^2$. Once K^2 is found by graphs of ϕ against z, the size of a *critical* reactor can be calculated from the standard formulas

$$K^2 = \left(\frac{\pi}{R}\right)^2 \quad \text{for a sphere,}$$

or $$K^2 = \left(\frac{\pi}{a}\right)^2 + \left(\frac{\pi}{b}\right)^2 + \left(\frac{\pi}{c}\right)^2 \quad \text{for a parallelepiped}$$

Problems

17.1 Find the time of flight of a thermal neutron through a 15-ft distance from an experimental opening in a reactor. Repeat for 1-ev neutrons and for 1-kev neutrons.

17.2 A neutron velocity selector is constructed according to the specifications of Fermi, Marshall and Marshall (see References): length of sandwich 2 in., composed of 1/32-in. Al foils alternating with approximately 0.006-in. Cd foils. If the speed of rotation is 15,000 rpm, what is the lowest neutron speed that can get through the assembly?

17.3 Compute the wavelength of thermal neutrons. At what angle will the first-order interference pattern be observed for scattering on rock salt, for which the lattice spacing is 2.814×10^{-8} cm?

17.4 What fraction of the neutrons in the thermal maxwellian distribution have speeds below that corresponding to $T = 25°K$?

17.5 Plot the flux along the z axis of a graphite exponential pile on semi-log graph paper using the following data: $a = b = 6$ ft; $L = 50$ cm.

17.6 The activity of an indium foil that has remained in a neutron flux for 1 hr is found to be 10^6 d/sec-cm³. What is the neutron flux in the vicinity of 1.44 ev? Assume a foil mass of 0.1 g.

References

HUGHES, DONALD J., *Pile Neutron Research*. Cambridge, Mass.: Addison Wesley Press, 1953.

HUGHES, D. J., "Pile Neutron Research Techniques." *Nucleonics*, February (1950); May (1950).

SNELL, ARTHUR H., "The Nuclear Reactor as a Research Implement." *Amer. Journ. of Phys.*, *20*, 527 (1952).

BECK, C. K., "Uses and Limitations of a Low Power Research Reactor." *Nucleonics*, May (1951) p. 18.

HOOVER, J. I., W. H. JORDAN, C. D. MOAK, L. PARDUE, H. POMERANCE, J. D. STRONG, and E. O. WOLLAN, "Measurement of Neutron Absorption Cross-sections with a Pile Oscillator." *Phys. Rev.*, *74*, 864 (1948).

WEINBERG, A. M. and H. C. SCHWEINLER, "Theory of Oscillating Absorber in a Chain Reactor." *Phys. Rev.*, *74*, 851 (1948).

ANDERSON, H. L., E. FERMI, A. WATTENBERG, G. L. WEIL, and W. H. ZINN, "Method for Measuring Neutron-Absorption Cross-sections by the Effect on the Reactivity of a Chain Reacting Pile." *Phys. Rev.*, *72*, 16 (1947).

FERMI, E., J. MARSHALL, and L. MARSHALL, "A Thermal Neutron Velocity Selector and Its Application to the Measurement of the Cross-section of Boron." *Phys. Rev.*, *72*, 193 (1947).

BRILL, T. and H. V. LICHTENBERGER, "Neutron Cross-section Studies with the Rotating Shutter Mechanism." *Phys. Rev.*, *72*, 585 (1947).

ZINN, W. H., "Diffraction of Neutrons by a Single Crystal." *Phys. Rev.*, *71*, 752 (1946).

SAWYER, R. B., E. O. WOLLAN, S. BERNSTEIN, and K. C. PETERSON, "A Bent Crystal Neutron Spectrometer and Its Application to Neutron Cross-section Measurements." *Phys. Rev.*, *72*, 109 (1947).

WOLLAN, E. O. and C. G. SHULL, "The Diffraction of Neutrons by Crystalline Powders." *Phys. Rev.*, *73*, 830 (1948).

ANDERSON, H. L., E. FERMI, and L. MARSHALL, "Production of Low Energy Neutrons by Filtering Through Graphite." *Phys. Rev.*, *70*, 815 (1946).

CAMPBELL, E. C., L. O. WYLY, and E. I. HOWELL, *Measurements on the ORSORT Uranium Graphite Exponential Pile*, ORNL-860. Oak Ridge National Laboratory, October 30, 1950.

GLASSTONE, S. and M. C. EDLUND, *The Elements of Nuclear Reactor Theory*. New York: D. Van Nostrand Co., 1952.

WEINBERG, A. M., *Pile Neutron Physics*, MDDC-1720. Oak Ridge National Laboratory, February 10, 1948. Theory of exponential pile.

TITTLE, C. W., "Slow Neutron Detection by Foils I, II." *Nucleonics*, June (1951); July (1951).

BURGY, M. T., G. R. RINGO, and D. J. HUGHES, "Coherent Neutron-Proton Scattering by Liquid Mirror Reflection." *Phys. Rev.*, *84*, 1160 (1951).

SNELL, A. H., F. PLEASONTON, and R. V. McCORD, "Radioactive Decay of the Neutron." *Phys. Rev.*, *78*, 310 (1950).

ROBSON, J. M., "Radioactive Decay of the Neutron." *Phys. Rev.*, *78*, 311 (1950).

CHAPTER 18

USES OF RADIOACTIVE AND
STABLE ISOTOPES

Prior to the recent large-scale development of atomic processes, isotopes were largely considered as scientific curiosities. Deuterium, the stable isotope of hydrogen, was the only isotope that had been separated, and it was collected only in limited quantities. Except for the use of radium for curative purposes, no widespread application of either natural or artificial radioactivity had been made. At present, in contrast, isotopes are being so widely used for medical, biological and industrial research that they may well have an important effect on our civilization. In this chapter we shall describe the virtues of the two types of isotopes: stable, and radioactive (including fission products), and point out a few of their many uses in medicine, agriculture, biology and industry, as well as for the investigation of physical and chemical processes. No attempt is made to be complete; the choice of examples is made on the basis of importance and in some cases interest, and to suggest that there are many ingenious uses not yet discovered.

18.1 Advantages and disadvantages of two types of isotopes

Stable isotopes are those that occur naturally in the elements of the periodic table, but which must be isolated by some physical means. The various methods of separation were described in Chapter 4. Some of the important isotopes other than deuterium and U^{235} are Li^6, B^{10}, O^{18}, and Hg^{198}. The principal advantages of using stable isotopes in research are:

(1) There is no time factor to be concerned about. Since the material does not decay, the long term effects can be studied with accuracy;

(2) When administered to a living organism in small quantities, physiological effects are negligible. The disadvantage is that a mass spectrograph is needed for analysis. Such an instrument is expensive and requires time and training to keep in best operating condition.

There are three main sources of radioactive isotopes. Until the nuclear reactor was developed, the only method of preparing active materials in quantity was by a cyclotron or other high-energy particle accelerator. Protons, deuterons and alpha particles served as the projectiles that bombarded and converted the target particles to new radioactive isotopes. Irradiation of samples with neutrons in a reactor is at present the principal source of isotopes, although several important substances are separated fission products, which constitutes the third source. Typical of the reactor produced isotopes are C^{14} and P^{32} formed as follows:

$$_0n^1 + {_7}N^{14} \rightarrow {_6}C^{14} + {_1}H^1 \quad (C^{14}\ t_H = 5700 \text{ yr})$$

$$_0n^1 + {_{15}}P^{31} \rightarrow {_{15}}P^{32} + \gamma \quad (P^{32}\ t_H = 14.3 \text{ days})$$

Other important isotopes are S^{35}, Ca^{45} and Fe^{59}. The advantages of active isotopes are: the smallest amount of material that can be detected is far beyond the ability to weigh; the apparatus needed to measure the decay products is relatively simple, consisting of a counter or a photographic plate; individual isotopes have identifying half-lives. It is an advantage that the radiations, by virtue of their penetration and ionization, can be used to destroy malignant tissue; it is a disadvantage in that radiations can be harmful when isotopes are used in contact with normal tissue or for the study of small organisms or cells. A large variety of stable and radioactive isotopes is available from the Oak Ridge National Laboratory by arrangement with the Isotopes Division of the Atomic Energy Commission. Irradiations of special materials in the reactor or bombardments in the proton cyclotron to produce a desired isotope may also be arranged.

18.2 Uses in chemistry, biology, medicine, and agriculture

Chemistry. The nature of a complex chemical reaction or the history of a substance in an organism can be studied by the use of compounds containing a radioactive element. Carbon[14], produced by neutron absorption in nitrogen, has become available and widely used since the advent of nuclear reactors. A sample of a nitrate such as $Ca(NO_3)_2$ is inserted in a capsule that is irradiated in a slug opening. Since its half-life is 5700 yr, the beta active C^{14} may be used very conveniently in long term experiments. Detection of the low-energy (0.155 mev) beta rays is achieved with a thin walled counter.

In many organic compounds, carbon atoms are located in two distinct parts of the molecule. For example, acetic acid CH_3COOH consists of the methyl group CH_3 and the carboxyl group $COOH$. It is possible by a sequence of chemical reactions to synthesize three isotopic varieties of acetic acid with radioactive carbon in either or both of the positions. These "labeled" compounds in turn can be used to construct more complicated molecules.

An alternative method of preparing labeled compounds, called biosynthesis, is performed by living organisms. The starch from plants grown in a radioactive CO_2 atmosphere contains C^{14}; conversion to various sugars can be achieved by subsequent treatment. The compound penicillin has been tagged with S^{35} by exposing the microorganisms that generate penicillin to a radioactive culture medium.

Biology. Radioactive or stable "tracers" may be used to follow accurately the progress of foods and minerals in the plant and animal body. One of the interesting conclusions that has been reached by their application is that there is a continual interchange between administered elements and those that are already present in the tissues of the body. This differs from the former concept that such materials were immediately used for energy and repair, while the remainder was stored for future emergency.

Radioactive iron Fe^{59} ($t_H = 46.3$ days) has been used to study the fundamentals of blood processes. It was discovered that iron in the red blood cells is re-used when the cells are destroyed, rather than being voided, as expected. Thus very little iron needs to be taken from the food to maintain the normal level in the body.

The importance of and interrelationships between the elements calcium and phosphorus in animal metabolism have been investigated by the isotopes Ca^{45} (152 days; β, 0.25 mev) and P^{32} (14.3 days; β, 1.7 mev). The widely differing energies allow selective measurements to be made in the presence of both isotopes.

The rate of absorption of Ca^{45} in poultry has been measured. Traces of Ca^{45} were found in the shell of an egg laid 15 min after the hen was given an injection of the isotope. Whites of eggs laid 24 hr after Ca^{45} was administered were found to contain much more activity than the yolks.

The stable isotope O^{18} has served as an important source of information about plant processes. The basic reaction in photo-synthesis is

$$CO_2 + H_2O \rightarrow \text{carbohydrates} + O_2$$

where sunlight serves as the source of energy and chlorophyll acts as a catalyst. A simple, but unexpected result found in experiments on photo-synthesis was that the oxygen liberated by plants comes from the water rather than from the carbon dioxide. Some of the study of this reaction is undoubtedly prompted by the hope that it might be developed and accelerated to harness the sun's energy for practical purposes.

No long-lived radioactive isotopes of nitrogen or oxygen have been formed, so tracer work with these elements must be done with O^{18} from heavy water production and with N^{15}, separated by chemical exchange methods. Since proteins and amino acids are nitrogen compounds, their interchanges in the body may be studied with N^{15} as the tracer.

Medicine. Blood circulation defects have been studied with radioactive iron Fe^{55} ($t_H = 2.9$ yr) and Fe^{59} (46 days) as well as with Na^{24} (14.9 hr). A solution is injected into a vein in the arm and the history of the active material followed through the body with a timing-counting device. Two isotopes of iodine, cyclotron produced I^{125} (56 days) and I^{131} (8 days), a fission product, have provided much information about the function of the thyroid gland and are used in the treatment of thyroid disorders. In cases of hyperactivity, the gamma rays of the iodine that concentrates in the thyroid destroy enough tissue to diminish the activity to normal.

Another use of the isotope I^{131} is in the location and definition of brain tumor tissue. An iodine compound di-iodo-fluorescein has the property of being selectively absorbed by such tissue. The compound is formed from the iodine that is the decay product of Te^{131}. It is injected, and a counter placed by the head may be used to locate the growth.

Considerable success has been attained in the use of the gamma emitter Co^{60} (5.3 yr) as a relatively inexpensive substitute for radium in the treatment of cancer. Cobalt needles are irradiated with neutrons in a reactor, coated with a thin metal layer to screen out the beta rays, and inserted in the offending tissue. Very intense gamma ray sources have been prepared in the Chalk River and Brookhaven reactors, at costs far below the equivalent of radium. Gram for gram, the activity of Co^{60} is several hundred times as great as that of radium; the dosage per disintegration is twice as large as for Ra.

Agriculture. Important information on methods of cultivation and fertilizing has come from the use of radioactive phosphorus P^{32} on corn, cotton and tobacco. The relative usage of minerals from the soil and from the fertilizer at different times in the plant's growth have been studied by N. S. Hall, et al., at North Carolina State College. One conclusion was that the young plant utilizes more phosphorus from the fertilizer than from the soil, a condition that tends to reverse in the mature plant. Further, the fertilizer should be placed close to the stalks of the young plant and far from those of the adult, to obtain maximum benefit. The study of the role played by *trace elements* such as boron, copper, cobalt and manganese by animals and plants in minute quantities is greatly facilitated by the use of the appropriate isotopes.

A few tests of the effects of radiation on fungi that attack plants or make their products non-edible have been successful. It is probably not practical to use radioactivity for large-scale extermination operations, because of the amounts of active material that would be needed. The criterion for applications of this sort is that it must be possible to bring the commodities to be treated to the source of radioactivity, as has been proposed for the pasteurization of milk by exposure to Co^{60} or fission product radiations. One variation from this principle, however, has been reported. Male mosquitoes have been sterilized by exposure to radiation and released. Because of the monogamous nature of the insects, the rate of reproduction of the species is reduced.

18.3 Industrial application of isotopes

Surprisingly small relative quantities of isotopes are used for industrial purposes, as evidenced by the list of shipments of isotopes from the Oak Ridge production centers. Among the reasons for this may be the lack of familiarity with the field, fear of radiations or of lawsuits, and complacency regarding established methods. A large variety of interesting uses has been reported, however.

The classic example is the study of engine friction and wear with radioactive piston rings. Neutron irradiation in a reactor yields active iron. As the engine in which the rings are installed is operated, the weight of iron that wears off may be detected down to 10^{-5} ounce by oil sampling. Wear patterns are obtained by lining the cylinder walls with photographic film.

The amount of gear wear has been measured using radioactive

methods. The system of Borsoff, Cook and Otvos may be described as illustrating the technique. A pinion gear was made active by irradiation for 30 days in a thermal neutron reactor. The main isotopes produced in the metal were Fe^{55} ($t_H = 2.9$ yr), Fe^{59} (46 days), Cr^{51} (26.5 days) and Co^{60} (5.3 yr). The radioactive part was meshed in a gear with another similar driving gear, and operated under various loads (see Fig. 18.1). Oil pumped through the gear box picked

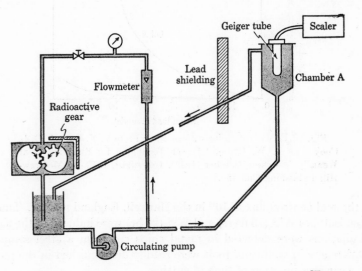

Fig. 18.1. Oil cycle in study of radioactive gear wear. [From V. N. Borsoff, D. L. Cook, and J. W. Otvos, "Tracer Technique for Studying Gear Wear." *Nucleonics*, October (1952). Copyright, 1952, by McGraw-Hill Publishing Co., Inc.]

up radioactive particles worn from the radioactive surfaces. A circulating pump transported the oil to a chamber with an inserted Geiger tube. A comparison was made of activity in terms of counts per minute with and without oil flowing. The standard for comparison consisted of a solution of ferric naphthenate made from a tooth broken from the radioactive gear. The relation between mass of metal in the test oil and counts per minute was found to be accurately linear. Since the operation took a period longer than the half-lives of some of the isotopes, the activity of the irradiated gear was determined on each day the experiment was performed. Comparisons of wear with two different oils as a function of load, Fig. 18.2, shows strikingly the type of information that can be obtained by the method.

A similar experiment in Sweden is reported by Colding and Erwall. Tungsten-carbide machining tool tips were irradiated for an hour in

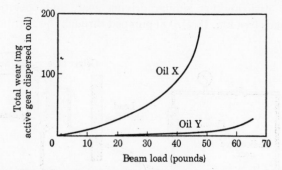

Fig. 18.2. Wear data for various oils. [From V. N. Borsoff, D. L. Cook, and J. W. Otvos, "Tracer Technique for Studying Gear Wear." *Nucleonics*, October (1952). Copyright, 1952, by McGraw-Hill Publishing Co., Inc.]

a thermal neutron flux of 10^{12} in the Harwell, England reactor. Tungsten isotopes W^{185} (76 days) and W^{187} (24 hr) were induced in the tips. Radiations were detected in metal chips cut from a steel sample. Differences in quality of tools were readily distinguished in the plots of wear as a function of time of cutting.

The process of self-diffusion in metals, where atoms migrate through the lattice arrangement of a crystal, may be studied quantitatively by coating a surface with a thin layer of a radioactive metal such as Fe^{59}, Co^{60}, or Cu^{64}. Successive layers of the solvent metal are milled off and analyzed for radioactive content. Alternatively, the reduction in surface activity over and above that due to radioactive decay can be taken as a measure of the diffusion into the depths of the metal.

Nuclear radiations may be used for locating one constituent in a solid solution or alloy. Tungsten[185] has been used as a tracer for a nickel alloy composed of 70 per cent Ni, 25 per cent Cr, 5 per cent W. A high-intensity gamma ray source such as Co^{60} can be applied to the detection of flaws in metals as accurately as with x-rays, but with the advantage that no maintenance of equipment is required.

Several examples of the detection of fluid transfer in closed systems have been reported. A radioactive sample inserted in a pipeline between high and low grades of oil allows the separation of the two at some point hundreds of miles down the pipeline. Radioactive floats may be used in chemical plants where the process vessels must be kept closed for safety. The flow of water pumped into depleted oil wells to improve recovery can be observed by gamma tracers. A leakage into adjacent wells that are still productive can be detected quickly, and a concrete barrier between the wells may be constructed. Pollution in streams by industrial wastes can also be studied by the introduction of an isotope in the effluent.

Uses of fission product wastes. The existence of large quantities of fission products from reactor operation was reviewed in Chapter 15, along with an indication of the problems in storage and disposal of the wastes. Several studies of possible practical uses of raw fission products have been made, in which many novel ideas are presented. One of the advantages of fission products as sources of gamma or beta rays over a machine yielding x-rays or electrons is clearly the freedom from maintenance and repair. A few of the uses, some of which have been tested successfully, are listed below.

(1) Activation of phosphors for luminous road signs, house markers or outdoor advertising.

(2) Eliminators for static electricity. The charge built up by friction in machines such as printing presses or textile looms is dispersed by the ionized air near a layer of fission products.

(3) Starters for fluorescent light bulbs. The gas in the tube is always partly ionized, making starting quicker.

(4) Gamma ray source as substitute for x-rays in radiographical examination of specimens.

(5) Sterilization of foods, drugs and medical supplies. Usual handling techniques to preserve aseptic conditions in the preparation of drugs such as penicillin are very costly. Fission product sources that give doses of the order of 10^6 r in a reasonable time may be substituted. The "cold" sterilization of foods appears to produce no discoloration or changes in flavor as sometimes normal "hot" sterilization does. Raw milk has been shown to be completely sterilized by 750,000 rep. The startling differences in appearance of peas, beefsteak and beans with and without gamma radiation may well be duplicated by general fission product irradiation.

(6) Irradiation of stored products to destroy insects. Co^{60} gamma irradiation doses of around 300,000 r have reduced the life span of various insects, adults and larvae, by a factor of 20 or more. An equivalent fission dose is probably practical.

(7) Effecting beneficial mechanical changes in materials. Electron bombardment of polyethylene at the General Electric Research Laboratory is reported to yield containers that withstand heat treatment at elevated temperature. Plastic containers that would melt under steam sterilization may thus be used for pharmaceuticals. Beta particle energies from fission products are in the proper range for similar applications. In many rubbers and plastics, irradiation causes hardening which is useful in some manufactured articles.

(8) Operation of heat engines by radiation energy. The absorption of gamma and beta rays in a water or metal core through which fission products are dispersed can be shown to result in sufficient heat for a small power supply. "Refueling" would not be needed more often than two- or three-month periods.

The examples of uses of separated stable and radioactive isotopes and fission products are intended only as a compact introduction to the field. For a more complete picture, including the handling and analysis techniques, the reader should refer to the many books and papers in the literature.

Problems

18.1 What is the maximum number of millicuries of I^{132} that a person suspected of thyroid defect can be given to guarantee that the dosage to the thyroid gland is less than five roentgens? Assume the tissue affected weighs twenty grams.

18.2 Calculate the specific activity (curies per gram) of pure P^{32}. If it is possible to detect disintegration rates as low as 10 d/sec, what weight of P^{32} is needed in a tracer experiment?

18.3 Investigate the problem of coating a drive belt in a manufacturing plant with a beta emitter to eliminate static electricity.

18.4 A proposal is made to add radioactive carbon to a plastic paint for purposes of measuring thicknesses of layers. Examine the feasibility of this idea and the health problems, if any.

References

GUEST, G. H., *Radioisotopes: Industrial Application*. Toronto: Sir Isaac Pitman and Sons, 1950.

AEBERSOLD, P. C., "Isotopes and Their Application in the Field of Industrial Materials." *Am. Soc. Testing Materials, 48*, 1 (1948).

SIRI, W. E., *Isotopic Tracers and Nuclear Radiations; with Applications to Biology and Medicine.* New York: McGraw-Hill Book Co., 1949.

GLASSTONE, S., *Sourcebook on Atomic Energy.* New York: D. Van Nostrand, 1950.

Isotopes—A 5-Year Summary of United States Distribution, Washington, D. C.: Atomic Energy Commission, U. S. Government Printing Office, August, 1951.

BRADFORD, JOHN R., *Radioisotopes in Industry.* New York: Reinhold Publishing Corp., 1952.

BEHRENS, C. F., Ed., *Atomic Medicine.* New York: Thomas Nelson & Sons, 1949.

CROMPTION, C. E. and N. H. WOODRUFF, "Chemical Syntheses of Labeled Compounds I, II." *Nucleonics,* March (1950); April (1950).

WOODRUFF, N. H. and E. E. FOWLER, "Biological Synthesis of Radio-isotope-Labeled Compounds." *Nucleonics,* February (1950).

References on Therapeutic and Tracer Uses of Radioisotopes, Circular D-5. Oak Ridge: Isotopes Division (AEC).

Isotopes: Radioactive, Stable. Oak Ridge National Laboratory. Catalog and price list; issued periodically.

BORSOFF, V. N., D. L. COOK, and J. W. OTVOS, "Tracer Technique for Studying Gear Wear." *Nucleonics,* October (1952) p. 67.

COLDING, B. and L. G. ERWALL, "Wear Studies of Irradiated Carbide Cutting Tools." *Nucleonics,* February (1953) p. 46.

Industrial Uses of Radioactive Fission Products. Stanford, Cal.: Stanford Research Institute, September, 1951. Also see *Nucleonics,* May (1951) p. 5; August (1951) p. 11.

"Problems in the Use of Fission Products." *Nucleonics,* January (1952) p. 45.

RYAN, J. W., "Effect of Gamma Radiation on Certain Rubbers and Plastics." *Nucleonics,* August (1953) p. 13.

HASSETT, C. C. and D. W. JENKINS, "Use of Fission Products for Insect Control." *Nucleonics*, December (1952) p. 42.

O'MEARA, J. P., "Radiation Chemistry and Sterilization of Biological Materials by Ionizing Radiations." *Nucleonics*, February (1951) p. 19. Extensive bibliography.

CHAPTER 19

NUCLEAR PROPULSION OF AIRCRAFT, SUBMARINES, AND ROCKETS

The problem of harnessing nuclear power to mobile systems is more difficult than that for stationary systems, principally because of the shielding weight that must accompany the reactor. In this chapter we shall review the advantages of nuclear energy for propulsion and attempt to demonstrate the importance of weight in the case of the nuclear airplane. The possibility of rocket propulsion is discussed briefly, even though such developments will probably be undertaken only after nuclear transportation with other vehicles has been well tested.

19.1 Survey of the propulsion problem

The anticipated advantage of a nuclear powered machine over those propelled by gasoline or other chemicals lies in its small fuel usage.

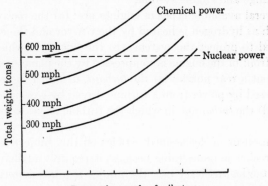

Fig. 19.1. Speed-range-weight relations for aircraft.

Ideally, one might expect that a machine the size of our present large planes could travel large distances, comparable to that around the earth, at supersonic speeds. Such a feat is far from realization by

349

chemically powered aircraft because of the excessive fuel weight. The situation can be represented by the graph of consistent values, speed, and flying range for ordinary aircraft of different weights, as in Fig. 19.1. Because of the negligible fuel consumption, the nuclear airplane would be represented by a horizontal line, indicating a range essentially unlimited by weight or speed.

Studies made by the project NEPA (Nuclear Energy for Propulsion of Aircraft) in collaboration with other research groups such as the Oak Ridge National Laboratory have established that reactor power systems are feasible for this use; an assignment to the General Electric Company to design and build such a reactor has been made. By combining information on airplane design characteristics, nuclear reactors and conventional power plants, we are able to outline the various choices to be made and problems that probably must be solved. The basic system is simple to visualize. Heat generated by fission in the reactor is extracted by some fluid, and converted into kinetic energy of jet gas or propeller rotation. The plane must be heavy enough to support shielding, and capable of periodic servicing under conditions of radioactive contamination, but can be otherwise conventional. The choice of method of converting heat into thrust is dependent, however, on a compatible reactor type, fluid coolant, heat exchange and engine system.

The several available types of engines are: (a) the *rocket*, in which a fuel such as hydrogen is heated by the reactor and the exhaust gas thrust used to project the system; (b) the *ramjet*, in which entering air in the front of the engine is compressed by the plane speed, heated, and sent out a rear nozzle; (c) the *turbojet*, in which the entering air is compressed by power from a turbine driven by gases heated in the reactor; (d) the *turboprop*, in which the turbine drives a conventional propeller.

The consensus of declassified articles on this subject seems to be that the rocket is undesirable because it requires auxiliary fuel and has little tactical military use; the ramjet requires materials of construction that must withstand an excessive temperature. Of the remaining two engines, objections to the turboprop have been raised on the basis of the low speed. In terms of an effectively unlimited fuel for long flights, this objection would not seem to be too serious. Since both the turboprop and jet engine methods employ a turbine in one way or another, they will be discussed with equal emphasis.

A further choice may be made between a system in which the reactor cooling fluid is expendable and used once (open cycle), and a system in which it is recirculated (closed cycle). An air coolant would fall in the first category while helium, mercury, and steam would be

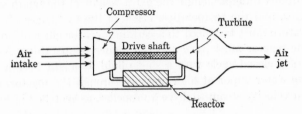

Fig. 19.2. Open-cycle air turbojet.

in the second. For an open cycle the reactor coolant would be the medium driving the turbine; in the closed cycle, the fluids might well be different, an arrangement that would be favorable if the intermediate heat exchanger were efficient. The many possible arrange-

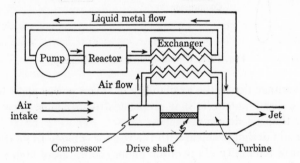

Fig. 19.3. Closed-cycle metal-air turbojet.

ments of the basic components have been outlined by Ohlinger. We shall select several of these types, largely on the basis of variety. The advantage of an open cycle using air, for instance, is simplicity, as can be illustrated by a schematic engine diagram, Fig. 19.2. Its disadvantages are the danger of oxidation of hot metal surfaces in the reactor, and the large volume of air that would have to be put through the reactor to remove the requisite heat. The advantage of a closed cycle is that the coolant for the reactor may be chosen appropriate to that component while the second fluid is suitable for driving the turbine. As an example, liquid metal might be circulated through the reactor and a heat exchanger, with air again serving to propel the unit, as shown in Fig. 19.3. The activity in the metal is not transmitted to the turbine, allowing its safe replacement after use.

The disadvantages include the extra weight of the pump and heat exchanger, and the temperature losses in the exchanger. If the air temperature must be raised to a certain level for efficient operation, then the reactor must have an even higher temperature. As an example of a closed cycle with a single fluid, it might be practical to circulate water vapor at high pressure through the reactor, and use the high velocity steam to drive a propeller, as sketched in Fig. 19.4.

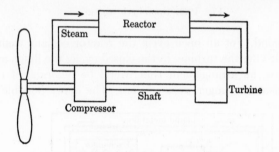

Fig. 19.4. Closed-cycle steam turboprop.

The advantage lies in the availability of steam power-plant information; the disadvantage is that propeller driven planes have a lower velocity than jet driven machines.

The main design problem with the reactor is likely to be the establishment of reliability of operation under conditions of high temperature and neutron bombardment. The fact that the metal parts are not moving may be offset by the displacement of particles in their lattice structure by neutron or fission fragment bombardment. Very little is known about the strength of materials at temperatures in the range 1000–2000°F, particularly in the presence of neutrons.

An entirely separate overall design factor is the neutron-gamma shielding. Assuming that the airplane is conventional in that it requires a crew, it is obvious that the greatest distance must be put between reactor and personnel. Letting this be provided by the wing span has the difficulty of giving an unbalance of weight. It would seem that the nose-tail separation would be most logical. As has been already computed, simple inverse square attenuation is by no means sufficient. Thus a heavy-metal gamma shield like lead and a light thermalizing medium such as graphite or water in conjunction with a highly absorbing substance like cadmium or boron for neutrons would have to be inserted in the space. However, the heavier the shield, the more power is needed to lift the plane; the higher power is associated with more neutron and gamma flux, which raises the shielding thickness again. The useful weight should not exceed the initial gasoline load of a conventional plane. This qualitative summary of the design problems can be put on a firmer basis by a specific example, making assumptions as needed.

19.2 The relation of weight and shielding in aircraft

A schematic analysis of the weight-shielding relation for a hypothetical example will illustrate one of the problems facing the designers

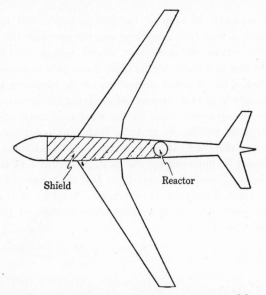

Fig. 19.5. Airplane (B-47) modified for reactor propulsion. Overall length = 108 ft; wing span = 116 ft; wing sweepback = 35 deg; overall height = 28 ft; weight = 125,000 lb.

of reactor propelled aircraft. Let us assume that we want to modify an existing airplane to be operated with nuclear heat instead of chemical energy. No improvement in speed or altitude will be expected; the main advantage will be in the increase in range, without refueling. As a specific machine, let us take the Boeing Stratojet (B-47), as sketched in Fig. 19.5.* It is a bomber propelled by six General Electric J-47 turbojet engines. Some of its characteristics are listed:

Weight: 125,000 lb basic,
185,000 lb with fuel and 20,000-lb payload,
Speed: Approximately 600 mph
Altitude: 35,000 ft,
Effective wing area: 1800 ft² (estimated),
Range: 1000 miles.

Whether or not an adaptation of this airplane would be desirable will not come under our scrutiny. It is used for illustrative purposes only.

We shall continue to employ the jet principle, but modify the engines in such a way that a nuclear reactor provides the necessary heating of the intake air. A reactor, shield, piping, auxiliaries, and whatever increase in weight results from the engine modification, will be substituted. The standard procedure for determining the effects of design changes in aircraft consists of studying the lift-drag relation. Lift L is the aerodynamic force on the wing that must just balance the total airplane weight W in level flight, or contribute vertical acceleration for climbing. Drag D is the force that resists forward motion. It must be balanced by the forward thrust T of the engines for steady flight. T must be larger than D if the plane is to gain forward speed. Each force may be expressed in terms of the primary quantities of speed v, wing area (plus effective area of fuselage) S, and air density ρ. Thus,

$$L \text{ (lb-force)} = \frac{C_L[v \text{ (ft/sec)}]^2 \, \rho \text{ (lb/ft}^3) \, S \text{ (ft}^2)}{2g \text{ (ft/sec}^2)}$$

$$D \text{ (lb-force)} = \frac{C_D[v \text{ (ft/sec)}]^2 \, \rho \text{ (lb/ft}^3) \, S \text{ (ft}^2)}{2g \text{ (ft/sec}^2)}$$

* Data provided by George Snyder, Chief, Preliminary Design, Boeing Airplane Company, Seattle, Washington, are greatly appreciated. Security of classified information will make it necessary, however, for us to estimate some of the design parameters.

The lift and drag coefficients C_L and C_D are dimensionless factors obtained from wind tunnel experiments. They depend on the shape of the airfoil and on the angle that it makes with the direction of oncoming air. Figure 19.6 shows the relation of C_L and C_D for a wing shape that may simulate the B-47 wing (NACA airfoil 65–410). We take the velocity at 35,000 ft to be $v = 524$ mph, 768 ft/sec. With $S = 1800$ ft^2, $\rho = 0.024$ lb/ft^3, $L = W = 185,000$ lb,

$$C_L = \frac{(2)(32.2)(185,000)}{(0.024)(1800)(768)^2} = 0.46$$

This value must be corrected from the idealized airfoil to the shape corresponding to the actual wing. From best estimates, this raises C_L to 0.53. From Fig. 19.6, the drag coefficient is found to be 0.0103.

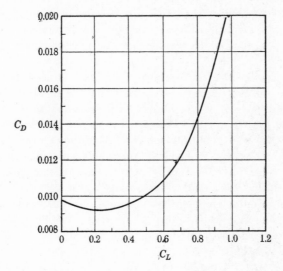

Fig. 19.6. Relation of lift and drag coefficients, NACA airfoil No. 65-410.

We add a 10-per cent increase for the induced drag associated with finite wing span. The result is $C_D = 0.0113$. Insertion in the drag formula yields the wing drag

$$D_w = \frac{(0.0113)(768)^2(0.024)(1800)}{2(32.2)} = 4500 \text{ lb}$$

The additional drag due to tail, fuselage and engines may be added.
Taking typical coefficients for each component and reasonable choices
of effective area yields a total extra drag of 8300 pounds. Thus the
drag (and therefore thrust) force for the original system is 12,800 lb.
The thrust horsepower needed to overcome this drag is given by the
relation

$$\text{hp} = \frac{T \text{ (lb-force) } v \text{ (mph)}}{375}$$

which turns out to be about 18,000 hp. Using the conversion factor
1 hp = 0.746 kw, we find the power to be

$$P = 13,400 \text{ kw} \quad \text{or} \quad 13.4 \text{ mw}$$

Everything else being equal, the reactor must give the same useful
power as does the jet system. The actual reactor power level must
be considerably higher than 13.4 mw because of inherent efficiency
factors. Let us estimate the overall efficiency (propulsion and heat)
to be 15 per cent, which means that the reactor power should be
90 mw.

The next step is to find out what shielding is needed to protect
the plane and ground crews. It is clear that we should separate the
reactor and plane crew by the largest possible distance to take advantage of inverse square spreading. Let us put the reactor near the
tail of the airplane, about 50 feet away from the crew compartment.
Adequate protection is by no means provided by distance, as indicated
in Chapter 14. The safe distance from a bare reactor with as low a
power as 10 kw was found to be a quarter of a mile. Two principal
radiations must be stopped—gamma rays and fast neutrons. If we
can slow the fast neutrons down, there are several materials such as
boron that will absorb the resultant thermals sufficiently. The fission
rate in a 90 mw reactor is

$$(90 \text{ mw})(3 \times 10^{16} \text{ fissions/sec-mw}) = 2.7 \times 10^{18} \text{ fissions/sec}$$

The number of fast neutrons emitted per second is thus 2.5 times
this, or 6.75×10^{18}; the number of 2-mev gammas is about five times
the fission rate or 13.5×10^{18}. We shall neglect completely the problem of radiation scattering by air to the crew. For simplicity, let us
use lead to stop the gammas and water to slow down the neutrons.
We may estimate separately the thicknesses x of spherical shell shields
of the two materials that are needed to achieve tolerance at a 50-ft

distance from the center of the reactor. For 2-mev gamma rays, the absorption coefficient in lead is taken as 0.53 cm^{-1}. Let the gamma ray leakage from the core be an arbitrary 22 per cent so that the initial flux is 3×10^{18}. The tolerance flux is assumed to be 800.

$$\frac{e^{-(0.53)x}}{4\pi[(50)(30.5)]^2} = \frac{800}{3 \times 10^{18}}$$

Note that the core radius is neglected as small in comparison with the 50-ft distance in the inverse square attenuation. Simplifying,·

$$e^{0.53x} = 1.28 \times 10^8, \quad x = 35 \text{ cm} = 1.15 \text{ ft}$$

If the reactor core is a sphere of arbitrary 3-ft radius, the shell volume is

$$\frac{4\pi}{3} [(4.15)^3 - (3)^3] = 186 \text{ ft}^3$$

With a density of $(11.3)(62.4) = 705$ lb/ft^3, the weight is 130,000 lb or 65 tons.

We may repeat the process for the water shield, assuming the fast neutron attenuation length of 8 cm and an 11-per cent leakage from the reactor core (7.5×10^{17} neutrons/cm^2-sec). Take the tolerance flux as 22 neutrons/cm^2-sec:

$$\frac{e^{-x/8}}{4\pi[(50)(30.5)]^2} = \frac{22}{7.5 \times 10^{17}}$$

or $\qquad e^{x/8} = 1.2 \times 10^9, \quad x = 167 \text{ cm} = 5.48 \text{ ft}$

If the water lies outside the lead, its volume would be

$$\frac{4\pi}{3} [(9.63)^3 - (4.15)^3] = 3440 \text{ ft}^3$$

and its weight is

$$3440 \times 62.4 = 215,000 \text{ lb} = 107.5 \text{ tons}$$

The total shield weight, lead plus water, is thus 172.5 tons. Recalling that the plane weight fully loaded is only 92.5 tons, we find that the assumed weight of the shielding is completely out of reason. In order to reduce weight, protection for the surrounding area when the plane is on the ground must obviously be sacrificed. Let us assume that the crew is protected with a sector of the spherical shield, weighing perhaps one-fifth of the total, or 34.5 tons. Let the average density of the reactor proper be 125 lb/ft^3, which implies a weight of about

7 tons. If the experimental flights are made without conventional fuel or the 10-ton payload, and recalling that the basic airplane weight was 62.5 tons, we find an effective increase in weight of the system of a net 11.5 tons, or 23,000 lb, or 12 per cent. The lift must be larger, as must the thrust. Let us make the rough assumption that each must increase by 12 per cent, which implies an increase in reactor power of 12 per cent, which in turn necessitates even more shielding. Let us estimate the added thickness of water Δx that is needed to stop the excess in fast neutrons. The necessary condition is

$$e^{-\Delta x/8} = \frac{1}{1.12}$$

since the 50-ft distance is unchanged. The thickness is only 0.91 cm, or 0.03 ft, which appears to be negligible. The weight of this shell at a radius of 9.63 ft is, however,

$$4\pi(9.63)^2(0.03)(62.4) = 2200 \text{ lb}$$

or more than one ton. A vicious circle is thus set up. The increase in shielding requires more propulsion power, which results in a need for more shielding, etc. In practice, of course, the analysis might be set up in a form so that a compatible power level, shielding thickness and weight could be found immediately. It is believed that the above approach helps one visualize the problem more easily, however.

19.3 Aircraft power plants

The next problem of interest is the jet engine modification. We shall make only a few general remarks on this subject. On the basis that the General Electric Company designs the nuclear airplane, it is very logical to assume a G.E. jet engine for a model. The unit in the F-86D "Sabre" jet plane built by North American Aviation is sketched in Fig. 19.7. The principle of operation of the standard unit is relatively simple. Air enters through an intake at the front of the engine and is compressed to several atmospheres pressure by a compressor driven by the turbine in the rear. The compressed air enters a set of eight combustion chambers or "cans" mounted in a circle about the drive shaft. Fuel from tanks separate from the engine is sprayed into the cylinders, and the mixture is ignited by a spark plug. The heated air drives the turbine wheel and escapes into the chamber behind. The booster or after-burner consists of a region in which further heat is supplied the gas by the ignition of additional fuel. The high pressure built up in the rear chamber forces the air out the nozzle in a high speed stream. By the law of conservation of momentum, the forward thrust (in lb-force) given to the engine is

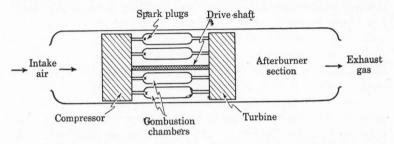

Fig. 19.7. Conventional jet engine. [Courtesy General Electric Co.]

equal to the product of mass flow rate (lb/sec) and the velocity (ft/sec) at which it issues. It will be necessary to replace the heat from the burning fuel by heat from nuclear fission. Two possibilities come to mind immediately: (a) place a reactor in each engine as in Fig. 19.2, or (b) heat all engines by a single reactor. In the first case one would presumably insert a cylindrical reactor in the space formerly occupied by the combustion chambers, leaving a hole down the central axis for the turbine compressor shaft. Incoming air could serve both as the reactor coolant and the medium that provides the engine thrust. The set of combustion chambers occupy a space about three feet long and three feet in diameter, which sets a starting point for the reactor size. From our previous studies we have seen what a problem it is to achieve the necessary large surface area for heat transfer to air in a reactor of this size. The volume of voids for cooling ducts causes an increase in neutron leakage proportional to the square of the density ratio. One advantage of having the reactor at the engine is that the heat transfer is direct, from the reactor to the air; no conduction and radiation losses of long piping systems would be experienced. From a military standpoint, there would be both advantages and disadvantages with this arrangement. The exposed reactor is more vulnerable to light anti-aircraft fire than a reactor surrounded by shielding in the fuselage. On the other hand, the loss of one propelling reactor out of the six would necessarily cripple but not lose the airplane. One might also question what would happen to the reactivity of the reactor if its geometry were disturbed, for example, if a local compression of the moderator were to occur. These arguments break down, of course, if guided-missile attacks are considered. Another disadvantage of the individually powered engines lies in the difficulty of shielding the crew. The problem is not insurmountable, since one might use an aircraft design with wings nearer the tail than the nose. The second possibility of a single, more centrally located reactor fits in with the considerations on shielding in the previous section. In this case the combustion chamber would be replaced by heat exchangers, using a reactor coolant such as a liquid metal as in Fig. 19.3. The volume of an exchanger, as shown in Section 10.6, can be much smaller than a reactor. Now only the ducts for the coolant and the flowing air contribute to the space since the fuel and moderator are now located elsewhere. One would sacrifice some loss in heat and efficiency with this system, as mentioned earlier; but until a nuclear reactor is as familiar as a conventional airplane engine, it would be preferable from an operation standpoint to have to deal with only one reactor instead of six. A liquid metal need not be the only choice of primary coolant, of course. Gases such as air or helium could be used, but with associated problems stemming from low heat capacity and conductivity.

19.4 Submarine propulsion

The unclassified aspects of the history of the nuclear-powered submarine, sponsored by the AEC and the U.S. Navy, have been fully recorded in many popular articles. Only a brief mention of this important development is made here. The shielding weight limitations in a submarine reactor are not as serious as for an airplane, because of the relative weights of the two machines. Thus the submarine reactor can more nearly approximate a stationary system. Two programs are now well along toward success. (1) A water cooled reactor was built and put into operation (May 1, 1953) by Westinghouse Corporation at the Reactor Testing Station, Arco, Idaho. For this unit, a water-to-water heat exchanger provides steam for turbines that in turn drive the propeller shaft. This submarine thermal reactor (STR) is composed of enriched U^{235} in heterogeneous form. The first atomic submarine, the *Nautilus*, built by the Electric Boat Company, Groton, Connecticut, was launched in January, 1954. One new feature of its reactor is the use of "canned" pumps. In these, the pump and its motor are both sealed within a water duct. Possible leaks of radioactive water through bearings, as in conventional pumps, are thus eliminated. (2) Another version, the Submarine Intermediate Reactor, was placed under construction by General Electric Company, near Schenectady, New York. As indicated by its name, it operates on intermediate energy neutrons. The coolant in this unit is liquid sodium, again with an exchanger to provide steam power.

19.5 Space travel with nuclear rockets

In the discussion on the problem of the propulsion of military or commercial aircraft, the rocket method was assumed to be less desirable because of the amount of fuel that had to be carried. When the nuclear airplane, with its essentially unlimited terrestrial range has been perfected, attention may be focused on flight outside the earth, for example to the moon. For propulsion outside the earth's atmosphere, the turbojet principle described in Section 19.3 fails for lack of air propellant, and the rocket method must be adopted. We shall review here three basic aspects of the problem: the fundamentals of rocket motion, the necessary conditions to escape the earth's gravitational force, and the prospects of using nuclear reactor heat energy to provide the rocket thrust.

Maximum rocket velocities. The popular misconception that the rocket moves forward because of the reaction of expelled gases on the air behind it can be dismissed by a brief restatement of the law of conservation of momentum:

If a fraction dm of the fuel is ejected in a time dt with a velocity v_f (with reference to the rocket), and thus a momentum $(dm)v_f$ is lost, the rocket, including the fuel it has at that time, must increase in momentum in the forward direction by the same amount.

However, by Newton's second law, force equal to rate of change of momentum, we have

$$F = \frac{(dm)v_f}{dt}$$

The rate at which the fuel is released, $dm/dt = a$, is presumably constant, and thus the thrust is constant. The mass of the rocket is continually decreasing because of the fuel loss, resulting in a higher acceleration as time goes on. The equation of motion for vertical flight with gravity neglected $m\, dv/dt = av_f$, where $m = m_0 - at$, may easily be integrated to obtain a relation between the exhaust velocity of fuel v_f, the final speed of the empty rocket v, and the masses of the empty, m, and full, m_0, rocket.

$$v = v_f \log_e \frac{m_0}{m}$$

This is the basic rocket equation. For vertical flight with gravity and air resistance included, the ultimate velocity will be lower than this value.

Escape from the earth. Two modes of interplanetary flight have been considered: (a) direct and complete escape from the earth's gravitational force; (b) establishment of an intermediate satellite orbit of the order of a thousand miles above the earth's surface. The requirements on final rocket velocity are considerably less stringent in the latter case. Let us estimate the needed speeds in the two cases. We may calculate the final speed a rocket must have to overcome completely the force of gravity by imagining the rocket to be similar to a bullet of mass m fired vertically from the earth. In order to get away, the bullet would have to have a kinetic energy $\frac{1}{2}mv^2$ at least as large as the work done in carrying it from the earth's surface to infinity. From the way the gravitational force varies with distance r from the earth's center, $F = GMm/r^2$, where M is the mass of the earth, and G is the gravitational constant, we find the work to be

$$W = \int_{r_e}^{\infty} F\, dr = \frac{GMm}{r_e}$$

Here r_e is the earth's radius. Thus $\frac{1}{2}mv^2 = W$, or

$$v = \sqrt{2GM/r_e}$$

Using known values of the constants, the velocity is found to be 36,700 ft/sec. The speed of a satellite v_s at a height h above the earth surface is found from the balance of the centrifugal acceleration $v_s^2/(r_e + h)$, and the gravitational acceleration $g_0[r_e/(r_e + h)]^2$, where g_0 is its value on the earth's surface. Solving for v_s, we have

$$v_s = r_e\sqrt{g_0/(r_e + h)}$$

For an orbit at 1075 miles above the earth, the speed must be $v_s = 23{,}000$ ft/sec. The maximum exhaust speed of chemical fuel is quoted to be 11,000 ft/sec. The mass ratio m_0/m to achieve escape or an orbit can now be determined from the basic rocket formula. For the two cases we find: escape $m_0/m = 28$; satellite, $m_0/m = 8$. In the first case this means that at least $\frac{27}{28}$ of the system at the start must be fuel, or that for every pound of the rocket hull, equipment or personnel, there must be 27 lb of fuel. For the satellite case $\frac{7}{8}$ must be fuel. The satellite condition is thus much easier to obtain. It is clear that if a nuclear reactor can provide the necessary heat to give the gas a higher exhaust speed than 11,000 ft/sec, the weight ratio would be even more favorable.

Possible application of reactor. In a rocket such as the V-2 type, both fuel (alcohol) and oxidizer (liquid oxygen) are provided. Since

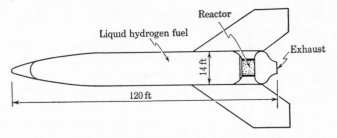

Fig. 19.8. Nuclear rocket.

the reactor is supposed to supply the heat energy and no chemical reaction occurs, a gas such as hydrogen stored in liquid form would probably serve as propellant. One might visualize its use first as a coolant for the rocket surface as air friction heats it up. The most desirable reactor design from the standpoint of heat transfer and material stress would be a porous system through which hydrogen flows. A homogeneous mixture of very small particles of graphite and enriched uranium carbide would allow a rapid transfer of fission heat to the coolant. The principles discussed in Section 10.3 for fluid flow in porous media would be applied to determine the pressure drop needed. The heat transfer properties would best be determined by experimental test on a small scale, in view of the limited information on heat removal by this method. Let us make an estimate of the reactor power needed to achieve a speed comparable to the orbit speed. Assume that the reactor proper has weight one-tenth of the originally loaded system, and that the fuel weighs eight-tenths of the total. Further, let the reactor be a cylinder of 6-ft diameter, 6-ft length, with porosity of 0.5. With a normal graphite density, of 1.65 g/cm^3, this implies a reactor mass of 8740 lb, a fuel load of 70,000 lb, and a remainder of 8740 lb. The size of the system is indicated in Fig. 19.8. The exhaust gas speed to obtain a final rocket speed of 23,000 ft/sec must be

$$v_f = \frac{23,000}{\log_e (1.0/0.2)} = \frac{23,000}{1.61} = 14,300 \text{ ft/sec}$$

The thrust T must certainly be somewhat greater than the original weight of 87,400 lb to launch the rocket and overcome air resistance in the earth's atmosphere. We take an arbitrary thrust value of twice the initial total weight, or approximately 175,000 lb. The lower limit on the necessary reactor power P is the product Tv_f, which from the numbers above is

$$P = (175,000 \text{ lbf})(14,300 \text{ ft/sec})$$
$$= 2.5 \times 10^9 \text{ ft-lbf/sec}$$
$$= 3.4 \times 10^9 \text{ watts} = 3400 \text{ mw}$$

The important question is whether, with this rather high power level, the operating temperature of the system is reasonable or not. We find the mass flow rate of hydrogen from the relation $T = av_f$:

$$a = \frac{175,000 \text{ (lb) } 32.2 \text{ (ft/sec}^2)}{14,300 \text{ (ft/sec)}}$$
$$= 394 \text{ lb/sec} = 1.79 \times 10^5 \text{ g/sec}$$

If the flow rate is constant the fuel will be exhausted in a time

$$t = \frac{70,000 \text{ lb}}{394 \text{ lb/sec}} = 178 \text{ sec}$$

At high temperatures, the specific heat of hydrogen approaches 4 calories/g-°C (or 16.7 joules/g-°C). Thus, the temperature rise is

$$\Delta T = \frac{Q}{ca} = \frac{3.4 \times 10^9 \text{ watts}}{(16.7 \text{ joules/g-°C})(1.79 \times 10^5 \text{ g/sec})}$$
$$= 1130°C$$

The reactor temperature is presumably only a little above this figure. The melting point of uranium carbide is 2260°C; carbon sublimes around 3600°C. The numbers above merely establish the rough boundaries of the problem of reactor design. This superficial survey indicates, however that reactor powered rockets are not outside the realm of possibility.

Problems

19.1 The J-47 turbojet engine has a thrust of 5200 lb at 600 mph at sea level. Find the horsepower of the B-47 airplane at 35,000 ft altitude, if the thrust of each of the six engines is $\frac{1}{3}$ that at sea level.

19.2 What weight saving would be achieved if the crew of the nuclear powered airplane were allowed to receive a total dosage during a 5000-mile flight of one roentgen of gamma rays instead of the tolerance?

19.3 Continue the airplane weight analysis one step further to find the additional power required by the addition of a layer consisting of 2200 lb of water.

19.4 What reactor power would be needed to achieve the rocket escape velocity of 36,700 ft/sec?

19.5 The basic rocket equation was derived for motion in free space. How must it be changed if a constant gravitational force is acting during the burning period?

References

OHLINGER, L. A., "Engineering Aspects of Nuclear Reactors." *Nucleonics*, December (1949); January (1950); February (1950); March (1950).

GOODMAN, C., Ed., *The Science and Engineering of Nuclear Power*. Cambridge, Mass.: Addison-Wesley Press, 1949, Vols. I, II.

KALITINSKY, A., "Atomic Power and Aircraft Propulsion." *Soc. of Automotive Eng. Transactions*, January (1949) p. 1.

KRAMER, A. W., "Nuclear Power for Mobile Use." *Power Generation*, February (1949) p. 78.

KOSHUBA, W. J., "Metallurgical Considerations in the Application of Nuclear Energy for Propulsion of Aircraft." *Metal Progress*, May (1949) p. 635.

HUNTINGTON, HARRIET E., *Aircraft, USA*. New York: Doubleday & Co., 1951.

ABBOTT, IRA H., *Theory of Wing Sections*. New York: McGraw-Hill Book Co., 1949.

WOOD, KARL D., *Technical Aerodynamics*. New York: McGraw-Hill Book Co., 1947.

PERKINS, COURTLAND D. and ROBERT E. HAGE, *Airplane Performance, Stability and Control*. New York: John Wiley & Sons, 1950.

WHYBRA, M. G., "Atomic Rocket Motor." *Rocketscience*. March (1949) p. 7; December (1949) p. 88.

KALITINSKY, A., "Nuclear Power for Aircraft." *Air Affairs*, Winter (1949) p. 539.

Semi-Annual Reports of AEC to Congress. Washington, D. C.: U. S. Government Printing Office. Issues July 1950 to present.

HEMKE, PAUL E., *Elementary Applied Aerodynamics*. New York: Prentice-Hall, Inc., 1946.

DURHAM, F. P., *Aircraft Jet Power Plants*. New York: Prentice-Hall, Inc., 1951.

CHAPTER 20

ELECTRICAL POWER FROM FISSIONABLE FUEL

At the time the existence of atomic weapons was revealed, almost every popular article on the subject pointed out that the new energy could also be applied to peacetime uses, particularly as a tremendous source of electrical power. Since then the larger part of the atomic energy program has been devoted to military problems, which has probably set back the goal of atomic electricity by at least five years. In this chapter, we shall review the factors that affect the practicality of building electrical power plants utilizing nuclear fuel, and attempt to assess the long range value.

20.1 Availability and cost of fuel

The abundance and cost of fuel is the first consideration. The two raw materials thorium and uranium are the seventh and ninth most abundant elements in the earth's crust, appearing as 11 and 4 parts per million respectively. They occur however, in low concentration in contrast with ores like gold and silver. The world supply of each element in commercially profitable form is estimated to be around 10^8 pounds.* Now the energy consumption per year in the world could be provided by 2×10^6 pounds of fissionable material. Thus the uranium-thorium deposits correspond to a 100-yr supply for the world. As an auxiliary source, these materials would last considerably longer than 100 years, of course. The cost of natural uranium in pure metal form appears to lie somewhere between $5 and $50 per pound. W. H. Zinn uses a figure of $35 per pound for illustrative purposes, which we shall adopt.† From these numbers we can estimate quickly what *ultimate* contribution the fuel cost would be to electrical power.

---

* These estimates, based on Menke's article (see References) make use of pre-war data. Much higher figures are currently reported.

† There is some evidence that the Canadian price is as low as $10 per pound. The $35 figure will be taken as an American cost for production.

A natural uranium reactor could presumably be operated by continually substituting the plutonium produced even after the original U^{235} content was used up. If the conversion factor were as high as unity (one Pu atom per fissionable atom burned), all of the uranium could eventually be converted for energy. The energy release was computed in Section 3.2 to be 10^7 kwhr/lb. The cost associated with fuel at a price of $35 per pound would be 3.5×10^{-3} mills/kwhr of *heat* energy. This is about 1/1000 of the cost of low price electrical energy, which is almost 4 mills/kwhr, for example as supplied by the Tennessee Valley Authority. No consideration of efficiency of conversion of heat energy into electrical energy has been included; the costs of construction, operation and handling of materials are completely neglected. This result, while completely unrealistic, shows us at once that nuclear power is not *basically* uneconomical.

In the previous paragraph it was assumed that both the U^{235} and U^{238} could be converted eventually into energy. Suppose for some reason that it were not possible to utilize plutonium as a replacement fuel, but one had to rely on U^{235} only. Assume further that only half of the U^{235} could be used because the reactor failed to function with less than 0.35 per cent U^{235}. The cost of energy would increase by a factor of twice 140, the ratio of U^{238} to U^{235} in natural uranium. If we then assume an arbitrary efficiency factor of 20 per cent, the cost of fuel *alone* now becomes 4.9 mills/kwhr which is larger than the cost of the cheapest electricity. Since we have still not incorporated the many other costs, competition with water power electricity is almost ruled out.

Within the span of the above two answers we have found the region for exploration. There are several ways of looking at the possibility of regenerative production. Let us first study the trend in costs with the breeding or conversion factor, which was unity for our first calculation, and effectively zero for the second, since we made no use of the plutonium. Let x be the number of Pu atoms produced per U atom used up by the processes of fission and radiative capture to form U^{236}. The simplest approximation to make is that Pu is effective as U^{235} from all aspects—energy release per fission, available neutrons per atom used, etc. If the materials are interchangeable, the same conversion factor x may be used to predict the number of Pu atoms produced per Pu atom used. The initial supply of U^{235} gives rise to x units of Pu. This in turn gives $x \cdot x = x^2$ units of Pu,

etc. The number of atoms that have been available and subsequently
used for power is

$$1 + x + x^2 + x^3 + \ldots = \frac{1}{1 - x}$$

so long as x is less than unity. The analogy to subcritical multiplication as described in Section 8.2, is evident. For $x = 0$, the case of no
regeneration, the amount of power on this scale is unity; for $x = 0.5$,
it is $1/(1 - 0.5) = 2$; for $x = 0.9$, it is $1/(1 - 0.9) = 10$. The last
case corresponds to a utilization of 7.1 per cent of the uranium rather
than 0.71 per cent. The limiting case of $x = 1$ gives infinity, or more
cogently, complete utilization of the uranium. Complete conversion
is evidently desirable, otherwise fuel would constitute an appreciable
part of the cost. The discovery of high grade deposits or the development of cheap methods of extracting uranium from low grade ores
would greatly affect the situation, of course. It should be pointed
out that our assumption about the relative values of Pu and U^{235} is
not quite correct. Table 20.1 demonstrates that the excessive neutron

TABLE 20.1

COMPARISON OF U^{235} AND PLUTONIUM AS FUEL

	σ_f	σ_c	σ_a	Fission (%)	Capture (%)	Neutrons per Fission	Neutrons per Absorption
U^{235}:	549	101	650	84.5	15.5	2.5	2.11
Pu:	664	361	1025	64.8	35.2	3.0	1.94

capture in Pu^{239} to form Pu^{240} reduces the number of neutrons *per
absorption* below that of U^{235}, even though ν, the number per fission
is higher. The next question that arises is "How can a high conversion factor be obtained?" With an η of 1.94, it is clear that there are
only 0.94 neutrons available after the one to preserve the chain has
been set aside. The maximum x in a Pu-Pu breeding cycle is thus
0.94. Any moderator, coolant, or poisoning absorption will rapidly
bring this down. The best available moderator is pure heavy water;
the best coolant is a gas such as helium, the best metal for ducts is
aluminum or zirconium. One may readily devise the optimum heterogeneous reactor from these materials to find the highest possible x.
A good estimate might be 0.7, which implies a gain of somewhat over
3 in uranium usage. The alternative is to abandon the thermal reactor as a breeder, in view of the high cross section of most materials
at low neutron energies, and make use of fast or intermediate neu-

trons, where the cross sections become much lower than at thermal energy. The Experimental Breeder reactor discussed in Section 20.4 is apparently an outgrowth of an argument like the one above.

20.2 Construction and operating costs

The fuel cost, although high, is not the dominant factor in the total cost of electrical power. One must list the following items as contributing additional costs:

(1) Materials.

(2) Construction of reactor, heat exchanger and generators, and transmission equipment.

(3) Operation of reactor and chemical processing equipment.

(4) Interest, taxes, and profit (unless government owned).

One approach to the economics of nuclear fuel is to tabulate costs of all components of a conventional plant, and make somewhat arbitrary adjustments to accommodate the nuclear heat source. It is probably not quite fair to compare nuclear power with that from TVA which largely uses water as a primary source of energy. Instead, let us draw a comparison with a system run on coal. We shall assume that conventional coal-burning steam generating stations of 100-mw capacity involve an investment of $90 per kilowatt. This cost unit is based on the rough rule that the total cost is proportional to the power output. Of this $90 per kilowatt, about $30 per kilowatt has to do with mechanical equipment: boiler, turbines and auxiliary steam equipment. The remaining $60 per kilowatt includes fixed-investment electrical equipment, building and service equipment (excluding the transmission system). Now let us examine a reactor-powered electrical station. A typical unit might be a natural uranium-graphite, liquid-metal cooled reactor, with a heat exchanger to transfer the energy into steam. Shielding and special control equipment would be needed. Now assume that the mechanical equipment would cost *three* times as much as in a standard system. The total cost is thus $150 per kilowatt or, for a 100-mw plant, the investment would be $15 million. Operating costs, exclusive of fuel, amount to approximately 15 per cent of the investment per year. The yearly cost would thus be $2.25 million. With an electrical production and complete utilization of $(100,000 \text{ kw})(8760 \text{ hr/yr})$ 8.76×10^8 kwhr/yr, the nuclear plant cost would be 2.6 mills/kwhr. If the system were loaded only to half capacity the cost would double, to 5.2 mills/kwhr. The coal-steam cost, with everything estimated in the same way except for the heat source investment, yields a yearly operating figure of $1.35 million, and an energy cost of 1.6 mills/kwhr at 100-per cent load factor, or 3.2 mills/kwhr at 50-per cent load factor. Now we may include fuel costs in the two cases.

Coal. The cost of coal varies with grade and transportation costs, but we shall take a figure of $10 per ton. The heat yield is approximately 8000 kwhr/ton. At 20-per cent efficiency, the effective yield is 1600 kwhr/ton, from which we deduce the fuel cost to be 6.2 mills/kwhr.

Nuclear. Let us use the basic figure of 4.9 mills/kwhr computed previously, for "one pass" operation of the natural uranium, with half of the U^{235} burned. In order to be complete, let us add another 50-per cent cost for slug fabrication and chemical processing to recover plutonium and isolate the fission products. This brings the effective fuel cost to 7.3 mills/kwhr.

Adding costs for the two cases as in Table 20.2, we arrive at a final

TABLE 20.2

COMPARISON OF COAL AND URANIUM POWER PLANT COSTS
(full capacity)

	Coal (mills/kwhr)	*Uranium* (mills/kwhr)
Investment and operation:	1.6	2.6
Fuel:	6.2	7.3
	7.8	9.9

estimate—coal plant 7.8 mills/kwhr; nuclear plant 9.9 mills/kwhr. It thus appears, at least to the degree of accuracy that our computations have been made, that nuclear power is in the range to compete with coal in producing electricity, but is not *cheaper*, as one might hope. The extra cost of the equipment might eventually be compensated for by the potentially lower fuel cost. It must be pointed out that the degree of pessimism or optimism taken by the estimator can change the figures markedly. The only real test of the economics is to design, construct and operate enough units to establish a standard for comparison. Such rough estimates as we have made indicate at least that such an experiment would be worth the trial, in the interests of tapping the new source of energy.

A factor that has been completely left out of the analysis is the value of plutonium, as weapons material, since we presumed at the outset that it would not be used for reactors. It is quite clear that any of the plutonium byproduct of a power reactor that could be sold, presumably to the government, would reduce the price of electrical power. Two questions logically arise: (a) Should the government thus subsidize private industry by agreeing to purchase plutonium? (b) Will there always be a demand for plutonium? These questions lead into the region of the economic policy of the government and international relations, respectively. It is not our function to examine the problems, but it is important to note that the problem of developing practical nuclear power is by no means purely technical in nature. One point of view that helps in estimating the value of Pu is to assume that the Atomic Energy Commission could build reactors to yield Pu (but not power) costing nearly as much to run as would the power reactors we have just discussed. They would not have all of the electrical equipment, of course. As a very rough guess, we suggest that the cost would be one-half of that for the privately owned power breeder. Subsidization as an alternative thus could cut the electrical power cost from about 10 mills/kwhr to 5 mills/kwhr. From an overall point of view, remembering where government money ultimately comes from, by one channel or another, it would seem to be of advantage to obtain whatever useful power is available at the same time the weapon material is accumulated. Whether private industry or the government should do this is a moot question.

Another approach to the estimate of Pu value is based on existing production data. We arrived at a power rating of 10^9 watts for the Hanford reactor from Smyth's quotation that up to 1 kg/day of Pu production was needed. General Groves, former director of the Manhattan Project, quoted a monthly operating cost for the Hanford works of $3.5 million. Let us assume that the reactor had been designed for the generation of electricity. Taking the probable electrical output at 200 mw (20 per cent overall efficiency), we arrive at an operating cost of

$$(\$4860/hr)/(2 \times 10^5 \text{ kw}) = 24 \text{ mills/kwhr}$$

It is very likely that the cost of operating an efficient plant under more nearly peacetime rather than wartime conditions would be lower than this, but the factor is unknown. If this factor were 2, industry could produce electricity for *nothing*, if the government paid the equivalent of 12 mills/kwhr for Pu.

20.3 Building heating by a nuclear reactor

The experimental reactor BEPO, at Harwell, England, has been put to work in providing heat for an 80-office building, with an ultimate expected saving of 1000 tons of coal per year (see Fig. 20.1). The

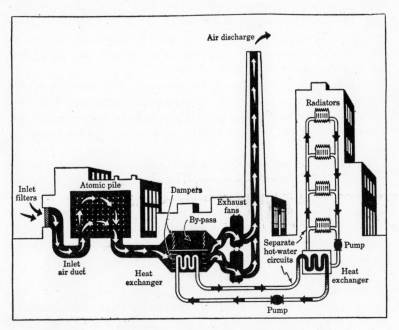

Fig. 20.1. Heating cycle in the BEPO system. [From *Popular Science Monthly*, February (1952).]

heating plant, weighing 8 tons, cost a modest $42,000. The reactor power is a 4-mw air cooled, cylindrical system, very much like the Brookhaven or Oak Ridge machines. Exhaust air at 212°F from the reactor passes through a heat exchanger, with a bypass to regulate flow according to the demand. The hot water at 160°F from the exchanger circulates through a second water-to-water heat exchanger, which is a part of the actual building system. The latter includes space heating and hot water supplies. The maximum output anticipated is 7 million Btu/hr, or approximately 1 mw, implying a 25 per cent efficiency of utilization of nuclear heat.

Calculations were made on a system composed of a chamber traversed by many bare water tubes, perpendicular to which the reactor air flows. The choice of optimum design of the heat exchanger was based on several factors:

(1) *The inlet and outlet water temperatures to the exchanger.* Two different exchangers were considered: (a) high-water outlet temperature; (b) low-water outlet temperature. In (a) the air-water temperature difference is small, the tube surface area must be large to draw off a given amount of heat and, thus, the resistance to air flow will be large. In (b) the reverse is true.

(2) *The pressure drop across the exchanger.* The insertion of the exchanger increases the overall resistance of the system. With constant-speed exhaust blowers, the flow through the reactor is reduced. The operating point is where blower capacity and system resistance are matched.

(3) *The air temperature drop in heat exchanger and its effect on the characteristics of the exhaust blower.* The air cooled by the exchanger is more dense than that normally handled by the blowers. The volume of air that must be displaced to achieve a given *mass flow* is thus smaller, and the blower capacity is modified.

(4) *The change in pressure drop through the reactor and the change in mass flow resulting from the insertion of the exchanger.*

(5) *Available space to locate the exchanger.*

(6) *Necessity of achieving useful hot water temperature.*

Any reduction in the flow through the reactor results in an increased exit air temperature and as well a rise in reactor temperature. This in turn tends to reduce its reactivity and the power level at which it can operate. The final choice of exchanger was a tank approximately 9 ft high, 10 ft wide, and 4 ft deep, with finned copper tubes. The air flow was set at 600,000 lb/hr at 12 lb/in.^{2} absolute pressure, 212°F. The pressure drop in the exchanger corresponds to 7 in. of water.

20.4 Fast breeder reactor

The feasibility of regeneration of fissionable material with useful power production has been demonstrated on a small scale. The Experimental Breeder Reactor at Arco, Idaho, designed by Argonne

National Laboratory, provides a power density of 4 kw/in.³ of the core, higher by a factor of 6 than the combustion chamber of a jet engine or the boiler of a high-pressure naval engine. The general features of the system are described below and illustrated in Fig. 20.2.

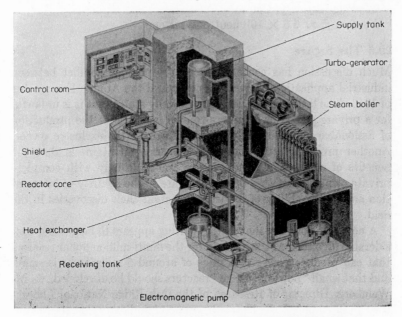

Fig. 20.2. Fast breeder reactor cycle. [From W. H. Zinn, "Basic Problems in Central-Station Nuclear Power." *Nucleonics*, September (1952). Copyright, 1952, by McGraw-Hill Publishing Co., Inc.]

No moderator is used, which requires that fission be caused by fast neutrons. The enriched U^{235} metal core, about the size of a football, is surrounded by a blanket of U^{238}, in which most of the plutonium is produced. The coolant is NaK, which is liquid at room temperature, with a boiling point of 1500°F. The alloy flows through the blanket, the core, a heat exchanger and thence to a receiving tank. An electromagnetic pump lifts the cool NaK to an elevated storage tank and the cycle starts over. Heat is removed from the exchanger by a separate circuit to restrict the amount of equipment for which shielding is needed. The heat in the secondary NaK circuit is taken up by a steam boiler; the steam drives a turbo-generator, is condensed, and returned to the boiler. Some of the operating characteristics of the EBR are listed below:

NaK *alloy exit temperature:* 660°F
Steam pressure at turbine: 400 psi
Generator capacity: 250 kw
Neutron flux: 6.5 × 10^{14} neutrons/sec-cm²

20.5 The future

Much discussion has centered about the possible conflict between industrial application of nuclear energy and the Atomic Energy Act of 1946. The latter, in Section 4, specifically states that it is unlawful for a private person or company to own facilities for the production of fissionable material. Only the AEC can be the exclusive owner. Another problem, some industrial concerns maintain, is that the benefits of commercial practices are realizable only with complete private ownership. Other problems relate to the security of information and to the ability of industry to patent their discoveries in the field.

A new point of view that at this writing appears to be gaining considerable favor is that the demand for the multi-million dollar reactors that can produce power at a price of around 5 mills/kwhr is small, and that small "power package" reactors should be developed. A. M. Weinberg, Director of Research of the Oak Ridge National Laboratory, in discussing L. R. Hafstad's proposal, indicates that the advantages of such 5 mw units are as follows:

(1) They could be used in remote locations where power is very expensive (a proposal to build a reactor in Nevada to pump water from mines has been widely discussed).

(2) Industries would be much more willing to invest a sum of $2.5 million to determine the practicality of nuclear power rather than $20 million, with government subsidy and partial control.

(3) The development of reactors is rendered much more flexible by the emphasis on small machines. Such a trend from the simple and cheap to the large and expensive has always characterized American technology.

It remains to be seen whether the Atomic Energy Act will be modified to allow interested companies to proceed with design and construction of power breeder reactors, or whether the trend will be to small package reactors in which power is the main goal, not the production of fissionable material. The growing awareness and interest in these problems is the most encouraging indication that practical electrical power in some form will be realized.

References

MENKE, J. R., *Nuclear Fission as a Source of Power*, MDDC-1104. Clinton National Laboratory, declassified June 30, 1947.

"Fundamentals of Nuclear Physics." *Westinghouse Engineer*, November 1945 to May 1947. Compilation of articles.

"Harwell Heats Office Building with Heat from BEPO Reactor." *Nucleonics*, January (1952) p. 70.

WALKER, J. and H. J. GRANT, "Utilization of Waste Heat from the British Experimental Pile." *Nucleonics*, March (1952) p. 58.

ZINN, W. H., "Basic Problems in Central-Station Nuclear Power." *Nucleonics*, September (1952) p. 8.

SHANNON, R. H., J. D. SHELBY, and M. B. DAGAN, *A Study of Electrical Power Generation Utilizing Heat Energy from Power Breeder Reactors*, KAPL-591. Knolls Atomic Power Laboratory (AEC), November 19, 1951.

ELLIOTT, R., *Economic Factors in the Selection of Steam Temperatures in Nuclear Power Plants*, NAA-SR-145. Downey, Cal.: North American Aviation, Inc., August 20, 1951.

KINGDON, K. H., "Progress Report on Nuclear Power." *Nucleonics*, April (1952) p. 18.

BOSKEY, BENNETT, "The Atomic Energy Act and the Power Question." *Nucleonics*, November (1952) p. 31.

WEINBERG, ALVIN M., "Wanted: Smaller and More Reactors." *Nucleonics*, November (1952) p. 31.

"World Progress in Atomic Energy." *Nucleonics*, December (1952) p. 7.

"Progress Report on Industrial Nuclear Power." *Nucleonics*, December (1952) p. 40.

BECKERLEY, J. G., "Declassification Problems in Power Reactor Information." *Nucleonics*, January (1953) p. 6.

HOCHWALT, C. A. and P. N. POWERS, "Dual Purpose Reactors." *Nucleonics*, February (1953) p. 10.

WEIL, G. L., "Power Only Reactors." *Nucleonics*, April (1953) p. 12.

EVERETT, R. W., "Market for 'Package' Nuclear Power." *Nucleonics*, April (1953) p. 32.

JOINT COMMITTEE ON ATOMIC ENERGY, *Atomic Power and Private Enterprise.* Washington: U. S. Government Printing Office, December, 1952.

Appendix A

REACTOR THEORY

Derivation of reactor equation

Many of the mathematical methods of reactor theory are analogous
to those of *heat flow*. The general expression for the rate of heat
flow across a unit-area surface in a medium of conductivity k where
the temperature varies from point to point is

$$Q = -k \frac{dT}{dx}$$

where the negative sign signifies that the flow is *opposite* to the
direction in which the temperature rises. If T decreases with x,
then the gradient dT/dx is negative, and the flow is in the positive
x direction. The basic postulate of neutron diffusion theory is that
the net flow of neutrons across a surface is due to a variation in the
number of neutrons n, or the flux $\phi = nv$ at different points. The
neutron current, or flow across a unit surface, is

$$J = -D \frac{d\phi}{dx} \quad \text{or} \quad -D\phi'$$

where D is the diffusion coefficient, equal to $\lambda_t/3$, where λ_t is the
transport mean free path. The term D is an experimentally measur-
able quantity. It may be seen that the direction of flow of neutrons
is from the regions where ϕ is large to those where it is low. Now,
imagine a reactor that is very broad and flat, as shown in Fig. 6.3,
such that there is a variation of neutron density along the x direction
but not along y and z. It is reasonable to expect that the neutron
density (and thus ϕ) is high in the center and low near the edges.
Take a block of the medium that has 1-cm² area and infinitesimal
thickness dx. The *net flow out* is the difference between the current
leaving through the right face and that entering the left face J_{in}.
Let us call the net flow the "leakage" from the volume element:

$$\text{leakage} = J_{out} - J_{in}$$

379

We know that in terms of the flux values at the two surfaces, the J's are $-D\phi'_{x+dx}$ and $-D\phi'_x$ respectively, where the subscripts indicate at what point the gradient is measured. Now assume that the gradient at $x + dx$ can be written as a linearly changing function

$$\phi'_{x+dx} = \phi'_x + \left(\frac{d\phi'}{dx}\right) dx$$

where $d\phi'/dx$ is the rate at which the gradient changes with position. Thus

$$\text{leakage} = J_{\text{out}} - J_{\text{in}}$$

$$= -D(\phi'_{x+dx} - \phi'_x) = -D\left(\frac{d\phi'}{dx}\right) dx = -D\frac{d^2\phi}{dx^2} dx$$

which is the net *loss of neutrons* from a volume element of thickness dx, area unity. The rate of *neutron absorption* may also be computed. It is $\phi \Sigma_a$ per unit volume, or $\phi \Sigma_a dx$ in the small slab. The final contribution to the thermal neutron balance is the *production*, by slowing down. For a steady state condition, we must have

$$\text{production} = \text{leakage} + \text{absorption}$$

or

$$q\, dx = -D\frac{d^2\phi}{dx^2} dx + \phi \Sigma_a dx$$

where q is the number of thermal neutrons appearing each second in a unit volume. Rearranging,

$$D\frac{d^2\phi}{dx^2} - \phi \Sigma_a + q = 0 \tag{A-1}$$

This is the reactor differential equation. The flux must satisfy this equation, just as the number of radioactive atoms at any time must satisfy a simpler linear equation. The equation is handled differently for the cases of homogeneous and heterogeneous reactors.

Homogeneous reactors

The source term q for a homogeneous mixture of uranium and moderator is constructed as follows:

(1) The number of neutrons absorbed in 1 cm^3 each second is $\phi \Sigma_a$.

(2) If each neutron absorbed gives rise to k_∞ fission neutrons, then the number of fast neutrons produced per cubic centimeter is $k_\infty \phi \Sigma_a$.

(3) Of these only a fraction $e^{-K^2\tau}$ get to thermal without escaping from the reactor. Thus the source is

$$q = k_\infty e^{-K^2\tau} \phi \Sigma_a$$

The reactor equation (A-1) becomes

$$D \frac{d^2\phi}{dx^2} - \phi \Sigma_a + k_\infty e^{-K^2\tau} \phi \Sigma_a = 0$$

The equation simplifies to

$$\frac{d^2\phi}{dx^2} + K^2\phi = 0 \qquad \text{(A-2)}$$

if we let

$$K^2 = \frac{\Sigma_a}{D}(k_\infty e^{-K^2\tau} - 1) \qquad \text{(A-3)}$$

By trial, we may show that $\phi = \phi_c \sin Kx$ will satisfy Eq. (A-2). If, in addition, we let $K = \pi/a$, where a is the reactor thickness, the flux $\phi = \phi_c \sin \pi x/a$ will go to zero at the reactor surfaces and be symmetric about the median plane, with an arbitrary maximum value ϕ_c on that plane. The size, shape, and physical properties of a critical reactor are related by Eq. (A-3). If we let $D/\Sigma_a = L^2$ (the square of the thermal diffusion length) and rearrange, Eq. (A-3) becomes

$$1 = \frac{k_\infty e^{-K^2\tau}}{1 + K^2 L^2} \qquad \text{(A-4)}$$

K^2 takes on values as indicated below for other geometries besides the slab. The infinite slab is a useful fiction for purposes of deriving

TABLE A-1

REACTOR FUNCTIONS

Geometry	Laplacian	Flux distribution	Size-shape factor K^2
Infinite slab:	$\dfrac{d^2}{dx^2}$	$\phi_c \sin \pi x/a$	$(\pi/a)^2$
Rectangular parallelepiped:	$\dfrac{d^2}{dx^2} + \dfrac{d^2}{dy^2} + \dfrac{d^2}{dz^2}$	$\phi_c \sin \pi x/a \sin \pi x/b$ $\sin \pi x/c$	$(\pi/a)^2 + (\pi/b)^2$ $+ (\pi/c)^2$
Sphere:	$\dfrac{d^2}{dr^2} + \dfrac{2}{r}\dfrac{d}{dr}$	$\phi_c \dfrac{\sin \pi r/R}{\pi r/R}$	$(\pi/R)^2$
Finite cylinder:	$\dfrac{\partial^2}{\partial r^2} + \dfrac{1}{r}\dfrac{\partial}{\partial r} + \dfrac{\partial^2}{\partial z^2}$	$\phi_c \sin \dfrac{\pi x}{H} J_0\left(\dfrac{2.4048r}{R}\right)$	$\left(\dfrac{2.4048}{R}\right)^2 + (\pi/H)^2$

the reactor equation; no one dimensional system exists. The actual shapes of reactors are circular cylinders, rectangular parallelepipeds (of which the cube is the most common form) and spheres. The generalized second derivative ∇^2 or "Laplacian" that takes the place of d^2/dx^2 for one dimensional systems has a characteristic value for each of the coordinate systems that are conventional for these geometries. ∇^2, the proper solutions of the reactor equation $\nabla^2\phi + K^2\phi = 0$, and the size-shape factor K^2 are listed in Table A-1.

Heterogeneous reactor

The solution of the reactor equations for this type of reactor will be demonstrated for the case of a single cylindrical slug of effectively infinite length, in a concentric cylindrical moderator. It is supposed that neutrons become thermal in the moderator only. Further, the number that slow down to thermal energy in each cubic centimeter per second, q, is taken to be the same throughout the moderator. Let us distinguish the two regions by subscripts 0 and 1 on all quantities. The moderator may be described by the differential equation (A-1)

$$D_1\nabla^2\phi_1 - \phi_1\Sigma_1 + q_1 = 0 \quad \text{(moderator)}$$

∇^2 is the Laplacian applicable to this cylindrical geometry:

$$\nabla^2\phi = \frac{1}{r} \cdot \frac{d}{dr}\left(\frac{rd\phi}{dr}\right)$$

With no slowing down in the uranium, $(q_0 = 0)$, Eq. (A-1) becomes, for the slug,

$$D_0\nabla^2\phi_0 - \phi_0\Sigma_0 = 0 \quad \text{(slug)}$$

now let

$$K_0{}^2 = \frac{\Sigma_0}{D_0} \quad \text{and} \quad K_1{}^2 = \frac{\Sigma_1}{D_1}$$

Then the two equations become

$$\frac{1}{r} \cdot \frac{d}{dr}\left(r\frac{d\phi_0}{dr}\right) - K_0{}^2\phi_0 = 0$$

$$\frac{1}{r} \cdot \frac{d}{dr}\left(r\frac{d\phi_1}{dr}\right) - K_1{}^2\phi_1 + \frac{q_1}{D_1} = 0$$

Their solutions are as follows:

$$\phi_0 = \phi_c \mathcal{J}_0(K_0 r)$$

$$\phi_1 = C\mathcal{J}_0(K_1 r) + F\mathcal{K}_0(K_1 r) + \frac{q_1}{\Sigma_1}$$

where ϕ_c is the central flux, C and F and q_1 are constants to be determined, and $\mathcal{J}_0$ and $\mathcal{K}_0$ are modified Bessel functions. The values of $\mathcal{J}_0(x)$ and $\mathcal{K}_0(x)$, and their derivatives $\mathcal{J}_1(x) = d\mathcal{J}_0(x)/dx$ and $\mathcal{K}_1(x) = -d\mathcal{K}_0(x)/dx$, are collected in various mathematics tables. The constants may be calculated by applying the following boundary conditions:

(1) The flux is continuous across the slug-moderator interface, i.e.,

$$\phi_0 = \phi_1 \quad \text{at} \quad r = r_0$$

Thus,
$$\phi_c \mathcal{J}_0(K_0 r_0) = C\mathcal{J}_0(K_1 r_0) + F\mathcal{K}_0(K_1 r_0) + \frac{q_1}{\Sigma_1}$$

(2) The current is continuous across this surface, i.e.,

$$-D_0 \phi'_0 = -D\phi'_1 \quad \text{at} \quad r = r_0$$

Thus,
$$-D_0 \phi_c K_0 \mathcal{J}_1(K_0 r_0) = -D_1 C K_1 \mathcal{J}_1(K_1 r_0) + D_1 F K_1 \mathcal{K}_1(K_1 r_0)$$

(3) There is zero current out of the cell,

$$-D_1 \phi'_1 = 0 \quad \text{at} \quad r = r_1$$

Thus,
$$-D_1[CK_1 \mathcal{J}_1(K_1 r_1) - F K_1 \mathcal{K}_1(K_1 r_1)] = 0$$

There are three equations in four unknowns, for which the ratios ϕ_c/q_1, C/q_1, and F/q_1 may be found. Graphs of the relative flux as a function of r may be plotted. The thermal utilization may be redefined as the ratio of neutrons absorbed in the uranium to the number slowing down, which is simply q_1 times the moderator volume V_1. Since ϕ_0 varies, the total absorption must be obtained by integration.

$$f = \frac{\int_{r=0}^{r=r_0} \Sigma_0 \, \phi_0 \, dV_0}{q_1 V_1} = \frac{\int_0^{r_0} \Sigma_0 \, \phi_c \mathcal{J}_0(K_0 r) 2\pi r \, dr}{q_1 V_1}$$

which reduces to
$$f = \frac{\phi_c}{q_1} \left(\frac{2\pi \, \Sigma_0 \, r_0}{K_0 \, V_1} \right) \mathcal{J}_1(K_0 r_0)$$

Since ϕ_c/q_1 can be obtained from the three simultaneous equations, f may be computed. A formula quoted by Weinberg for f takes account of all the preceding analysis, but does not yield the flux coefficients. It is, in adapted form,

$$\frac{1}{f} = \left(1 + \frac{V_1 \Sigma_1}{V_0 \Sigma_0} M \right) + \left(\frac{V_1}{V_0} N - 1 \right)$$

where
$$M = \frac{K_0 r_0}{2} \frac{\mathcal{J}_0(K_0 r_0)}{\mathcal{J}_1(K_0 r_0)}$$

$$N = \frac{K_1 r_0}{2}\left[\frac{\mathcal{J}_1(K_1 r_1)\mathcal{K}_0(K_1 r_0) + \mathcal{J}_0(K_1 r_0)\mathcal{K}_1(K_1 r_1)}{\mathcal{J}_1(K_1 r_1)\mathcal{K}_1(K_1 r_0) - \mathcal{J}_1(K_1 r_0)\mathcal{K}_1(K_1 r_1)}\right]$$

Since the computation of these terms for several reactor configurations becomes very tedious, it is desirable to find a simple but accurate approximation. This has been done by Atkinson* using the tabulated series expansions for the several Bessel functions. The result is

$$M = 1 + \frac{(K_0 r_0)^2}{8} - \frac{(K_0 r_0)^4}{192} + \cdots$$

$$\frac{V_1}{V_0} N - 1 \simeq \frac{(K_1 r_1)^2}{2}\left(\log_e \frac{r_1}{r_0} - \frac{3}{4}\right)$$

For natural uranium and graphite or heavy water, values of f computed from these expressions are correct to about 0.1 per cent, which is probably better than the accuracy of diffusion theory.

Age theory

The slowing down process of neutrons may be described by an approximate method due to Fermi, called *age theory*. One of the basic assumptions of this theory is that neutrons lose a small amount of energy per collision, which allows the use of differential equations to describe a process that is actually discrete. We shall be interested in finding the number of neutrons that cross, i.e., slow down past a given energy value E each second in a particular unit volume of a moderator. This quantity, labeled q, is called the *slowing down density*. It may be related to the flux ϕ of neutrons with energy in the vicinity of the level E by constructing several auxiliary quantities:

(1) *The number of collisions C to change the neutron energy by an infinitesimal amount dE.* As discussed in Section 2.6, C may be written

$$C = \frac{\log_e (E + dE) - \log_e E}{\xi} \cong \frac{dE}{E\xi}$$

(2) *The time t required for neutrons to slow down an amount of energy dE.* If the average distance between collisions is λ_s, the scattering mean-free path, and the average neutron speed is v, then the

---

* Ivan C. Atkinson, Master's Thesis, Physics Department, North Carolina State College, June, 1953.

time between collisions is $t_1 = \lambda_s/v$. For C collisions, however, the time is

$$t = Ct_1 = \frac{dE\lambda_s}{E\xi v}$$

(3) *The number of neutrons that have energy in the range dE at E.* An analogy with the properties of neutron flux may be drawn. If the time for a neutron to move a distance dx is $t = dx/v$, then the flux may be written

$$\phi = nv = n\, dx/t, \quad \text{or} \quad n\, dx = \phi t$$

Note that $n\, dx$ is the number of neutrons in a unit-area slab of thickness dx. Now the quantity q is a "flow" in the energy "space." If t is the time to move a "distance" dE, then the number of neutrons in the range dE is

$$n\, dE = qt = \frac{q\, dE\, \lambda_s}{E\xi v}$$

The corresponding *flux* of neutrons in the range is

$$\phi(E)\, dE = n(E)\, dE\, v = \frac{q\, dE\, \lambda_s}{E\xi}$$

These selected neutrons may now be treated as were thermal neutrons. We neglect the absorption process in forming a neutron balance equation of the selected neutrons that lie in a unit volume in a steady reactor and write

$$\text{production} = \text{leakage}$$

The left term is the difference between the number entering dE and leaving it, i.e.,

$$q = q_{\text{in}} - q_{\text{out}} = q(E + dE) - q(E) = \frac{\partial q}{\partial E}\, dE$$

The partial derivative is used because q is a function both of energy and position. The leakage term is of the form

$$\frac{-\lambda_t}{3} \nabla^2 \phi(E)\, dE$$

where ∇^2 is the generalized second derivative. See Table A-1. The leakage is thus

$$\frac{-\lambda_t}{3} \nabla^2 \phi(E)\, dE = \frac{-\lambda_t\lambda_s}{3\xi} \cdot \frac{dE}{E} \nabla^2 q$$

A new variable τ is now introduced as a substitute for energy, but closely related to it.

$$\tau = \int_{E_{\text{th}}}^{E} \frac{\lambda_t \lambda_s}{3\xi} \frac{dE}{E} \quad \text{and} \quad d\tau = \frac{\lambda_t \lambda_s}{3\xi} \cdot \frac{dE}{E}$$

This formula is the same as that given in Section 2.7. The balance equation may be written in this notation as

$$\nabla^2 q + \frac{\partial q}{\partial \tau} = 0$$

One important case is a medium containing a point source that emits n_0 neutrons per second. The solution of the differential equation for this case is the slowing down density q as a function of r and τ

$$q(r,\tau) = \frac{n_0 e^{-r^2/4(\tau_0 - \tau)}}{[4\pi(\tau_0 - \tau)]^{3/2}}$$

where τ_0 is the value of τ for $E = E_f$, namely, for neutrons that have slowed from fission energy to thermal. The number slowing through the thermal neutron level is found by setting $\tau = 0$,

$$q(r) = \frac{n_0 e^{-r^2/4\tau_0}}{(4\pi\tau_0)^{3/2}}$$

If we now let τ_0 be called the *square of the fast diffusion length, $L_f{}^2$,* we obtain the relation plotted in Figure 14.3.

An alternative use of age theory is to derive the fast leakage factor

$$\mathcal{L}_f{}^2 = e^{-K^2 L_f{}^2} = e^{-K^2 \tau}$$

as used in Section 6.2. We shall illustrate the method for the slab reactor. Two equations must be solved simultaneously, the age equation

$$\frac{\partial^2 q}{\partial x^2} + \frac{\partial q}{\partial \tau} = 0 \qquad\qquad \text{(A-5)}$$

and the diffusion equation

$$D \frac{d^2\phi}{dx^2} - \phi \Sigma_a + q = 0 \qquad\qquad \text{(A-1)}$$

Equation (A-1) may be written

$$\frac{d^2\phi}{dx^2} + K^2\phi = 0 \qquad\qquad \text{(A-2)}$$

by properly defining K^2.

We assume q is made up of two factors, the number of neutrons starting out fast $k_\infty \phi \Sigma_a$, multiplied by some unknown function of τ labeled $\mathcal{L}_f(\tau)$. When q refers to fission neutrons this function must be $\mathcal{L}_f(\tau_0) = 1$, to agree with the initial source. If we substitute $q = k_\infty \phi \Sigma_a \mathcal{L}_f(\tau)$ in Eqs. (A-5) and (A-2) and simplify, we obtain the equation

$$\frac{d\mathcal{L}_f(\tau)}{d\tau} + K^2 \mathcal{L}_f(\tau) = 0$$

The solution of this new differential equation is

$$\mathcal{L}_f(\tau) = e^{-K^2(\tau_0 - \tau)}$$

Thus, when q refers to thermal neutrons, $\tau = 0$,

$$\mathcal{L}_f(0) = e^{-K^2 \tau_0}$$

It is convenient to omit the subscript zero on τ_0. The fast leakage factor is thus $\mathcal{L}_f = e^{-K^2 \tau}$ as shown earlier.

Resonance escape probability

The derivation of the resonance escape probability p follows the logic below: a neutron of energy E has two possible fates in the resonance region—of being scattered by a moderator atom, with chance measured by Σ_s, or of being absorbed by uranium, measured by Σ_r. (The other possibilities, scattering by uranium and capture by moderator, are assumed negligible.) The chance of escaping on one collision is thus $\Sigma_s/(\Sigma_s + \Sigma_r)$. In slowing down, the number of collisions to go from an energy $E + dE$ down to energy E is the change in the logarithm of E, $(d \log_e E)$, divided by the average change in $\log_e E$, namely, ξ. Thus, $C = d(\log_e E)/\xi$. The chance of escaping on C collisions is

$$\left(\frac{\Sigma_s}{\Sigma_s + \Sigma_r} \right)^C = \left(1 - \frac{\Sigma_r}{\Sigma_s + \Sigma_r} \right)^C \cong e^{-[\Sigma_r C/(\Sigma_s + \Sigma_r)]}$$

This substitution may be justified by comparing the first three terms of the series expansions of each expression for small x:

$$(1 - x)^C = 1 - Cx + \frac{C(C - 1)}{2} x^2 - \dots$$

$$e^{-Cx} = 1 - Cx + \frac{C^2 x^2}{2} - \dots$$

For C collisions then

$$p_C = e^{-\Sigma_r d(\log_e E)/(\Sigma_r + \Sigma_s)\xi}$$

The product of probabilities for each energy interval is the probability for the whole slowing down region, by the property of exponential function

$$(e^a)(e^b)(e^c) \ldots = e^{a+b+c+\ldots}$$

The summation may be replaced by an integral over the complete energy range. Thus,

$$p = e^{-\int \Sigma_r \, d(\log_e E)/(\Sigma_r + \Sigma_s)\xi}$$

If Σ_r is small in comparison with Σ_s, and one can define an appropriate average value of Σ_s over the region in which resonances occur, the resonance escape probability may be approximated by

$$p = e^{-[\int \Sigma_r \, d(\log_e E)]/\xi \Sigma_s}$$
$$= e^{-Nv[\int \sigma_r \, d(\log_e E)]/\xi \Sigma_s}$$

Experiments have been performed to find the value of $\int \sigma_r d(\log_e E)$ called the "resonance integral." Now let "σ_U" be an effective *average* resonance absorption cross section

$$"\sigma_U" = \frac{\int \sigma_r d(\log_e E)}{\int d(\log_e E)}$$

The span of the (logarithmic) energy interval in the denominator is quoted to be 5.6, so that

$$"\sigma_U" = \frac{\int \sigma_r dE/E}{5.6}$$

We also define a fictitious absorption cross section

$$"\sigma_M" = \frac{\xi \sigma_s}{5.6}$$

on the basis that scattering events compete with uranium absorption to carry neutrons through the resonance peaks safely. Let "Σ_U" $= N_U$ "σ_U", and "Σ_M" $= N_M$ "σ_M" and substitute in the equation for p to obtain the symmetric result

$$p = e^{-("\Sigma_U"/"\Sigma_M")}$$

In a heterogeneous reactor, the two "absorptions" should be weighted by the volumes of media in which they occur V_M and V_U, and the respective average neutron fluxes $\bar{\phi}_U$ and $\bar{\phi}_M$. Thus,

$$p = e^{(-V_U "\Sigma_U" \bar{\phi}_U / V_M "\Sigma_M" \bar{\phi}_M)}$$

Now, if one defines a "resonance utilization" f_r in exact analogy with the thermal utilization f, the expression above may be converted to the form

$$p = e^{-(1/f_r - 1)^{-1}}$$

Appropriate resonance neutron constants are known. It is possible to compute $1/f_r$ by use of the same formulas that yield $1/f$ for thermal neutrons.

Temperature drop in a uranium slug

The rate of heat generation per unit volume in the slug at a radius r' is taken to be proportional to the local flux

$$q = A \mathcal{J}_0(K_0 r')$$

The total heat produced within an arbitrary surface bounded by r is

$$q_r = \int_0^r q 2\pi r' \, dr' = 2\pi A \int_0^r r' \mathcal{J}_0(K_0 r') \, dr'$$

$$= \frac{2\pi A r}{K_0} \mathcal{J}_1(K_0 r)$$

The constant A may be found in terms of the total heat developed in the slug q_1 by letting $r = r_0$.

$$q_1 = \frac{2\pi A r_0}{K_0} \mathcal{J}_1(K_0 r_0)$$

Thus,
$$q_r = q_1 \frac{r}{r_0} \cdot \frac{\mathcal{J}_1(K_0 r)}{\mathcal{J}_1(K_0 r_0)}$$

The temperature gradient at r is determined by the conductivity equation (10.4):

$$q_r = -k \frac{dT}{dr} (2\pi r), \quad \text{or} \quad dT = -\frac{q_1 \mathcal{J}_1(K_0 r) \, dr}{2\pi k r_0 \mathcal{J}_1(K_0 r_0)}$$

Integrating between limits $T = T_0$ at $r = 0$, and $T = T_s$ at $r = r_0$,

$$T_0 - T_s = \frac{q_1}{2\pi k (K_0 r_0) \mathcal{J}_1(K_0 r_0)} \left[\mathcal{J}_0(K_0 r) \right]_0^{r_0}$$

$$= \frac{q_1}{2\pi k (K_0 r_0) \mathcal{J}_1(K_0 r_0)} \left[\mathcal{J}_0(K_0 r_0) - 1 \right]$$

The temperature drop $T_0 - T_s$ is approximated by using the first few terms in the series expansion of the Bessel functions $\mathcal{J}_0$ and $\mathcal{J}_1$:

$$\mathcal{I}_0(x) \cong 1 + \left(\frac{x}{2}\right)^2 + \frac{1}{4}\left(\frac{x}{2}\right)^4$$

$$\mathcal{I}_1(x) \cong \frac{x}{2} + \frac{1}{2}\left(\frac{x}{2}\right)^3$$

Thus,
$$T_0 - T_s \cong \frac{q_1}{4\pi k}\left[\frac{1 + (K_0 r_0)^2/16}{1 + (K_0 r_0)^2/8}\right]$$

$$\simeq \frac{q_1}{4\pi k}\left[1 - (K_0 r_0)^2/16\right]$$

Appendix B

ATOMIC AND NUCLEAR DATA*

Atomic number, name	Element or isotope	Abundance (%)	Chemical atomic weight	Density (g/cm³)	Thermal cross sections		ξ	$\overline{\cos\theta}$
					σ_s	σ_a		
1 Hydrogen	H	...	1.0080	0.08988 (/l)	38 ± 4 (gas)	0.330 ± 0.007	1.0	0.667
	H¹	~100			...	...	0.7261	0.333
	H² = D	0.015	2.0147	0.17 (/l)	...	0.46 ± 0.1 mb	0.4281	0.168
2 Helium	He	...	4.003	0.177 (/l)	0.8 ± 0.2	...		
	He³	0.00013			...	n,p 5200 ± 300 0		
	He⁴	~100						
3 Lithium	Li	...	6.940	0.534	1.4 ± 0.3	70 ± 1	0.2643	0.097
	Li⁶	7.5			...	n,α 910		
	Li⁷	92.5				33 ± 5 mb (0.9 sec)		
4 Beryllium	Be⁹	100	9.013	1.85	7 ± 1	10 ± 1 mb	0.2078	0.074
5 Boron	B	...	10.82	2.34	4 ± 1	750 ± 10	0.1756	0.062
	B¹⁰	18.8			...	n,α 3990		
	B¹¹	81.2			...	<50 mb (0.03 sec)		

* REFERENCES: Isotopic abundances and cross sections from AECU-2040; atomic weights and densities from *Handbook of Chemistry and Physics*, 34th Ed.; ξ and $\overline{\cos\theta}$ for elements to mass 40 from chart by H. R. Kroeger, *Nucleonics*, October (1949). When the absorption cross section σ_a is not known, the activation value σ_{act} is given, with the half-life of the product following it.

391

ATOMIC AND NUCLEAR DATA (Continued)

Atomic number, name	Element or isotope	Abundance (%)	Chemical atomic weight	Density (g/cm³)	σ_s	σ_a	ξ	$\overline{\cos\theta}$
6 Carbon	C	...	12.010	1.65 (pure)	4.8±0.2	4.5 mb	0.1589	0.056
	C12	98.9				...		
	C13	1.1				1.0±0.3 mb (5800 yr)		
	C14	5800 yr				<200		
7 Nitrogen	N	...	14.008	1.2506 (/l)	10±1	1.78±0.05	0.1373	0.048
	N14	99.6			...	n,p 1.70±0.05 n,γ 0.10±0.05		
	N15	0.37				24±8 μb (7.4 sec)		
8 Oxygen	O	...	16.0000	1.429 (/l)	4.2±0.3	<0.2 mb	0.1209	0.0142
	O16	99.76			...			
	O17	0.037			...	...		
	O18	0.20			...			
9 Fluorine	F19	100	19.000	1.69 (/l)	4.1±0.3	0.21±0.04 mb (29 sec)	0.1025	0.035
10 Neon	Ne	...	20.183	0.8990 (/l)	2.4±0.3	<2.8	0.0967	0.033
	Ne20	90.9			...	...		
	Ne21	0.26			...	...		
	Ne22	8.8						
11 Sodium	Na23	100	22.997	0.971	4.0±0.5	0.49±0.02	0.0852	0.029
12 Magnesium	Mg	...	24.32	1.74	3.6±0.4	59±4 mb	0.0807	0.028
	Mg24	78.6			...	33±10 mb		
	Mg25	10.1			...	270±90 mb		
	Mg26	11.3				60±60 mb		
13 Aluminum	Al27	100	26.97	2.699	1.4±0.1	0.215±0.008	0.0730	0.025

14 Silicon	Si	...	28.06	2.42	1.7±0.3	0.13±0.03	0.0702	0.024
	Si28	92.22				80±30 mb		
	Si29	4.70				0.27±0.09		
	Si30	3.08				0.41±0.41		
15 Phosphorus	P31	100	30.98	1.82 (yellow)	10±2	0.19±0.03	0.0637	0.022
16 Sulfur	S	...	32.066	2.07 (rhombic)	1.1±0.2	0.49±0.02	0.0616	0.021
	S32	95.1				...		
	S33	0.74				...		
	S34	4.2				...		
	S36	0.016						
17 Chlorine	Cl	...	35.457	3.214 (/l)	1.5±0.5	31.6±1.0	0.0558	0.019
	Cl35	75.4				n,p 0.30±0.10		
	Cl37	24.6				0.56±0.12 (38 min)		
18 Argon	A	...	39.944	1.7837 (/l)		0.62±0.04	0.0497	0.017
	A36	0.35				6±2 (34 days)		
	A38	0.08				0.8±0.2 (265 yr)		
	A40	99.6				0.53±0.02 (1.8 hr)		
	A41	1.8 hr				<0.06 (>3.5 yr)		
19 Potassium	K	...	39.096	0.87	1.5±0.3	1.97±0.06	0.0507	0.017
	K39	93.1				1.87±0.15		
	K40	0.012				70±20		
	K41	6.9				1.19±0.10		
20 Calcium	Ca	...	40.08	1.55	9±2	0.43±0.02	0.0495	0.017
	Ca40	96.9				0.22±0.04		
	Ca42	0.64				...		
	Ca43	0.14				40±3		
	Ca44	2.1				0.63±0.12 (152 days)		
	Ca46	0.0032				...		
	Ca48	0.18				1.1±0.1 (8.5 min)		

Accurate values for all M above 40 given by

$$\xi \cong \frac{2}{M + \tfrac{2}{3}} \qquad \overline{\cos\theta} = \frac{2}{3M}$$

ATOMIC AND NUCLEAR DATA (Continued)

Atomic number, name	Element or isotope	Abundance (%)	Chemical atomic weight	Density (g/cm³)	Thermal cross sections	
					σ_s	σ_a
21 Scandium	Sc^{45}	100	45.10	3.02	...	23±2
22 Titanium	Ti	...	47.90	4.5	6±2	5.6±0.4
	Ti^{46}	8.0			...	0.6±0.2
	Ti^{47}	7.8			...	1.6±0.3
	Ti^{48}	73.4			...	8.0±0.6
	Ti^{49}	5.5			...	1.8±0.5
	Ti^{50}	5.3			...	<0.2
23 Vanadium	V	...	50.95	5.96	5±1	4.7±0.2
	V^{50}	0.2			...	...
	V^{51}	99.8			...	...
24 Chromium	Cr	...	52.01	7.1	3.0±0.5	2.9±0.1
	Cr^{50}	4.4			...	16.3±1.3
	Cr^{52}	83.7			...	0.73±0.06
	Cr^{53}	9.5			...	17.5±1.4
	Cr^{54}	2.4			...	<0.3
25 Manganese	Mn^{55}	100	54.93	7.2	2.3±0.3	12.6±0.6
26 Iron	Fe	...	55.85	7.85	11±1	2.43±0.08
	Fe^{54}	5.9				2.2±0.2
	Fe^{56}	91.6				2.6±0.2
	Fe^{57}	2.20				2.4±0.2
	Fe^{58}	0.33				2.5±2.0
27 Cobalt	Co^{59}	100	58.94	8.9	5±1	34.8±2.0

28 Nickel	Ni	...	58.69	8.90	17.5±1.0	4.5±0.2
	Ni58	67.9			...	4.2±0.3
	Ni60	26.2			...	2.7±0.2
	Ni61	1.2			...	1.8±1.3
	Ni62	3.7			...	15±3
	Ni64	1.0			...	2.6±0.4 (2.6 hr)
	Ni65	2.6 hr			...	6±3 (56 hr)
29 Copper	Cu	...	63.54	8.93	7.2±0.7	3.59±0.12
	Cu63	69.0			...	4.3±0.3
	Cu65	31.0			...	2.11±0.17
30 Zinc	Zn	...	65.38	7.14	3.6±0.4	1.06±0.05
	Zn64	48.9			...	0.5±0.1 (250 days)
	Zn66	27.8			...	n,α <20 μb
	Zn67	4.1			...	n,α 6±4 μb
	Zn68	18.6			...	n,α <20 μb
	Zn70	0.63			...	...
31 Gallium	Ga	...	69.72	5.91	4±1	2.71±0.12
	Ga69	60.2			...	2.0±0.2
	Ga71	39.8			...	4.9±0.4
32 Germanium	Ge	...	72.60	5.36	3±1	2.35±0.20
	Ge70	20.4			...	3.3±0.3
	Ge72	27.4			...	0.94±0.09
	Ge73	7.8			...	13.7±1.1
	Ge74	36.6			...	0.60±0.06
	Ge76	7.8			...	0.35±0.07
33 Arsenic	As75	100	74.91	5.73	6±1	4.1±0.2

ATOMIC AND NUCLEAR DATA (*Continued*)

Atomic number, name	Element or isotope	Abundance (%)	Chemical atomic weight	Density (g/cm³)	Thermal cross sections σ_s	σ_a
34 Selenium	Se	...	78.96	4.8 (gray)	13 ±1	11.8 ±0.4
	Se⁷⁴	0.87			...	48 ±7
	Se⁷⁶	9.0			...	82 ±7
	Se⁷⁷	7.6			...	40 ±4
	Se⁷⁸	23.5			...	0.4 ±0.4
	Se⁸⁰	49.8			...	0.59 ±0.06
	Se⁸²	9.2			...	2.0 ±1.4
35 Bromine	Br	...	79.916	7.59 (/l) (gas) 3.12 (liquid)	6 ±1	6.5 ±0.5
	Br⁷⁹	50.5			...	10.4 ±1.0
	Br⁸¹	49.5			...	2.6 ±0.4
36 Krypton	Kr	...	83.7	3.708 (/l)	7.2 ±0.7	28 ±5
	Kr⁷⁸	0.35			...	0.3 ±0.1 (34 hr)
	Kr⁸⁰	2.27			...	95 ±15
	Kr⁸²	11.6			...	45 ±15
	Kr⁸³	11.6			...	205 ±10
	Kr⁸⁴	57.0			...	<2
	Kr⁸⁵	10 yr			...	<15
	Kr⁸⁶	17.4			...	<2
	Kr⁸⁷	78 min			...	<470 (2.3 hr)
37 Rubidium	Rb	...	85.48	1.53	12 ±2	0.70 ±0.07
	Rb⁸⁵	72.2			...	0.72 ±0.15 (19.5 days)
	Rb⁸⁷	27.8			...	0.12 ±0.03 (17.5 min)
	Rb⁸⁸	18 min			...	<200 (15 min)

38 Strontium	Sr	...	87.63	2.54	10±1	1.16±0.06
	Sr⁸⁴	0.55			...	...
	Sr⁸⁶	9.8			...	1.3±0.4 (2.7 hr)
	Sr⁸⁷	7.0			...	...
	Sr⁸⁸	82.7			...	5±1 mb (53 days)
	Sr⁸⁹	53 days			...	<110 (25 yr)
	Sr⁹⁰	25 yr			...	1.0±0.6 (9.7 hr)
39 Yttrium	Y⁸⁹	100	88.92	5.51	3±2	1.38±0.14
40 Zirconium	Zr	...	91.22	6.4	8±1	0.18±0.02
	Zr⁹⁰	51.5			...	0.1±0.1
	Zr⁹¹	11.2			...	1.52±0.12
	Zr⁹²	17.1			...	0.25±0.12
	Zr⁹⁴	17.4			...	0.08±0.06
	Zr⁹⁶	2.80			...	0.1±0.1
41 Columbium (or Niobium)	Cb⁹³ (or Nb)	100	92.91	8.4	5±1	1.1±0.1
42 Molybdenum	Mo	...	95.95	10.2	7±1	2.4±0.2
	Mo⁹²	15.7			...	<0.3
	Mo⁹⁴	9.3			...	...
	Mo⁹⁵	15.7			...	13.4±1.3
	Mo⁹⁶	16.5			...	1.2±0.6
	Mo⁹⁷	9.5			...	2.1±0.7
	Mo⁹⁸	23.9			...	0.4±0.4
	Mo¹⁰⁰	9.5			...	0.20 ± 0.05
43 Technetium	Tc⁹⁹	...	99	...		

ATOMIC AND NUCLEAR DATA (Continued)

Atomic number, name	Element or isotope	Abundance (%)	Chemical atomic weight	Density (g/cm³)	Thermal cross sections σ_s	σ_a
44 Ruthenium	Ru	...	101.7	12.2	6±1	2.46±0.12
	Ru⁹⁶	5.7			...	10±4 mb (2.8 days)
	Ru⁹⁸	2.22			...	...
	Ru⁹⁹	12.8			...	...
	Ru¹⁰⁰	12.7			...	...
	Ru¹⁰¹	17.0			...	...
	Ru¹⁰²	31.3			...	1.2±0.3 (42 days)
	Ru¹⁰⁴	18.3			...	0.7±0.2 (4 hr)
45 Rhodium	Rh¹⁰³	100	102.91	12.5	6±1	150±7
46 Palladium	Pd	...	106.7	12.16	3.6±0.6	8.0±1.5
	Pd¹⁰²	0.8			...	...
	Pd¹⁰⁴	9.3			...	...
	Pd¹⁰⁵	22.6			...	...
	Pd¹⁰⁶	27.1			...	...
	Pd¹⁰⁸	26.7			...	11±3 (13 hr)
	Pd¹¹⁰	13.5			...	0.4±0.1 (26 min)
47 Silver	Ag	...	107.880	10.50	6±1	60±3
	Ag¹⁰⁷	51.9			...	30±2
	Ag¹⁰⁹	48.1			...	84±7
48 Cadmium	Cd	...	112.41	8.65	7±1	2400±200
	Cd¹⁰⁶	1.22				1.0±0.5 (6.7 hr)
	Cd¹⁰⁸	0.92			...	...
	Cd¹¹⁰	12.4			...	0.2±0.1 (49 min)

	Isotope	Abundance	Atomic weight	Density		Cross section
	Cd¹¹¹	12.8			...	...
	Cd¹¹²	24.0			...	20 ± 10 mb (5 yr)
	Cd¹¹³	12.3			...	19,500
	Cd¹¹⁴	28.8			...	0.14 ± 0.03 (43 days); 1.1 ± 0.3 (2.3 days)
	Cd¹¹⁶	7.6				1.4 ± 0.3 (2.7 hr)
49 Indium	In	...	114.76	7.28	2.2 ± 0.5	190 ± 10
	In¹¹³	4.2			...	56 ± 12 (50 days); 2.0 ± 0.6 (72 sec)
	In¹¹⁵	95.8			...	145 ± 15 (15 min); 52 ± 6 (13 sec)
50 Tin	Sn	...	118.70	7.31 (tetragonal)	4 ± 1	0.65 ± 0.05
	Sn¹¹²	0.95			...	20 ± 10 mb (30 min); 1.3 ± 0.3 (112 days)
	Sn¹¹⁴	0.65			...	...
	Sn¹¹⁵	0.34			...	...
	Sn¹¹⁶	14.2			...	6 ± 2 mb (14.5 days)
	Sn¹¹⁷	7.6			...	...
	Sn¹¹⁸	24.0			...	10 ± 6 mb (245 days)
	Sn¹¹⁹	8.6			...	...
	Sn¹²⁰	33.0			...	1 ± 1 mb (>400 days); 0.14 ± 0.03 (27 hr)
	Sn¹²²	4.7			...	0.16 ± 0.04 (40 min); 1.0 ± 0.5 mb (126 days)
	Sn¹²⁴	6.0			...	4 ± 2 mb (10 days); 0.2 ± 0.1 (10 min)
51 Antimony	Sb	...	121.76	6.691	4.3 ± 0.5	5.5 ± 1.0
	Sb¹²¹	57.2			...	5.7 ± 0.5
	Sb¹²³	42.8			...	3.9 ± 0.3

ATOMIC AND NUCLEAR DATA *(Continued)*

Atomic number, name	Element or isotope	Abundance (%)	Chemical atomic weight	Density (g/cm³)	Thermal cross sections	
					σ_s	σ_a
52 Tellurium	Te	...	127.61	6.24	5 ± 1	4.5 ± 0.2
	Te¹²⁰	0.091			...	70 ± 70
	Te¹²²	2.5			...	2.7 ± 0.9
	Te¹²³	0.88			...	390 ± 30
	Te¹²⁴	4.6			...	6.5 ± 1.2
	Te¹²⁵	7.0			...	1.50 ± 0.15
	Te¹²⁶	18.7			...	0.8 ± 0.2
	Te¹²⁸	31.8			...	0.3 ± 0.3
	Te¹³⁰	34.4			...	0.5 ± 0.3
53 Iodine	I¹²⁷	100	126.92	4.93 (solid) 11.27 (/l) (gas)	3.6 ± 0.5	6.7 ± 0.6
	I¹²⁹	(3 × 10⁷ yr)			...	11 ± 4 (12.5 hr)
	I¹³¹	(8 days)			...	600 ± 300 (2.4 hr)
54 Xenon	Xe	...	131.3	5.85 (/l)	4.3 ± 0.4	35 ± 5
	Xe¹²⁴	0.096			...	...
	Xe¹²⁶	0.090			...	...
	Xe¹²⁸	1.92			...	<5
	Xe¹²⁹	26.4			...	45 ± 15
	Xe¹³⁰	4.08			...	<5
	Xe¹³¹	21.2			...	120 ± 15
	Xe¹³²	26.91			...	<5
	Xe¹³⁴	10.4			...	<5
	Xe¹³⁵	9.2 hr			...	3.5 × 10⁶
	Xe¹³⁶	8.93			...	<5

Z	Element	Isotope	% abundance / half-life	At. wt.			
55	Cesium	Cs^{133}	100	132.91	1.873	20±5	29.0±1.5
		Cs^{135}	2×10⁶ yr			...	15±8 (13.7 days)
		Cs^{137}	37 yr			...	<2 (33 min)
56	Barium	Ba	...	137.36	3.5	8±1	1.17±0.10
		Ba^{130}	0.101			...	30±10 mb (12.0 days)
		Ba^{132}	0.097			...	6±3 (>20 yr)
		Ba^{134}	2.42			...	2±2
		Ba^{135}	6.6			...	5.6±0.9
		Ba^{136}	7.8			...	0.4±0.4
		Ba^{137}	11.3			...	4.9±0.4
		Ba^{138}	71.7			...	0.68±0.10
		Ba^{139}	85 min			...	4±1 (12.8 days)
57	Lanthanum	La	...	138.92	6.155	18±8	8.9±0.3
		La^{138}	0.089				
		La^{139}	99.9			...	8.4±1.7 (40 hr)
		La^{140}	40 hr			...	3±2 (3.6 hr)
58	Cerium	Ce	...	140.13	6.90	9±6	0.70±0.08
		Ce^{136}	0.19			...	25±25
		Ce^{138}	0.26			...	9±6
		Ce^{140}	88.4			...	0.63±0.06
		Ce^{142}	11.08			...	1.8±0.3
59	Praseodymium	Pr^{141}	100	140.92	6.5		11.2±0.6
60	Neodymium	Nd	...	144.27	6.95	25±5	44±2
		Nd^{142}	27.1			...	18.5±2
		Nd^{143}	12.2			...	290±30
		Nd^{144}	23.9			...	4.8±0.5
		Nd^{145}	8.3			...	52±4
		Nd^{146}	17.2			...	9.8±0.8
		Nd^{148}	5.7			...	3.3±1.0
		Nd^{150}	5.6			...	2.9±1.5

ATOMIC AND NUCLEAR DATA (Continued)

Atomic number, name	Element or isotope	Abundance (%)	Chemical atomic weight	Density (g/cm³)	Thermal cross sections σ_s	σ_a
61 Promethium	Pm^{147}	4 yr	147	...	...	60 ± 20 (5.3 days)
62 Samarium	Sm	...	150.43	7.7	...	6500 ± 1000
	Sm^{144}	3.1			...	<0.25 (60 days)
	Sm^{147}	15.0			...	...
	Sm^{148}	11.2			...	50,000 ± 20,000
	Sm^{149}	13.8			...	...
	Sm^{150}	7.4			...	7000 ± 2000
	Sm^{151}	122 yr			...	150 ± 40 (47 hr)
	Sm^{152}	26.7			...	5.5 ± 1.1 (25 min)
	Sm^{154}	22.5			...	4500 ± 500
63 Europium	Eu	...	152.0	...	...	9000 ± 3000
	Eu^{151}	47.8			...	5500 ± 1500
	Eu^{152}	5.3 yr			...	420 ± 100
	Eu^{153}	52.2			...	1500 ± 400
	Eu^{154}	5.4 yr			...	14,000 ± 4000
	Eu^{155}	1.7 yr			...	44,000 ± 2000
64 Gadolinium	Gd	...	156.9	...	...	<125 (225 days)
	Gd^{152}	0.20			...	...
	Gd^{154}	2.15			...	70,000 ± 20,000
	Gd^{155}	14.8			...	...
	Gd^{156}	20.6			...	160,000 ± 60,000
	Gd^{157}	15.7			...	4 ± 2 (18 hr)
	Gd^{158}	24.8			...	1.5 ± 0.5 (3.6 min)
	Gd^{160}	21.8			...	

Z	Element	Isotope	% abundance or half-life	Atomic weight			Cross section
65	Terbium	Tb^{159}	100	159.2	...	...	44±4
66	Dysprosium	Dy	...	162.46	...	...	1100±150
		Dy^{156}	0.052			...	...
		Dy^{158}	0.090			...	...
		Dy^{160}	2.29			...	...
		Dy^{161}	18.9			...	...
		Dy^{162}	25.5			...	...
		Dy^{163}	25.0			...	...
		Dy^{164}	28.2			...	...
		Dy^{165}	2.4 hr				2600±300 (1.3 min); <1000 (2.4 hr)
67	Holmium	Ho^{165}	100	164.94			5000±2000 (81 hr) 64±3
68	Erbium	Er	...	167.2	4.77		166±16
		Er^{162}	0.136			...	...
		Er^{164}	1.56			...	...
		Er^{166}	33.4			...	...
		Er^{167}	22.9			...	...
		Er^{168}	27.1			...	...
		Er^{170}	14.9				>7 (7 hr)
69	Thulium	Tm^{169}	100	169.4			118±6
70	Ytterbium	Yb	...	173.04		12±5	36±4
		Yb^{168}	0.140			...	11,000±3000 (33 days)
		Yb^{170}	3.03			...	...
		Yb^{171}	14.3			...	...
		Yb^{172}	21.8			...	...
		Yb^{173}	16.1			...	...
		Yb^{174}	31.8			...	60±40 (4 days)
		Yb^{176}	12.7			...	5.5±1.0 (1.8 hr)

ATOMIC AND NUCLEAR DATA (Continued)

Atomic number, name	Element or isotope	Abundance (%)	Chemical atomic weight	Density (g/cm³)	Thermal cross sections σ_s	σ_a
71 Lutetium	Lu	...	174.99	...	...	108±5
	Lu¹⁷⁵	97.4			...	35±15 (3.7 hr)
	Lu¹⁷⁶	2.60			...	4000±800 (6.7 days)
72 Hafnium	Hf	...	178.6	13.3	...	115±15
	Hf¹⁷⁴	0.18			...	1500±1000
	Hf¹⁷⁶	5.2			...	15±15
	Hf¹⁷⁷	18.4			...	380±30
	Hf¹⁷⁸	27.1			...	75±10
	Hf¹⁷⁹	13.8			...	65±15
	Hf¹⁸⁰	35.4			...	13±5
73 Tantalum	Ta¹⁸¹	100	180.88	16.6	5±1	21.3±1.0
74 Wolfram (Tungsten)	W	...	183.92	19.3	5±1	19.2±1.0
	W¹⁸⁰	0.14			...	60±60
	W¹⁸²	26.4			...	19±2
	W¹⁸³	14.4			...	11±1
	W¹⁸⁴	30.6			...	2.0±0.3
	W¹⁸⁶	28.4			...	34±3
	W¹⁸⁷	25 hr			...	90±40 (65 days)
75 Rhenium	Re	...	186.31	20.53	14±4	84±4
	Re¹⁸⁵	37.1			...	100±8
	Re¹⁸⁷	62.9			...	63±5
76 Osmium	Os	...	190.2	22.48	11±1	14.7±0.7
	Os¹⁸⁴	0.018			...	<200 (97 days)
	Os¹⁸⁶	1.58			...	...

Z / Element	Isotope	% / half-life	At. wt.	Density	σ	σ (details)
	Os^{187}	1.64			...	...
	Os^{188}	13.3			...	...
	Os^{189}	16.1			...	...
	Os^{190}	26.4			...	8 ± 3 (15 days)
	Os^{192}	41.0			...	1.6 ± 0.4 (32 hr)
	Os^{193}	32 hr			...	60 ± 20 (700 days)
77 Iridium	Ir	...	193.1	22.42	...	440 ± 20
	Ir^{191}	38.5			...	260 ± 100 (1.4 min); 700 ± 200 (70 days)
	Ir^{193}	61.5			...	130 ± 30 (19 hr)
78 Platinum	Pt	...	195.23	21.37	10 ± 1	8.1 ± 0.4
	Pt^{190}	0.012				...
	Pt^{192}	0.78				...
	Pt^{194}	32.8				90 ± 40 (4.3 days)
	Pt^{195}	33.7				...
	Pt^{196}	25.4				...
	Pt^{198}	7.2				1.1 ± 0.3 (18 hr); 50 ± 20 mb (82 days)
79 Gold	Au^{197}	100	197.2	19.32	9.3 ± 1.0	3.9 ± 0.8 (31 min)
	Au^{198}	2.7 days			...	94 ± 1
80 Mercury	Hg	...	200.61	13.546	10 ± 5	$16,000 \pm 8000$ (3.3 days)
	Hg^{196}	0.151				380 ± 20
	Hg^{198}	10.0				3100 ± 1000
	Hg^{199}	16.9				...
	Hg^{200}	23.1				2500 ± 800
	Hg^{201}	13.2				<60
	Hg^{202}	29.8				<60
	Hg^{204}	6.8				3.0 ± 0.8 (44 days)
81 Thallium	Tl	...	204.39	11.85	14 ± 2	0.43 ± 0.10 (5.5 min)
	Tl^{203}	29.5			...	3.3 ± 0.5
	Tl^{205}	70.5			...	11.0 ± 0.9
						0.77 ± 0.08

ATOMIC AND NUCLEAR DATA (Continued)

Atomic number, name	Element or isotope	Abundance (%)	Chemical atomic weight	Density (g/cm³)	σ_s	Thermal cross sections σ_a^*	σ_f^*
82 Lead	Pb	...	207.21	11.35	11 ± 1	0.17 ± 0.01	<100
	Pb^{204}	1.5			...	0.8 ± 0.6	<0.1 mb
	Pb^{205}	23.6			...	26 ± 5 mb	<2
	Pb^{207}	22.6			...	0.69 ± 0.05	<2
	Pb^{208}	52.3			...	<30 mb	
83 Bismuth	Bi^{209}	100	209.00	9.747	9 ± 1	32 ± 3 mb	
84 Polonium Po^{210}; 85 Astatine At^{211}; 86 Radon Rn^{222}; 87 Francium Fr^{221}							
88 Radium	Ra^{223}	11.2 days			...	...	
	Ra^{226}	1620 yr	226.05	5	...	15 ± 3	
	Ra^{228}	6.7 yr			...	36 ± 5 (<10 min)	
89	Ac^{227}	18.6 yr	227.05	...	...	500 ± 35	
Actinium							
90 Thorium	Th^{227}	18.6 days			...	...	1500 ± 1000
	Th^{228}	1.90 yr			...	...	<0.3
	Th^{229}	8×10^3 yr			...	...	45 ± 11
	Th^{230}	8.0×10^4 yr			...	45 ± 10 (25.5 hr)	<1 mb
	Th^{232}	100; 1.39×10^{10} yr	232.12	11.3	13 ± 2	7.0 ± 0.4	<0.2 mb
	Th^{233}	23.5 min			...	1400 ± 200 (24.1 days)	...
	Th^{234}	24.1 days			...	1.8 ± 0.5 (<10 min)	<0.01
91 Protactinium	Pa^{230}	17.3 days	231	...	...	...	1500 ± 250
	Pa^{231}	3.4×10^4 yr			...	260 ± 50 (1.3 days)	10 ± 5
	Pa^{232}	1.3 days			...	...	700 ± 150
	Pa^{233}	27.4 days			...	37 ± 14 (1.2 min)	<0.1
	Pa^{234}	(UX$_2$)(1.2 min)			...	...	<500
		(UZ)(6.7 hr)			...	...	<5000

Z	Element	Isotope	Half-life	% abund.	Mass			σ_a	σ_f
92	Uranium	U	...		238.07	18.68	8.2	7.42	3.92
		U^{230}	20.8 days					...	25 ± 10
		U^{231}	4.2 days					...	250 ± 100
		U^{232}	70 yr					...	80 ± 20
		U^{234}	2.5×10^5 yr	0.0057				89 ± 7	<0.65
		U^{235}	8.8×10^8 yr	0.714'				650	549
		U^{238}	4.50×10^9 yr	99.3				2.80	0
		U^{239}	23.5 min					22 ± 5 (14 hr)	...
93	Neptunium	Np^{234}	4.4 days					...	900 ± 300
		Np^{236}	22 hr					...	10^5
		Np^{237}	2.5×10^6 yr					150 ± 15 (2.1 days)	19 ± 3 mb
		Np^{238}	2.1 days					...	1600 ± 100
		Np^{239}	2.3 days		239			...	3
94	Plutonium	Pu^{238}	89.6 yr					425 ± 75 (2.4×10^4 yr)[b]	18 ± 2
		Pu^{239}	2.4×10^4 yr		239			1025	664
		Pu^{241}	~12 yr					400 ± 50 (~5×10^5 yr)	1080 ± 100
		Pu^{242}	~5×10^5 yr					40 ± 20 (5 hr)	...
95	Americium	Am^{241}	47.5 yr		241			700 ± 200 (16 hr); <50 (500 yr)	3.2 ± 0.2
		Am^{242m}	16 hr					...	2000 ± 1000
		Am^{242}	500 yr					8,000 ± 1000	3500 ± 1000
		Am^{243}	~10^4 yr					50 ± 25 (~25 min)	<25
96	Curium	Cm^{240}	27 days					...	20,000 ± 10,000
		Cm^{242}	162.5 days		242			...	<5
97	Berkelium	B	...		243			...	...
98	Californium	Cf	...		244			...	...

* Note that $\sigma_f + \sigma_{act} = \sigma_a$. If number listed in σ_a column has a half life, it is σ_{act}.

ATOMIC AND NUCLEAR DATA (*Continued*)

Atomic number, name	Element or isotope	Abundance (%)	Chemical atomic weight	Density (g/cm³)	Thermal cross sections		
					σ_s	σ_a^*	σ_f^*
99 Einsteinium	E	...	253	...			
100 Fermium	Fm	...	255	...			
101 Mendelevium	Mv	...	256	...			

Appendix C

LIST OF DEPOSITORY LIBRARIES

Essentially all of the AEC non-classified reports are available at the libraries listed below.

California
Berkeley, University of California General Library
Los Angeles, University of California Library
Colorado
Denver, Denver Public Library
Connecticut
New Haven, Yale University Library
District of Columbia
Washington, Library of Congress
Georgia
Atlanta, Georgia Institute of Technology Library
Illinois
Chicago, John Crerar Library
Chicago, University of Chicago Library
Urbana, University of Illinois Library
Indiana
Lafayette, Purdue University Library
Iowa
Ames, Iowa State College Library
Kentucky
Lexington, University of Kentucky Library
Louisiana
Baton Rouge, Louisiana State University Library
Massachusetts
Cambridge, Harvard University Library
Cambridge, Massachusetts Institute of Technology Library

Michigan
Ann Arbor, University of Michigan Library
Detroit, Detroit Public Library
Minnesota
Minneapolis, University of Minnesota Library
Missouri
Kansas City, Linda Hall Library
St. Louis, Washington University Library
New Jersey
Princeton, Princeton University Library
New Mexico
Albuquerque, University of New Mexico Library
New York
Buffalo, Lockwood Memorial Library
Ithaca, Cornell University Library
New York, Columbia University Library
New York, New York Public Library
Troy, Rensselaer Polytechnic Institute Library
North Carolina
Durham, Duke University Library
Raleigh, North Carolina State College Library
Ohio
Cincinnati, University of Cincinnati Library
Cleveland, Cleveland Public Library
Columbus, Ohio State University Library
Oklahoma
Stillwater, Oklahoma Agricultural and Mechanical College Library
Oregon
Corvallis, Oregon State College Library
Pennsylvania
Philadelphia, University of Pennsylvania Library
Pittsburgh, Carnegie Library of Pittsburgh
Tennessee
Knoxville, University of Tennessee Library
Nashville, Joint University Libraries
Texas
Austin, University of Texas Library

Utah
Salt Lake City, University of Utah Library
Washington
Seattle, University of Washington Library
Wisconsin
Madison, University of Wisconsin Library

INDEX